D1329863

BABI YAR

BABI YAR

A Documentary Novel

BY

Anatoly Kuznetsov

Translated by Jacob Guralsky

Illustrations by S. Brodsky

THE DIAL PRESS   1967   NEW YORK

A Note About This Book

Anatoly Kuznetsov was twelve years old when the Germans took Kiev in 1941. He lived near Babi Yar—Old Wives Gully—a ravine on the outskirts of the city. In this ravine the Nazis massacred almost 200,000 persons during the two-year occupation. Kuznetsov vowed that if he survived he would dedicate himself to writing the story of that occupation.

After the war Kuznetsov entered the Literary Institute in Moscow and became a writer, but it was nearly 25 years before he completed his book, *Babi Yar*. He buttressed his boyhood recollections by studying the leaflets, posters and newspapers of the occupation period, interviewed persons who had survived and wove the whole into a striking narrative, which he dubbed a documentary novel. It combined the warmth and buoyancy of a youngster's story with the moving account of a city in agony. Soviet reviewers compared it with *The Diary of Anne Frank*.

When Kuznetsov's book began to appear serially in the Moscow magazine *Yunost (Youth)* in the autumn of 1966, it created a sensation. The full story of Babi Yar had never been told. For many years the Soviet authorities had suppressed or played down the fact that the Nazis singled out the Jews as victims. Kiev's Babi Yar was most notorious as the scene of a gruesome slaughter of the Jews, and for a quarter of a century the Soviet press ignored the whole matter. No tablet marked the site. It is as if, say, the Polish public had never been told about the Auschwitz (Oswiecim) death camp. Indeed, thanks to this Soviet press policy, the Auschwitz camp in Poland and the Buchenwald concentration camp in Germany became far better known to the Soviet people than the Babi Yar on their own soil. Not until the start of the 1960's did the poet Yevtushenko electrify Soviet audiences by reading his poem which begins: *No monument stands over Babi Yar.* . . . But it remained for Anatoly Kuznetsov to recount exactly what happened at Babi Yar. Now it is reported that the Kiev authorities plan to mark the spot.

But it was not merely his disclosures about the massacre at Babi Yar that made Kuznetsov's book a sensation. For a long time after the war, Soviet citizens who had stayed behind under the Nazi occupation instead of fleeing with the Soviet Army were regarded with suspicion, whether they had actually been collaborators or merely innocent victims. This is perhaps the first Soviet novel about the occupation to describe everyday life under the Nazis realistically and to take civilians for its heroes, rather than soldiers or partisans; it does not conceal the collaboration of some Ukrainians; and, though the author was filled with a fierce hatred of the Nazis, he portrayed them as convincing characters. With all this, it is a touching story of boyhood, by a gifted writer, and something of a *tour de force* of popular history writing. It is a cry for human freedom. Small wonder that interest around the world has been intense.

Columbia University houses a magazine called *The Current Digest of the Soviet Press,* which I began in 1949. Each week the staff of this magazine issues a book-length collection of translations from Soviet newspapers and magazines, for use by researchers and scholars. *The Current Digest* had never published a novel, but when Anatoly Kuznetsov's reached these shores the editors felt it was such a vital account of "history in human terms" that it deserved the highest priority. Within two weeks *The Current Digest* printed the beginning of the book in a translation by Jacob Guralsky, an American translator who had spent many years in the Soviet Union, and Mary Mackler. Their translation was

A Note About This Book

edited by Barbara Appel. The Dial Press, which had successfully procured copies of the Russian magazine text in Europe —with the very valuable assistance of George Feifer, the well-known writer on Soviet affairs—then commissioned Mr. Guralsky to translate the text for this edition. Norman Sloan, Assistant Editor of *The Current Digest,* was of great help. Anne M. Barry of The Dial Press deserves credit for seeing the manuscript to press with what seems miraculous speed. My thanks to the publisher, Richard W. Baron, for his help and perspicacity, and to Patrice La Liberté, Charlotte Allstrom and Patricia Carlin for their invaluable assistance.

The illustrations, which originally appeared in *Yunost,* are by S. Brodsky.

A few words about terms that may require explanation. "Militia" is the Soviet word for "police" (Kuznetsov's father was a militiaman); the policemen under the German occupation, recruited mostly from among Ukrainian collaborators, were called *Polizei.* To avoid confusion, we have used the Russian and German words, rather than "policeman." The passports referred to in the story are not passports for foreign travel, but the internal passports that all Soviet citizens carry. They specify nationality, among other things, and the Nazis used them to identify Jews. Soviet citizens also have "labor books," in which their employment is recorded, but not nationality. As for other terms and places and names that may need clarification, explanations have been relegated to notes in order not to interrupt the flow of the author's narrative.

LEO GRULIOW
Editor, *The Current Digest*
of the Soviet Press

NEW YORK, JANUARY, 1967

Table of Contents

ix

BABI YAR

BY

YEVGENY YEVTUSHENKO

No monument stands over Babi Yar.
A drop sheer as a crude gravestone.
I am afraid.
      Today I am as old in years
as all the Jewish people.
Now I seem to be
      a Jew.
Here I plod through ancient Egypt.
Here I perish crucified, on the cross,
and to this day I bear the scars of nails.
I seem to be
      Dreyfus.
The Philistine
      is both informer and judge.
I am behind bars.
      Beset on every side.
Hounded,
    spat on,
      slandered.

Squealing, dainty ladies in flounced
Brussels lace
stick their parasols into my face.
I seem to be then
               a young boy in Byelostok.
Blood runs, spilling over the floors.
The bar-room rabble-rousers
give off a stench of vodka and onion.
A boot kicks me aside, helpless.
In vain I plead with these pogrom bullies.
While they jeer and shout,
               "Beat the Yids. Save Russia!"
some grain-marketeer beats up my mother.
O my Russian people!
                              I know
                                        you
are international to the core.
But those with unclean hands
have often made a jingle of your
purest name.
I know the goodness of my land.
How vile these anti-Semites—
                    without a qualm
they pompously called themselves
"The Union of the Russian People"!
I seem to be
               Anne Frank
transparent
               as a branch in April.
And I love
               And have no need of phrases.
My need
               is that we gaze into each other.
How little we can see
                    or smell!
We are denied the leaves,
                    we are denied the sky.

Yet we can do so much—
                    tenderly
embrace each other in a dark room.
They're coming here?
          Be not afraid. Those are the booming
sounds of spring:
                    spring is coming here.
Come then to me.
               Quick, give me your lips.
Are they smashing down the door?
                         No, it's the ice breaking . . .
The wild grasses rustle over Babi Yar.
The trees look ominous,
                    like judges.
Here all things scream silently,
                    and, baring my head,
slowly I feel myself
                    turning gray.
And I myself
          am one massive, soundless scream
above the thousand thousand buried here.
I am
     each old man
               here shot dead.
I am
     every child
               here shot dead.
Nothing in me
               shall ever forget!
The "Internationale," let it
                    thunder
when the last anti-Semite on earth
is buried forever.
In my blood there is no Jewish blood.
In their callous rage, all anti-Semites
must hate me now as a Jew.
For that reason
          I am a true Russian!

—From *The Poetry of Yevgeny Yevtushenko, 1953 to 1965*, translated by
George Reavey and published by October House, Inc.

A Necessary Explanation

Everything in this book is the truth.

When I told parts of this story to various people, they all said I ought to write a book. The longer I lived, the more I myself became convinced it was my duty.

The thing is that I was born and grew up in Kiev, in Kurenevka District, not far from the big ravine whose name used to be known only to local residents—Babi Yar.

Like other parts of Kurenevka, Babi Yar was, as they say, the scene of my childhood, a place where we played, and so on.

Then suddenly one day it became very well known.

For more than two years it was a forbidden zone, ringed with high-voltage barbed wire; it had a camp, and signboards announcing that anyone who approached would be fired upon.

Once I was even inside—in the office, it is true, and not in the gully itself; otherwise I would not have written this book.

A Necessary Explanation by the Author

We heard the bursts of machine-gun fire at irregular intervals: ta-ta-ta, ta-ta. I heard this, day after day, for two years, and it still rings in my ears.

At the end of the second year of the occupation thick, heavy smoke rose over the gully. It kept rising for three weeks.

When the German troops were driven from Kiev and it was all over, a friend and I, though we were afraid of mines, went to see what was left there.

It was a huge, one might even say majestic, ravine dividing three Kiev districts: Lukyanovka, Kurenevka and Syrets. A pleasant stream used to course through its bottom. The banks were steep, precipitous, sometimes overhanging; there were frequent landslides in Babi Yar. But in general it looked quite ordinary. There was also the neighboring Repyakhov Yar, very similar, and many other ravines.

A tattered old man carrying a sack was crossing the ravine, and from the confidence with which he walked we realized that this was not the first time he had walked here.

"Hey, uncle!" I shouted. "Was it here that they shot the Jews, or farther on?"

The old man stopped, looked me over from head to foot and said:

"And how many Russians were killed here, and Ukrainians and other nationalities?"

And he went his way.

We knew the stream like the palms of our hands. In

childhood we had dammed it to make ponds and bridged it with stepping-stones and gone swimming in it.

It used to have good, grainy sand, but now for some reason the sand was sprinkled with white pebbles.

I bent over and picked up a pebble. It was a burned piece of bone, the size of a fingernail, white on top, black on bottom. The stream had washed these pebbles down and was carrying them along. From this we concluded that they had shot the Jews, Russians, Ukrainians and other nationalities higher upstream.

So we walked for a long time over these bones until we came to the very mouth of the ravine, and the stream disappeared; it flowed from many sandy layers. The bones were being washed out from these layers.

The gully became narrow here and divided into several channels, and in one place the sand was gray. Suddenly we realized that we were walking on human ashes.

Nearby, a sand bank, washed by the rains, had caved in and exposed a granite outcropping—and a layer of coal. The coal layer was about ten inches thick.

Goats were grazing on the bank, while three goatherd boys, about eight years old, were chipping off lumps of the coal with hammers and crushing the lumps on the granite outcropping.

We came up to them. The coal was grainy and brown, as though locomotive ash had been mixed with paste.

"What are you doing?" I asked.

A Necessary Explanation by the Author

"See!" One of them reached into his pocket and brought out something shiny and dirty. He held it out in his palm.

It was a half-melted gold ring and some other bit of metal.

They were mining gold.

We wandered around and found many complete bones and a fresh, still damp skull and, again, lumps of dark ash in the sand.

I picked up one lump which weighed about five pounds, carried it off and kept it. It was the ashes of many people, all mixed together—international ash, so to speak.

Even then the thought came to me that someone should tell about this as it really happened, from the very beginning, omitting nothing and inventing nothing.

This is what I am doing, because I feel it my duty; because, as it says in Till Eulenspiegel, *"Klaas's ashes knock at my heart."*

Thus, the word "documentary" in the subtitle of this novel means that I am presenting only authenticated facts and documents and that here you will find not the slightest literary invention—that is, not "how it might have happened" or "how it should have been."

A. K.

THE GERMANS COME

FROM THE SOVIET INFORMATION BUREAU

EVENING COMMUNIQUÉ SEPTEMBER 21, 1941

Throughout September 21 our troops fought the enemy along the entire front. After fierce fighting lasting many days, our troops have left Kiev.

I saw our men leaving and realized that this was the end. Occasionally a few Red Army men in their faded khaki uniforms, some with packs on their backs and some without, ran through the courtyards and across the garden plots and jumped the fences.

It became very quiet. The battle had gone on for many days, with the thunder of artillery, the wail of sirens, one bombing after another; at night the whole horizon had been lit up with lightning flashes and the glow of fires; we had slept on our bundles in a slit-trench shelter, and the earth had shaken and poured down on our heads.

Then all was quiet—a stillness more frightening than any shooting. We could not tell whether Kurenevka now lay on our side of the front, on the other, or somewhere in between.

A machine gun chattered, distinct and near, from the side of the railway embankment. Twigs and leaves fell from the old willow that spread over our trench. I crashed through the hatch and into the shelter, where Grandfather snarled and slapped my face.

Our trench in the kitchen garden was a typical air raid shelter of those times: T-shaped, it was two yards deep and almost a yard wide. Such slits had been dug in every backyard and in all the streets and squares. The radio had told us how to dig them.

Grandfather and I had worked on ours for several days and had improved on the pattern. We had put boards along the earthen walls, covered the floor with bricks, and built a roof. We did not have the planks, of course, for a triangular roof, but laid our five-foot wooden hunting traps across the top and piled all the firewood and everything else we could find in the shed on top of them.

Grandfather figured that the bomb that hit our trench would have to plow through all that wood; the logs would fly apart, but the explosion would never reach us—not through all that hard firewood!

To make the whole thing as solid as possible, we covered the wood with dirt, and the dirt with cakes of grassy sod by way of camouflage. As a result we had a fairly impressive and striking hillock, underneath which, when the hatch at the entrance was in place, everything was as quiet and dark as a grave.

It was our great good luck that no explosions occurred anywhere near us and that we were not hit by a single sizable hunk of shrapnel, for if that had happened the whole woodpile would have come down on our heads. We did not realize this at the time and were proud of the job we had done, sure that we were sitting there luxuriously safe.

At first, before we had such a good bomb shelter, Grandfather, Grandmother and I used to hide from the bombs under the bed.

The bed was an old, solid affair, backed with sheet metal on which pictures had been painted in oils: a mill and a lake with swans on it. If a bomb came down, we thought, it would come through the ceiling and bounce on the feather bed and spring mattress. When it exploded, the feather bed and the two padded blankets would, naturally, keep the shrapnel from penetrating.

To avoid lying on the bare floor, Grandmother spread a blanket under the bed and put our pillows there, so that it was cozy.

When the shooting started and the windows vibrated to the howl of bombers, Grandfather would be the first to roll under the bed and press against the wall. I would tumble in next, taking the middle place, and Grandmother, always fussing around the stove, would catch up our tomcat Titus and lie down at the edge, protecting us all with her own body. That is how we kept saving ourselves.

Grandfather kept muttering prayers and cursing me:

"You *gomon!* What are you twisting about like that for? Got a worm in you, or what?"

When we had finished our mighty trench, we ran to and from it in the same order, Grandmother always burdened with the pillows and blankets (she never left them in the trench for fear they would grow damp). Our tomcat Titus got used to the war. At the first shell he would fly for the hatch of the trench in great leaps, his tail waving high. There he would meow, with agony in his eyes, until somebody lifted him in; he had learned to climb up the steep ladder, but not to get down.

3

I never found out what a *gomon* was. Grandfather died before I remembered to ask him. As for my worm of curiosity, it always tormented me. I would peek out to count the planes and see the gruesome crosses on them. Or I would try to see how the bombs exploded. But when the Red Army men went running past and it was clear that this was the end, I did not very much want to look, and was really terrified.

There was a kerosene lamp in our trench which gave off smelly fumes. Mama (until now she had been on duty day and night at her school) sat on a stool, with horror in her eyes. Grandfather kept eating. He always did that when he was excited. His forked beard bobbed up and down, for, because of his dentures, he never chewed his food, but only "squelched" it, as Grandmother used to say; and the crumbs kept falling down his beard. Grandmother prayed on and on, almost inaudibly. She crossed herself at intervals before the Mother of God, the icon she had brought here. I had knocked a nail into the wall to hang it on. I liked this icon. It was my favorite among all the ones Grandmother had.

There was always a quiet rustling, a fuss and stirring in the walls behind the boards. Ants, beetles and worms went about their lives there, oblivious of the war. The earth at last stopped rocking and seeping through the chinks in the ceiling. In that eerie silence one felt something awful was about to happen, an explosion of unthinkable dimensions.

I sat there, barely breathing, waiting for the detonation.

Suddenly there were hasty footsteps overhead. The hatch went up, and we saw the face of our neighbor Yelena Pavlovna.

"What are you sitting there for? The Germans have come!" She was wrought up, not at all herself.

I was twelve years old. Many things were happening for

4

the first time in my life. This was the first time that Germans had turned up. I bounced out of the trench. Squinting in the bright light, I noticed that the world had changed somehow, though everything seemed to be as it was before.

Waving her hands, Yelena Pavlovna breathlessly continued:

"A young fellow, such a young one, standing there! My windows face the street. The truck left, but the young fellow is still there."

I sped across the yard and reached the top of the fence in one bound.

Right there on our Petropavlovskaya Square stood a low-slung, predatory, long cannon on fat, inflated tires. And beside it there was indeed a very young, straw-haired, rosy-cheeked German soldier in an extraordinarily clean and well-fitting gray-green uniform. His rifle lay cradled in his arm, and when he noticed that I was watching he stiffened proudly. I liked the way he stiffened; he was showing off.

I had a friend who was three years older than I. His name was Bolik Kaminsky, and I shall tell about him later. He was evacuated with his factory school. Now, this fellow was very much like Bolik. I had expected all sorts of things: The fascists would turn out to be fearful giants or would all be riding on tanks, wearing gas masks and horned helmets. I was shaken to see this ordinary, commonplace boy, altogether like Bolik.

So he was showing off! Well, so would I if I had a cannon like that.

The incredible explosion I had been waiting for came at that instant. I gasped for breath, hit my chin on the fence and nearly fell off. The little soldier was squatting disgracefully, bunched up in fright against his artillery piece.

But he recovered at once, stood up and stared at something over my head. I turned and saw the blue sky filled with falling tree crowns, boards and bits of planks whirling and sailing about.

"So they blew up the bridge after all!" said Grandfather, putting his nose over the fence to get his view of the first German. "Oho! Now that's something! How can anyone fight them? They're a real army. Just look at the way he's dressed!"

The soldier was indeed well-dressed. In cartoons and films German troops had always looked like ragged tramps and bandits. In life they turned out to be somewhat different. A square, angular, mean-looking truck dashed up in a cloud of dust, swung rakishly about (Grandfather and I watched, fascinated) while two more soldiers as agile as circus athletes coupled the cannon to the truck, sprang onto the running boards and flew off toward Podol, one hanging on each side.

"Well," said Grandfather, shaken, "The Soviet regime is finished. Go ahead and help carry the things into the cottage. They got wet in the trench."

I went to the trench, but not very willingly. Mama handed up some bundles from the black pit, suitcases and stools. Grandmother took the things from her and heaped them together, while I started carrying them to the house.

We had done the same thing ever so many times of late: into the trench, out of the trench; down, up. If only we had had something decent to hide; but it was always the same rubbish: a patched, moth-eaten leather coat from Tsarist times, pillows and such. In short, it was no job for a man.

Shurka Matsa, my second lifelong friend, appeared from behind the fence. Wide-eyed, he shouted, "The Germans are marching up the streetcar line! Let's go!"

I was off like the wind before Grandmother could say so much as "Wait a minute!"

Frunze Street (the old people still called it Kirillovskaya) was filled with trucks and carts from end to end, as far as you could see. They were angular trucks with jutting parts of all kinds, with grills and brackets.

Every truck or car has a face. It can look at the world indifferently with its headlights, or angrily, or pitifully, or surprised. But these were like the first, the one that had carried the cannon away. They had that mean look. I had never seen such machines before and thought them very powerful because of the roaring and smoke with which they filled the street.

The bodies of some of the trucks were entire little houses, with cots and tables that screwed to the floor. Soldiers looked out from these trucks. Some of them strolled along the street in gray-green, clean-shaven, fresh and cheerful. They laughed at the slightest pretext, joked and shouted to the first people who ventured out into the street. Helmeted motorcyclists darted through the traffic of carts loaded with ammunition and bundles. Each motorcyclist had a machine gun fitted to his handlebars.

Huge, fiery-red draught horses with straw-colored manes, horses the like of which we had never seen, advanced slowly and importantly on their shaggy legs. Harnessed in teams of six, they hauled the big guns with no effort at all. Our little Russian horses, with which the Red Army retreated, would have seemed like foals alongside these giants.

Officers in visored caps with silver insignia sat cheerfully chatting in dazzling black or white limousines. Shurka and I could hardly breathe. We could not see enough. Taking a chance, we dashed across the street. The sidewalks were quickly filling with people.

Nearly all the Germans carried little Russian phrase books. Leafing through them, they kept calling to the girls on the sidewalks:

"*Panenka,* girl! Bolshevik finished! Ukraine!"

"*Ukrá-ina,*" the girls corrected them.

"*Ja, ja! Ukrá-ina!* Come for a walk, *spazieren, bitte!*"

A crowd came moving down Bondar Lane, flowing solemnly in one direction, heads bobbing, and finally emerged as a procession of superannuated men and women. The old man at the head carried a towel slung over his shoulder, a round loaf of bread and a salt shaker on a tray. People crushed in from all sides to see the scene.

The old people stood confused for an instant. Were they too late? To whom should they offer their bread and salt? The leader moved toward the nearest of the white cars, where several officers sat smiling, and proffered his tray with a bow. Shurka and I were parted somehow, but I pushed forward with all my strength. They were saying something there. I heard laughter, and the people at the back of the crowd kept asking, "What did he say? What did he say?" But the column moved on. As the car rolled by I saw an officer in the front seat of the car hand the bread and towel on to those in the back.

Everybody was saying that the Germans had shouted "Butter and rolls!" and had dropped a case of butter and a basket full of rolls right on the streetcar tracks, as though to say "Help yourselves!" This set me scurrying about, trying to find where it had happened. I ran toward the bridge on Vyshgorodskaya Street.

There were neither rolls nor butter by the bridge, but

8

instead I saw a fire. A brick house on a corner stood burning serenely, slowly. The fire had started when a shell had plunged through one of its windows. The fence had been pulled down and lay on the flowers skirting the house. People tramped all over them. Two women and a girl kept shoveling dirt into the flames because there was no water. A man came out of the crowd of gapers and smashed a window with a stick.

A German sprang from a truck and took out his camera. Now squatting, now standing, he took close-ups and long shots.

The man who had broken the window climbed into the house and began to hand chairs and boxes of linen from a clothes closet to the women and the girl outside. He hurled a coat and a dress into the street, and everybody praised him, saying what a fine man he was. I thought so too. A brave man!

The troops kept coming from the bridge, clouds upon clouds of them. The sun was bright, and there was no shooting. There was only the roar of motors, wheels thudding, voices calling and laughing. All this made me dizzy after my long confinement in our shelter. Unsteadily, I made for home to report everything I had seen.

A soldier in gray-green stood in our yard with a gun slung over his shoulder and a rope in his hands. A simple-looking fellow with fair eyelashes and a flushed forehead, he stood looking about indifferently, while Grandfather beckoned to him, inviting him into the shed.

"There's nothing in the house, *nichts, nichts*. But over here, maybe there is. Come have a look, *bitte*."

The soldier shuffled reluctantly toward the small shed.

"They're looking for prisoners," said Grandmother from the porch.

9

Inside the shed was a hatch leading to a little cellar, and the soldier pointed to it.

"Matches, matches!"

Handed a match, he struck it and looked cautiously into the hole.

"There's a partisan in there!" said Grandmother, loudly and ironically.

The soldier sprang back as if he had been stung, turned his head and stared.

"I'm joking," soothed Grandmother. "Go ahead, don't be afraid. No partisans."

The soldier grumbled, however, and did not want to climb into the cellar. Instead, he pointed severely to our red house flag, the one Grandfather hung out at the gates on holidays.

"That."

"Yes, yes!" Grandfather began fussing about. Snatching the flag, he tore it from its pole. "Marfa, throw it into the stove, quick!"

Another soldier turned up, also carrying a rope. He shouted something excitedly to the first, and the two ran off. Grandmother beckoned me into the hallway of our house.

"Take this up to the garret. Wrap it in a newspaper and hide it up there."

I knew why. Climbing into the garret, I reached a far corner by crawling on my belly and shoved the packet behind a beam. I descended, eating a lot of spider webs on my way, and found Grandmother at the gate with Yelena Pavlovna.

Grandmother was calling to Grandfather, "Come quick. They're bringing a partisan!"

Our soldier with the flushed forehead was driving a fat, dirty pig down the street. He was lashing its sides with his rope, while a second soldier lashed it from behind with a switch. A cluster of several other soldiers accompanied them, chortling happily.

Wide-eyed and breathless, Yelena Pavlovna related that the soldiers were not looking for prisoners at all, but simply plundering. They had taken Kaminsky's pig and had stolen some leather coats. They had also looked into her, Yelena Pavlovna's, closet and under her bed. They had peeled the pillowcases off her pillows and taken the towel from where it hung on its nail. Her neighbor hadn't wanted to give up his pig, so they had given him a receipt for it, saying, *"Offizier, Offizier* pay!" We were lucky to have been robbed of nothing. Maybe they had been ashamed to take anything from us, because Grandfather had kept saying those German words.

Grandfather's eyes followed that valiant armed procession, headed by a pig.

"Come on," he said gruffly. "Let's carry the things back into the trench. The devil take them, I completely forgot that as conquerors they're entitled to rob us for three whole days."

CHAPTER II

LOOTING TAKES KNOW-HOW

Our neighbor took his receipt to the school, which now apparently served as staff headquarters. I tagged after him, thinking, "They'll give him some German money, and I'll ask him to show it to me."

I stayed at the gate, while he told somebody in the yard what he had come for and then entered a door. Then I saw him fly out of the door with a crash, his arms waving wildly. The soldiers yelled at him and clicked the bolts of their guns. Afraid they would start shooting, I dived around the corner.

Troops were still moving across the square, though more sparsely now. Some shady-looking characters came running from the marketplace, toting bags and bundles. Sure that the marketplace was just where I belonged at the moment, I darted in that direction.

The windows of the hardware store had been smashed, and people were hauling drums of paint, locks and bundles of shovels out of the store. I plunged into the thick of them, working my elbows, trying to get to the counter, but people

13

had clambered up on it. I could glimpse only a forest of boots trampling the spilled chalk and putty. The crowd heaved for one of the stockroom sheds behind the store and I went along, and in the doorway earned a punch on the head and another on the mouth. With a running start I wedged myself between a pair of *muzhiks* and got such a squeezing that I nearly heard my ribs crack; but there, under my nose at last, stood a box that had been broken open.

Inside, covered with straw, lay some kerosene lamps, brand-new, though innocent of any glass chimneys. I reached for them, pushed someone else's hands aside, clutched one, then another, and found—that there were no more. Gone.

I ran into the street and could have howled with disappointment. They had broken into the haberdashery—and to think that I had seen it intact on my way here!

Twisting into the shop, I managed to grab a box from a shelf. Someone tried to snatch it from me, but I hung onto it like a cat to a hunk of meat. My soul was nearly shaken out of me until the box came apart, scattering buttons apparently meant for a coat. I filled my pockets with them.

I noticed clothes brushes being kicked about underfoot, snatched for them and caught about five, but lost one of my lamps and saw it grabbed up by someone at once.

Battered and swaying on my feet, I came into the open and saw people hauling bags of salt from the grocery. By the time I got there I found nothing but a lot of paper and empty crates. I was ready to cry. I wasn't a greedy boy, really. Grandmother had brought me up to be such a well-behaved and polite grandson! But the spirit of plunder had swept over me like a hot avalanche, and I could hardly breathe from greed and eagerness. I seemed to have missed everything; everywhere I was just a bit too late. As a small compensation, I took the weights from the scale on the counter and made for home with my spoils.

People looked out of windows and from behind gates, and our neighbor Pavel Sochav remarked loudly and ironically, for the whole street to hear, "So Tolya has been plundering, too. Go on home and tell your mother to give you a good spanking."

I felt as though someone had thrown a pail of cold water over me. A moment before I had been so proud, carrying my lamp and brushes, but now I scurried into the yard and dumped my spoils in the hallway.

"What's all this?" Mama gasped.

Grandmother shook her head sadly.

"Haven't we enough lamps of our own, child?"

Praise came from Grandfather, however:

"Good for him! Leave him alone! You'll be a good householder, you will! And I've missed it all, everything! Shatkovsky brought home half a grocery store. What a chance I had! Meanwhile, only we are being robbed!"

It turned out that while I was away at the marketplace, six soldiers had arrived, demanding, "Eggs, milk!" They had scoured the house, making themselves quite at home, and had taken our potatoes, cabbages and tomatoes.

"Just look what's going on! While some are plundering out there, others are doing it right here. What a business!"

I was still quivering with excitement and ran off to call Shurka Matsa. Together we chased down to the marketplace again. But it was empty now. Rummage about as we would, we found nothing at all. The place had been swept clean. The shops were littered only with paper, straw and broken glass.

We went into the street and watched the troops marching, marching into the town. Tractors, heavy-duty trucks, columns of soldiers on bicycles, carts and plain wagons. Those who had already come in and found quarters were loaded down with bundles and various rubbish, some of them with cloaks slung over their shoulders.

A wind blew up, chasing wisps of straw and paper and the smoke from the German trucks and other machines, and the German columns kept marching in endlessly, like a bank of clouds; and then they all got down to grabbing and hauling things away, all of them together and as thoroughly as locusts. This was cool and judicious sacking, apparently normal and quite accustomed robbery. This was on Friday, September 19, 1941.

KIEV IN HANDS OF GERMAN TROOPS

THE FUEHRER'S HEADQUARTERS   SEPTEMBER 20.

The high command of Germany's armed forces reports:

As operations proceeded for the encirclement of the Soviet armies in the East, an offensive was launched against Kiev, the capital of the Ukraine. After valiantly penetrating strong fortifications on the western bank of the Dnieper, our troops entered the city. The banner of the German army has flown over the Kiev citadel since this morning.

Offensive operations are moving irresistibly eastward from the Dnieper. We have scored major successes in the battles for the approaches to Leningrad. . . .[1]

CHAPTER III

WE ENTER THE "NEW LIFE"

When the fascists took Kiev, the newspaper *Ukrainskoye slovo* had already published fifteen issues; it had been printed in Zhitomir prior to the capture of Kiev. It was sold by the occupationists, or just handed out in the streets. Grandfather got a copy of it somewhere, triumphantly brought it home and eagerly got down to reading it. But not being very good at reading small print on poor paper—it was very like wrapping paper—he entrusted the task to me, while listening and contributing his philosophical interpretations.

I shall quote headlines from that newspaper:

"KIEV IN THE HANDS OF THE
GERMAN TROOPS."
"POLTAVA TAKEN."
"OUTSTANDING SUCCESSES AT LENINGRAD."
"MORE TERRITORY OCCUPIED NEAR
LENINGRAD."
"100,000 KILOGRAMS OF BOMBS HIT
PORT OF ODESSA."

"GREAT ADVANCE OF GERMAN TROOPS
IN BATTLES FOR TERRITORY ALONG
LOWER REACHES OF DNIEPER."
"THE STRUGGLE OF THE UKRAINIAN
PEOPLE."
"RESURRECTION OF CHURCH IN
KHOLM PROVINCE."
"GROWTH OF ART IN ZHITOMIR."
"TO KIEV," a poem by Yakov Nagorny.

Here I shall have to make a traditional digression and give
at least a sketchy account of the members of our family,
explaining who we were, what we were like and why. I hate
such digressions in a book myself and don't mind skipping
them; so, if you find mine uninteresting, you may safely skip
it, since it is not the main thing anyway. As for me, I shall
have to pay my due to tradition, since some of the situations
and dialogue may be incomprehensible or confusing otherwise.

Fyodor Vlasovich Semerik, my grandfather, disliked Soviet
rule, to put it plainly. No, he was neither a fascist nor a mon-
archist, nor a nationalist nor a Trotskyite, nor a Red nor
a White; he hadn't the faintest idea about any of these.
A poor peasant by extraction, and in social status a worker
with a long labor record, he was actually a terrified, greedy
little inhabitant of this world.

He was born in 1870, the same year as Lenin, but there
the resemblance between the great man and my grandfather
ended. The great man died; and as Grandmother often put it
when quarreling with Grandfather, "Good people pass away,
but you, you parasite, you go on living and living."

Grandfather grew up in the village of Shenderovka, in

18

Kanev District, in a really desperate rural family with eleven children, all of them living in a tumbledown hut. Leaving his family forever, he spent his youth as a farmhand for German settlers in Kherson Province. When he finished his military service he went to Kiev in search of a living, loafed around looking for work, got a job as a janitor in a general's house, married a laundress, became a streetcar conductor, and began dreaming of having his own cottage and a life of plenty. That is, to be able to eat until he wasn't hungry anymore and not to have to worry about tomorrow or even the day after tomorrow—this was the outermost limit of his dream.

He went hungry and cold, saved every kopek, made a mess of Grandmother's youth, but finally bought a patch in a swamp in Kurenevka, drained it and built his cottage —and then the Revolution broke out.

It did not bring him any special changes, nothing edible anyway, but it robbed him of his dream of getting rich. For many years after that he worked as a plumber in the buildings of Shoe Factory No. 4 and never ceased to fume at the Soviet "paupers' regime"; he was forever complaining, "There are no real managers."

Grandfather was not the slightest bit impressed with collectivization, industrialization, the conquest of the North Pole or of the skies, for such things cannot be put on the table and eaten with porridge. And when he got a cow, he had a lot of trouble feeding it. The queues of people waiting to get mixed fodder were endless. There was a huge meadow beside a nearby embankment, but he was not allowed to turn his cow loose there. How he had had to twist and turn and bribe to get any hay at all! He had trotted all over both Babi and Repyakhov ravines with scythe and bag. He never drank any milk himself, but sent Grandmother to sell it all at the

19

market. In short, he was a great entrepreneur. He was also incredibly envious. He was envious of half of Kurenevka and particularly of those who had good kitchen gardens and hauled baskets of radishes and tomatoes to the market. Kurenevka had been doing this from time immemorial, besides raising cows and suckling pigs. It was deaf to all science, to all the arts and to politics—it demanded but one thing from politics: permission to go on selling radishes.

Grandfather, however, was a long way from being a true Kurenevka higgler. His kitchen garden could have been covered with the palm of a hand, so to speak. He had a patch of it around his cottage and his small shed. The rows of the collective farm vegetable garden reached up to our fence. Grandfather dug some fresh postholes one night and moved the fence half a yard, stealing five square yards of ground from the vegetable gardeners of the collective farm. They never noticed a thing, and Grandfather was in high spirits all week, gloating and scheming to move the fence another half yard in a few years.

He was always inviting quarrels; he surreptitiously picked his neighbor's pears if they happened to hang over "his land"; and sometimes he tried to club the neighbor's chickens when they strayed onto our territory. He was at war, therefore, with the entire street. When he lunged into a cursing match with his saliva flying, he could be heard all the way to the marketplace: "U-tu-tu-tu!" And that is why everybody called him "Semerik-tru-tu-tu."

He was too stingy to drink vodka and never smoked or went to the movies. If he had to get on a streetcar, he tried to ride for nothing; and he wore his pants and jacket until they rotted and just fell apart on him. If a haycart came down the street and lost a wisp or two, he'd be the first onto the road and would sweep the hay into a pile with a stick and bring it solemnly home.

The cow failed to justify her existence and had to be sold.

Grandfather then tried his hand at raising ducks. We used to go down to the pond with them and poke about with a splintered old basket, looking for duckweed to feed them. On such feed the ducks grew up bony and scrawny, so Grandfather switched to chickens, since these went about by themselves and scratched in the dirt for their own feed. The starving hens pecked the seeds out of the garden and just wouldn't lay eggs. Grandfather decided to raise suckling pigs, so that the slop and crumbs wouldn't go to waste. The pigs grew up to be as long-legged, muscular and lean as greyhounds. Both of them came down with distemper and died just about the time the Germans arrived. Both had to be buried. Energetic as Grandfather was, fighting and fussing from dawn to dusk, he could not get rich, and he blamed the authorities for everything.

Whenever he had a guest there was only one thing he could talk about: how wonderful everything had been in the old days, how people had got rich then, and how the Bolshevik ragtag and bobtail had ruined everything. When his crony, old man Zhuk, was arrested one night in 1937 for telling a stupid joke in public, Grandfather was terribly frightened and bereft of two-thirds of his theme. Now he could discourse only on how wonderful everything had been in the old days.

For some reason he never recalled his father's tumble-down hut on a rented patch of somebody else's land, but talked about how wonderfully the general had lived and how cheap everything had been under the Tsar, a roll costing five kopeks and a herring only two. As for his hatred for the

Bolsheviks, he talked only to God about that now, sure he would never be betrayed from on high.

A German leaflet came fluttering down on our roof soon after the war began and stuck to our chimney with the morning dew. Grandfather spotted it, brought a ladder and told me to get it. With some trouble I peeled the wet sheet off, and soon we were reading it.

The leaflet said that Germany had been ordained to destroy the Bolsheviks and establish a new and just order under which "everybody who works honestly will get what he deserves." It told us that life was magnificent in the liberated territory, butter costing only ten kopeks a pound, bread seven kopeks and a herring only three.

Grandfather's eyes started from his head. This was a message personally for him. He learned the contents of the leaflet by heart before tearing it up. He was over 71 by now, but his old dream was returning.

Marfa Yefimovna Dolgorukova, my grandmother, was born and raised in the village of Deremezn, in Obukhov District, in a thrice-cursed shack where, as in Grandfather's family, one could not spit in any direction without hitting a child. There were so many of her family out there, in Deremezn or in Peregonovka or doing odd jobs in Kiev, that I never rightly understood how many of them there were in all and just how they were related to me: Gapka and Konon, Ganna and Nina, Foma and feeble-minded Katya, and so on. They came to see us sometimes, and Grandmother would feed them, giving one of them an old skirt, another a patched pair of galoshes, and so on.

Grandmother went out into the world at twelve, becoming a servant, then a children's nursemaid, and finally a laundress. No matter how I pleaded, she could never recall

anything about her youth or her love—perhaps because there
was nothing to remember but dross.

She was completely illiterate, unable even to read numbers. She could tell paper money by the patterns and colors
of the bills, and coins by their sizes.

Since my mother was a schoolteacher who worked two
shifts at the school and also stayed behind after lessons, I
grew up with Grandmother alone. She woke me in the morning, washed me, fed me, spanked me, bemused me with her
fairy tales. She was forever trudging about, cooking, mixing,
pounding, preparing mash for the suckling pig, chasing out
the cat, bending over the vegetable rows in the kitchen garden or hewing wood, and always complaining of the pains
in her back. She was soft, flabby, with a coarse peasant face,
and always she wore a gray shawl or polka-dot kerchief.

Like Grandfather, she was thrilled by neither the airplanes nor the dirigibles that flew in those days, but was
rather afraid of them. Bundling me to bed atop the stove,
she related:

"When I was a little girl, the lot of us would huddle
together on the stove, clinging to one another, naked, bare-
footed and as hungry as worms, while Grandmother, who's
been dead for many years now, would frighten us, saying,
'You're sitting up there nice and quiet and be glad of that,
for other times will come, terrible times when the whole
world will be entangled in wire, when the enemy will come
across the land, when iron birds will fly above and peck at
people with their iron beaks. When those times come, it will
be the end of the world.' We listened and prayed, our baby
teeth chattering. God forbid that one should live to see such
times. But God didn't listen, and everything has come about
as Grandmother said it would: the wire, the iron birds, and
soon, probably, the end of the world."

In expectation of it, evidently, Grandmother cared nothing about her "property," and gave things away for the salvation of others. We might have lived better, but Grandmother could do without food herself to give it to someone else. She took the kopeks she saved to the church, where the beggars sat, or suddenly got up a parcel for someone in the hospital, for friends, neighbors or relatives. Grandfather was furious, and growled, "The good-for-nothings! Whom are you feeding? We're hungry ourselves!" But Grandmother merely waved him away. The "good-for-nothings" hid themselves when he came home from work, while Grandmother, to avoid sin and quarrels, sank to her knees and prayed.

She had many icons, indeed an entire icon stand in the corner, with a mysteriously glowing icon-lamp, tufts of grass, two wooden crosses—one for Grandfather and one for herself, to be placed in their hands when they lay in their coffins—and family registers, in which I entered the numerous names of relatives "still living" or "passed away," just as she dictated.

My father was a Communist and my mother a schoolteacher, so that a christening was ruled out when I was born. But when my parents were away at work one day, Grandmother wrapped me up and carried me off to the Church of St. Peter and St. Paul, where I was plopped into the font. Grandmother could not bear to leave me without Kingdom Come when I died. She disclosed the secret when I was ten, recalling how I had howled and caught the priest by the beard. It is a consolation to know I gave him what resistance I could.

Tutored by Grandmother, I was a backward person burdened with religion until the age of six. Grandmother would set me before the icon, take my hand in her rough brown palm, and teach me to cross myself and pronounce

24

the magic words which she could not understand herself, as I later found. Here is how she chanted them in her Church Slavonic and how I was to remember them all my life: "Ahfath! Whoart in Heaven, haloed be thy name, thy kingdomcome, thy willbedone on earth as it is in Heaven. Give us this day our dairy bread, do not forgive us our trespasses nor deliver us from evil."

Grandmother never suspected that the mysterious word "Ahfath" meant "Our Father." She thought it was merely the name of the prayer. As for me, I thought it was God's name and that it shone in the dark because it was "haloed." I also assumed that she was praying for "dairy bread," and dutifully reiterated her plea, "Do not forgive us our trespasses nor deliver us from evil."

But Mama, in whom I had ever so much faith, one day declared, "There is no God. Fliers have been all over the sky and have never seen Him."

This was shattering news, and I hastened to convey it to Grandmother, together with the devastating proof. She was annoyed and said it was not given to godless persons like fliers ever to see the Almighty. I thought things over and came to the conclusion that God would have been wiser to show Himself at least to the famous fliers Chkalov and Baidukov, for they would have come down and told everybody that He truly existed. Moreover, if He really existed, why did He have to hide and why did He allow those cursed bombers to fly? Which made me think He was not as almighty as He thought He was.

This launched Grandmother and me on a series of theological squabbles that led nowhere. She stuck to her opinion, and I to mine; but I never prayed anymore.

I asked Grandfather about it, but he was cautious about questions of divinity. He recalled that when he had been a

25

farmhand and was due to go into the army, back in 1890, he had prayed very hard not to be drafted. He had in fact kissed every icon in church, but had been taken into the army just the same. The proof offered by those fliers was convincing, he thought; but whenever he got himself into debt or ardently hoped that his turn would finally come in the queue for mixed fodder, he would spend a long time on his knees, bowing again and again, sweeping the floor with his beard, nagging God and wheedling.

Unlike Grandfather, Grandmother had no enemies, but only friends all down the street. Everybody came to her when in trouble or in need. She helped them all, lent them things, settled family disputes, minded other people's children, gave the neighbors herbs when they had stomach-aches, and helped them to get rid of tapeworms.

Maria Fyodorovna Kuznetsova, my mother, was my grandparents' only daughter, and it was she who gained a lot from the Revolution. She too would have been a servant or a laundress if she had not attended the new teachers' training courses. She became a teacher of grades one through four. She began teaching in 1923.

A pretty girl, well read and capable, she sang and played in the amateur arts circle of the People's Clubhouse. Then Grandfather noticed that he was beginning to have trouble with the militia (the police). Vasya Kuznetsov, the militiaman on the beat, kept coming and coming to the house, complaining that the street had not been swept or that the house number had to be painted afresh. Vasily was soon elected to the Kiev City Soviet, and Grandfather decided he would be an ideal son-in-law, for as a member of the City Soviet, thought Grandfather, Vasily would manage to get just about anything he wanted.

26

How mistaken Grandfather was! This was the biggest mistake of his life. Afterwards he was never able to forgive his son-in-law for never having brought anything home. When Grandfather had to go to the militia office with our house's register of occupants from time to time, he even had to wait in line with the other people to see his own son-in-law. Vasily Kuznetsov was a Bolshevik.

A real Russian type, a Kursk man, he was standing beside his lathe in 1917 when a friend came up and said, "Vasya, do we sign up with the Red Guards?" "We certainly do," was the answer. Vasya went off to hammer the bourgeoisie in the Civil War. He joined the Party in 1918, fought as a partisan in the Ukraine, stormed Kakhovka with General Frunze, took Perekop as the commander of a machine-gun squad, and hurled the White Guard General Wrangel into the Black Sea. He was an extraordinary man, I thought. How well he sang! He had a handsome baritone, was always laughing and, for some reason, could never relate anything seriously.

"Well, tell us how you vagabonds knocked about in the Crimea in the Civil War!" demanded Grandfather.

"Why not?" laughed Father. "The Crimea is a good place, plenty of wine. All the wineries were open when we came. I looked into the vats the minute we got there and sure enough, one of our group was floating in one already, up to his ears, his boots and machine-gun belt still on. Then I bet the fellows a Mauser pistol that I could drink a pail of port wine at one go."

"Why, that's three quarts!" gasped Grandfather.

"And I did, too."

"That's all they were good for!" spat Grandfather. "You'd better tell us what good the Guards did you, you hunger-monger!"

"I was recommended for the Order of the Red Banner," boasted Father. "But we were a hot-headed lot in those days. We were absolute ramrods. Those were the very first Orders. They had just been introduced into the Red Army. Frunze decorated several men. But we raised a row. 'They had Orders like that under the Tsar; are we now to have those pendulums again? We aren't fighting for those trinkets,' we said. So I refused to accept mine."

"Fool!" wailed Grandfather, clapping his hands together. "The award carries a regular monthly cash payment that you could be receiving! As it is, all you got was a pair of militiaman's trousers!"

Having exchanged his army uniform for that of a militiaman after the Civil War, Father indeed had nothing but that uniform. Grandmother and Mama had laboriously made his first suit. Grandfather never missed a chance to reproach him for this. Father finally left the militia and entered a workers' school. From there he went on to the Polytechnical Institute, bending over his drawing board night after night. Later, he went off to Uman for a long time, conducting the work of collectivization. On the day he defended his diploma dissertation he took me along. Everybody applauded when he finished. He had become a foundry engineer.

That was when he began to clash seriously with Grandfather.

"You're hiding your head in the sand, Father-in-law," Father would thunder. "You're a malingerer, a reproach to the Revolution! Just look: Your daughter got an education, and your son-in-law too. There's no speculation now, nor competition nor cheating either. And wait till you see what's coming!"

"If you're so smart," sneered Grandfather, "then allow me to keep a dozen cows and give me a field to plow."

"The fields belong to the collective farms. If you like cows, why don't you join a collective farm?"

"Join your paupers' farm yourself, if you like."

The quarrels between Father and Mother had also come to a head by that time, though for a different reason —jealousy. Mama was very jealous. I understood nothing at that time, but felt that Father and Mother had very strong tempers indeed. The quarrels were continuous now, and there was a constant flow of tears. From Grandmother I suddenly learned that my parents had gone to court and got a divorce long ago, but were unable to part for the time being. Father at last gathered his blueprints under his arm and set off for a job at the Gorky Automobile Plant. Though he married there, Mother continued to love him and never married again.

When the war began and the danger arose that the Germans might enter Kiev, Mother sent Father several anguished telegrams begging him to take us away, but there was no answer.

Mother wept hysterically at night, and Grandmother tried to soothe her:

"Don't worry, Marusya, we'll get along here."

"But what shall I do if the Germans come—teach the children to say 'Heil Hitler'?" quavered Mother, horrified. "I'm going to take Tolik and go away, no matter what happens."

"What will become of us then?" wept Grandmother.

She was right, for Mother's salary was the mainstay of the family. She was a proud woman and demanded no alimony from Father for a long time. It was only shortly before the war that Grandfather's prodding prompted her to take the step. We began to receive money orders through the bookkeeping department of the marriage registration office, but these were interrupted by the war.

Mother worked two shifts at the public school and sometimes earned a little extra money at evening school. She was allowed to do this because she was an exceptionally conscientious and gifted teacher. Her pupils at the evening school, all of them workers and fully grown up, used to call on us to court Mother. Grandfather liked them for bringing sausage, canned food and drinks. He would discuss things with them and ask them to bring scarce goods. Mother would sit in on such parties angrily for a minute or two and then go to bed. Her wooers finally soured and disappeared.

Mother had been on duty beside the telephone in the empty school of late, in the event of incendiary bombs. No provision had been made to evacuate the teachers. We packed our luggage but never got away. Mother was terrified by the advent of the Germans, expecting nothing good to come of it.

Titus the cat was the faithful companion of all my childhood. I have thought it over and decided that I would be sinning against truth if I did not mention him as a member of the family, for that is what he was, to me at any rate, besides playing an important role in my life, as I shall later recount.

He was an old cat, affectionate by nature, but very earnest and important. Familiarity was distasteful to him. He had a subtle way of knowing who really liked him and who was only fawning and currying favor.

Grandmother loved him, but Grandfather hated him desperately, mainly for exacting his food for nothing.

Grandfather once shoved him under his shirt, got on a streetcar and rode all the way to Pushcha-Voditsa, nine miles off and all surrounded with forests. He released him there and chased him into the woods.

Titus came home in a week, very hungry, frightened and unhappy.

Really angry now, Grandfather stuffed Titus into a bag, carried him across the whole city to Demiyevka and tossed him into Goloseyev Forest.

This time Titus came back in three months, with a crushed paw and minus an ear. He had had to cross the whole of our great city. Grandfather let him alone after that. Later, when I read Ernest Thompson Seton's heart-rending story about a cat who stubbornly swam across rivers and plodded through cities to reach the garbage can where he was born, I believed every word of it.

Though Titus learned to hide in our trench from the fascist planes, he had no real grasp of politics and could be said to have been the most apolitical of us all. This was foolish of him, of course, for the new life was to affect him too.

That is what we were like when the fascists came, or rather by the beginning of the war: insignificant noncombatants, two old people, a woman and a little boy, that is, the sort who least want war, but who, for some pernicious reason, suffer from it more than anyone else.

You are much mistaken, however, if you think that this story is going to show that war brings a lot of suffering to old folk, women and children. It is hardly necessary to prove such a thing. I have mixed a lot of personal matters in all this, of course, but I stress and stress again that this story is least of all meant to tell of all sorts of personal troubles.

31

This book is about something quite different.

"What sort of medals are these?" asked Grandfather, eyeing the newspaper.

A whole page of it was filled with "The Struggle of the Ukrainian People"—an historical outline, with pictures of medallions stamped with the portraits of Prince Svyatoslav, Princess Olga, Vladimir the Baptist, Bogdan Khmelnitsky, Mazepa, Shevchenko, Lesya Ukrainka and Simon Petlura.[1]

"So they haven't rejected Shevchenko?" marveled Grandfather.

"No."

"Nor Bogdan?"

"Nor Bogdan."

"That's remarkable! Mazepa, too. Petlura? Hmm." Grandfather stroked his beard. "As for that devil, I don't really know. I saw Petlura myself. He was a parasite and cutthroat. You can't imagine the things he and his men did around here!"

Mother came in to have a look at the newspaper. She had been in the next room, remaking my coat for the winter.

"I can't believe it," she muttered. "It's a nightmare. I still can't believe they surrendered Kiev. I just can't."

"You're a fool," said Grandfather cheerfully. "Forget the Bolsheviks. Forget them forever and aye!"

I got down to reading the details about the resurrection of the church in Kholm Province and about the marvelous upsurge of art in Zhitomir. Grandfather listened with deep satisfaction, nodding importantly to emphasize the words.

"That's fine," he said. "That'll be very good. The Germans know what they're about. Listen to me. When I was young, working for the German settlers, I realized even then that they were real managers. They like to work and hate people who are lazy. You'll get exactly what you earned. There'll be no cheating. And they've no thievery among them. When they go off anywhere they just latch their doors with a bit of wood—no locks! And if they do happen to catch a thief, they just beat him and keep hitting him until he's dead. You'll see what sort of a life we'll lead: Heaven on earth!"

"Nothing will come of it," said Mother, in a strange voice. "Our side will come back."

We did not argue with her, for we knew what she had on her mind, something she would not tell anyone. She was thinking that the old times might come back and with them Father, whom she loved and would continue to love to her dying day.

She shrugged and went back to her sewing. Grandmother was half-buried in the oven, moving the pots around, so that the newspaper remained an exclusively male affair.

"How lucky you are!" commented Grandfather. "The new life has come to Grandmother and me only in our old age. Marusya doesn't understand a thing. And you're lucky because you're young."

Why, that's great, I thought. I'm really young, and now the Germans have come, really good managers all. There won't even be any thieves. Mother has turned ashen with fear, but what does she know about it? She never saw them before, but Grandfather, he worked for Germans. I felt queer and a little anxious on the threshold of the new life.

"All right, to hell with them, let them put Petlura in the icons if they want!" said Grandfather in a sudden gust of hatred. "As long as it's not those ragged-arsed hunger-mongers who've brought the country to ruin. You could strangle, trying to get a bit of miserable cloth. Why, I could have bought a bale of it when I was a farm hand in the days of the Tsar."

"There's no fool like an old fool!" sighed Grandmother beside the stove. "Did you buy such a lot of it then?"

"I could have bought it!" exploded Grandfather. "It used to be that only the man in the house worked, but he fed a family of seven. But under the Bolsheviks the man works, the wife works, the children work, and they can't make a living, the lot of them!"

"But it was bad under the Tsar!" I piped.

"That's what they taught you in school. I know! But you never saw life under the Tsar yourself."

"What about all the people who were put in prison and exiled?"

"Idiot!" snorted Grandfather. "People have always gone to prison."

"Wagging your tongue again!" fumed Grandmother. "Only the grave can cure the humpback! What twaddle, what drivel! Soviet rule gave you a pension, you old fool and parasite; you could at least be grateful! You've forgotten your father's smoke-shack, haven't you? He wants the bourgeoisie!"

"The bourgeois is a louse!" cried Grandfather. (It's beginning again, I thought. Now they'll be at it all day!) "The bourgeois is a louse, but he knows his business."

"Don't argue with him, Mama!" pleaded Mother. "You can't tell him anything. He doesn't want to listen."

"No, there never was any order in Russia and never will be with such managers," said Grandfather, not in the least inclined to listen. "We need the Germans, that's what! Let them teach us. They won't waste their time on nonsense. If you want to work, then work, they'll say. And if you don't, then go to hell. We've no use for parasites and gasbags— What else does the newspaper say?"

I dug into the newspaper and found an announcement that confirmed Grandfather's words. It stated that "some unemployed men between the ages of 16 and 25 are AVOID-ING WORK!" They were ordered to turn up for registration at once.

"There you are!" said Grandfather, raising a triumphant finger.

CHAPTER IV

CONCERNING HEAVEN ON EARTH

We had to make a long trip, across the whole city, to Zverinets, and Grandmother therefore put bread, apples and two bottles of water into her shopping bag.

Kirillovskaya Street was littered with straw, paper and horse droppings. No one had swept it. All the store windows had been smashed, and the glass crunched underfoot. Women could be seen at open windows here and there, washing the crossed strips of paper off the glass. These had been pasted on the panes to keep them from shivering to bits in the bombing.

The crowds were drawing water from the brook dribbling out of the ravine called Babi Yar. They scooped up the water with cups, glasses and pails. The water mains were empty, and the whole city, swinging pails and other containers, was heading in long lines toward the Dnieper and the various brooks. Basins and barrels were set under drainpipes to collect rain.

A streetcar stood on the tracks exactly where it had

stopped when the current was turned off. I jumped aboard, ran about among the seats, ensconced myself in the driver's place and tinkled the bell. This was really fun. I had the car to myself and could do what I liked with it. The electric bulbs had already been unscrewed and people had begun to take the window glass too.

Abandoned streetcars stood all along the line at intervals. Some of them had been stripped not only of their glass, but their seats as well.

Soviet placards with caricatures of Hitler could still be seen on walls, but new ones had been pasted over them on one wall. Pictures of the happy life about to set in had been printed in yellow lines on a black background. Stout *muzhiks* with Ukrainian forelocks and flowing trousers plowed the land with oxen and then scattered seed recklessly from bast baskets. Then they cheerfully mowed the wheat with scythes and threshed it with chains. The final frame showed a whole family having dinner under Hitler's portrait, decorated with husks.

Suddenly, alongside those pictures I read a statement that made me rub my eyes:

"ZHIDY, LYAKHI AND MOSCALI ARE THE WORST ENEMIES OF THE UKRAINE!" These are derogatory terms for Jews, Poles and Russians, respectively.

Standing there beside that placard, I thought of my origin for the first time in my life. My mother was a Ukrainian, my father a full Russian, which meant I was half Ukrainian and half *moscal,* or an enemy to myself.

My best friends were Shurka Matsa, who was half Jewish, *ergo,* a *zhid,* and Bolik Kaminsky, who was half Polish and therefore a *lyakh.* This was utter confusion, and I had to ask Grandmother about it right away.

"Pay no attention to it, child," she urged. "Those were big fools who made that placard."

I decided that they were really fools; but who had allowed them to print such gibberish and paste it on the walls?

In Podol District people were milling about, preoccupied and busy. Everybody was dragging or carrying something. An old man and an old woman were straining with all their might to move a big wardrobe with a looking glass in it. A drayman with a drunken face had a gleaming grand piano on his cart. All the stores, barbershops and savings banks had been smashed open and were littered with glass. German soldiers, singly and in groups, were also laden with trash. They were not molesting anyone and passed unnoticed. Each man plundered on his own.

The closer we got to Kreshchatik Avenue, the more officers we saw. They walked with measured stride, their heads in the air, each with a silver-badged cap low on his forehead. Red German flags hung in various places, flaunting white disks with black swastikas in the center. The yellow-and-blue-striped flag of the Ukrainian nationalists flew beside the German bunting here and there, which meant that these flags were friends.

It was a splendid autumn day. The chestnut trees were yellowing and the sun was still warm. Grandmother trudged and trudged along, while I scurried from side to side like a borzoi puppy. We finally crossed Kreshchatik, where people were dragging the seats out of a motion picture house, and ascended to Pechersk, which was jammed with troops. Suddenly, there was the Lavra monastery.

The Kiev-Pechora Lavra constitutes an entire town surrounded with crenellated walls, a fantastic town of church upon church, cupola upon cupola, snow-white buildings and belfries, all steeped in greenery. I had come to know this place and was very fond of it, for it contained all the main museums of Kiev. "Museum town" was indeed what it was called.

There were awesome labyrinths in the Lavra, with saints in their coffins under glass. Excursions went through these labyrinths by the dim light of electric bulbs strung out in the caverns. In the middle of the Lavra stood the ancient Cathedral of the Assumption, with the tomb of Kochubei[1] and the executed Mazepa beside its walls. Pushkin had once stood here, copying the verses cast on the iron plaque in ancient letters. That is how he began his epic, *Poltava*. Even Yury Dolgoruky,[2] the founder of Moscow, was buried here.

Grandmother and I sat down in the grass and looked around. The churches, the walls and the cupolas glittered in the sun. We sat looking for a long time, peaceful and contented.

After a while Grandmother remarked:

"Don't trust people who wear caps pulled down over their foreheads, child."

"Why not?"

"Because they're bad men."

"Why?"

"I don't know. That's what my mother always said. When I saw the Germans today, my heart fell. Enemies! They're the enemy, child. These are hard times."

Grandmother used the word "enemy" in a very wide sense. Sickness came to a person because an enemy had nested within him. It also signified the Antichrist: "The enemy shall roam the earth."

40

"But Grandfather said we're going to have Heaven on earth."

"Don't you believe that old chatterbox. Heaven's in Heaven—where God is. It was never on earth and never will be. How many times have people been promised Heaven on earth, by just about everyone! They all promise it, but unhappy man has always had to slave for a piece of bread by the sweat of his brow. He's still slaving away, though Heaven is still being promised him. Your grandfather remembers herrings and good cloth, but does he remember how I washed clothes for strangers from dawn to dusk for fifteen kopeks? Ask him to tell you how the Petlura bandits nearly shot him at Pushcha-Voditsa. It's no use talking about it, I've never seen anything good on earth. Heaven? It's over there."

She nodded at the Lavra and began muttering a prayer.

I grew worried and uncomfortable, for I had been an atheist for a long time, having gone to a Soviet school, and knew perfectly well that Grandmother's Heaven did not exist either.

Aunt Olya and her husband lived in Zverinets District. Both of them had worked at the Arsenal Plant and had been evacuated with it. They had built a small house in Zverinets just before the war. Before leaving, they had installed a spinster named Marusya in the house, but had given all the documents and power of attorney to Grandmother, asking her to visit the place from time to time to keep an eye on it.

The little house had been neither razed nor sacked. Marusya received us very well. A cheerful, dark, unshaven man was in the house with her, and she promptly introduced him as her husband.

41

Grandmother congratulated her, of course, and kissed her.

When the neighbor Grabarev called to Grandmother from over the fence, she gasped with surprise.

"What are you doing here?"

"It was a stupid mistake," he answered. "I helped evacuate the Arsenal Plant, Marfa Yefimovna. I reached the Urals and waited for my family. I sent them telegram after telegram, but they couldn't come for some reason. Then I dropped everything, hurried back here, and found that they had been evacuated shortly before. I tried to return, but Kiev was surrounded. So they got away, while I'm stranded here."

He was downhearted, bent and aged. I noticed his cap, tilted back and almost falling off his head, and felt sorry for him.

"Good God!" fretted Grandmother. "But you're a Communist!"

"Do you think no other Party members were stranded in Kiev on account of the encirclement? Besides, what sort of a Communist was I! I just belonged and paid my dues. And they expelled me from the Party last summer, didn't you hear? Only they didn't put it down in my record—the war broke out, and they didn't get around to it. Anyway, now that I have stayed on occupied territory it's the same as though I were expelled."

Grandmother shook her head in commiseration.

"What are you going to do?"

"I'll work. I'm a carpenter."

He filled my cap with apples and handed it back to me across the fence.

We spent the night in the little house, and I slept very well in this new place until Grandmother woke me up:

"Boy! Wake up, child!" she urged. "Get under the bed, quick!"

The floor and the windows shook with the heavy fire of guns, and aircraft howled abominably. Grandmother and I lunged under the bed, where she had already spread a blanket, and clung to each other. Those were Soviet planes doing the bombing this time, and in the pitch dark their bombs seemed especially near and powerful. The bed kept shaking and rocking, as did the whole house, as though in an earthquake.

"Ahfath! Whoart in Heaven!" whispered Grandmother passionately as she shook me. "Pray! Pray!"

"Thy kingdomcome thy willbedone on earth as it is in Heaven," I mumbled. "Give us this day our dairy bread—"

In the morning Marusya told Grandmother:

"I respect you very much, Marfa Yefimovna, but don't come here anymore. This house is going to belong to me and my husband. The Soviets will never come back, and you don't need the place. We're going to put it in our own name."

Grandmother brought her hands together in surprise.

"That's what everybody is doing," explained Marusya. "The homes of those who were evacuated are being taken by those who need them; and this house belonged to a Communist. The Communists' time is finished! Now don't show me that power-of-attorney of yours; it's a Soviet one and invalid. And don't forget, too, that you're the relative of a Communist yourself."

The cheery, unshaven husband came and stood in the doorway, arms akimbo. Grandmother appealed to his conscience and to God and said she would complain, but he only laughed and sneered.

Our return journey was a sad one. Grandmother was downhearted.

At the foot of Kreshchatik Avenue we were suddenly stopped by a patrol.

"*Juden?*" the soldier asked Grandmother. "Passport!"

Badly frightened, Grandmother reached for her passport. The documents of a little old man were being checked alongside of us.

"Yes, I'm a Jew," he quavered.

"*Komm!*" ordered the German, leading him away.

"I'm a Ukrainian, a Ukrainian!" said Grandmother, terrified.

The soldier returned her passport and went away. We hurried down Kirov Street to Podol, where a woman told Grandmother:

"This morning we saw a Jewish girl running along the street, firing a revolver. She killed two officers and shot herself. Now they're picking up all the Jews. I heard they're going to make them pull the barricades down. Lord, first it's build them, then it's take them down. And they're going from house to house, chasing everybody out."

A crowd stood around a billboard studying the announcements, and I pushed through at once. Those were the first orders published by the commandant. I shall quote from memory:

"**FIRST.** Everything taken from stores, offices and empty apartments must be returned to its original place no later than tomorrow morning. Whoever fails to obey this order WILL BE SHOT.

"**SECOND.** The entire population is required to turn in surplus food. Each person may retain

44

supplies sufficient for 24 hours. Whoever fails to obey this order WILL BE SHOT.

"**THIRD.** The entire population is required to turn in whatever weapons, ammunition, military equipment and radio sets it may have. Firearms and radios are to be delivered to the commandant's office on Kreshchatik, and military equipment to Kreshchatik 27. Whoever fails to obey this order WILL BE SHOT."

My hair stood on end and I must have been very pale as I edged away from the crowd, for I was thinking of the brushes I had stolen, the lamp, the buttons and the weights of the scales.

Only now did I notice that there were no more looters in the streets, only clusters of people reading the announcements and then dissolving as each went his separate way.

Grandmother and I came home greatly troubled. Mama gathered all the things I had stolen into a heap and briefly commanded, "Take them back."

"But not the weights from the scales!" wailed Grandfather. "We have a pair of scales of our own. How can they prove those weights don't belong to us? As for the buttons, I'll throw them into the toilet."

I was finally compelled to return the lamp and the brushes because everybody in the street had seen me carrying them. I was ashamed to go to the bazaar. Nobody had brought anything back yet. I was the first, and I waited a long time until there was nobody in sight. Choosing the right moment, I shoved the lamp through the broken shop front, tossed the brushes after it, and took to my heels.

There was a worried discussion at home as to what to do

about our food supplies. Careful stock was taken of our peas, buckwheat and sugar. There was enough for a week or a week and a half, we figured, but Grandfather was ready to face execution rather than give any of it up.

"They're just trying to scare us!" he moaned. "Let people like Shatkovsky hand in their food. Why, he stole butter by the barrel. Let's first see what happens."

I was sent out to have a look at the situation toward evening. The shops were just as shattered and empty as before. My lamp had vanished from the store window, and the brushes were gone, too.

No one returned or delivered anything, but, to be on the safe side, Grandfather hid our food under the hay in the shed. Our bundles and suitcases were hidden underground, in the trench. None of us had ever owned any weapons or a radio.

We quaked when two soldiers came the next day, but they only walked through the rooms, took one of Grandmother's old kerchiefs, and left without a word. We watched them, dumbfounded. We could not get used to this. Grandmother said:

"You were right, locks really aren't needed now, we might as well latch the door with a clothespin. It's more than three days since they entered the city, but they're still robbing us."

"Which means that they've extended it to five days," retorted Grandfather, unwilling to change his mind. "Kiev is a big city. It's the capital. So they've been allowed to go on plundering for five days. They'll be finished on the 24th."

He was greatly mistaken.

The trouble only began on the 24th.

The Author Speaking

To you young people who were born in the forties or later and didn't see or live through anything of this kind, all this is simply history.

Some of you probably dislike dry school history.

I am sure you sometimes regard it as a conglomeration of dates and bookish horrors.

You have been told again and again how lucky you are to spend your youth in peacetime and that horrors are things you know only from the books you have read. You listen and listen, and sometimes say:

"We're tired of it all."

Some young people do not want to hear anything about war and politics and just want to dance and love—to live, in short. It is fine to live, to dance and to love; but do you know what I would add to this? I would add, on the strength of my own and everybody's experience, reflection and anxieties: woe to him who forgets politics nowadays.

Now that you've picked up this book and got this far into it, I earnestly advise you to be patient and read on to the end.

After all, this is not an ordinary novel; it contains no invention; I have described everything just as it happened.

Use your imagination a bit and imagine yourself *in my place. That should not be so hard. If you had been born an historic instant earlier, you might indeed have found yourself in my place; and all this would not be just a book to you, but a slice of life itself.*

As you read on, try to imagine that all this is happening not to me, but to you.

Today. Now.

Join me on a street in Kiev at the end of September, 1941. The city is in German hands.

It is a warm autumn day.

CHAPTER V

KRESHCHATIK AVENUE

The German troops marched into Kreshchatik Avenue from both ends on September 19, 1941.

Some of the columns approached from Podol District. They were the ones we had met in Kurenevka, smart and cheerful Germans in autos and trucks. The others came from the opposite side, from Bessarabka District. On motorcycles, sooty, directly from the front, they swept in, cloud after cloud of them, riding the sidewalks and filling the whole of Kreshchatik with the roar and smoke of their machines.

The whole thing looked like a colossal, very disorganized parade, full of traffic jams, confusion and muddle.

The troops began to occupy the empty buildings along Kreshchatik, evidently according to a prearranged plan. There were more offices and stores here than apartments, and most of the latter had been evacuated. Kreshchatik was really deserted.

The commandant's office found a building to its liking on the corner of Kreshchatik and Proreznaya Street. Its first floor had belonged to the well-known Children's World department store. The German staff headquarters occupied

49

the huge Continental Hotel. The Doctors' Club was turned into the German officers' club.

Everything had been thought out and organized efficiently. Mobile power plants were set up in the street in front of the buildings to furnish them with electricity. Water was brought up from the Dnieper in cisterns.

The looting on Kreshchatik began somewhat later than on other streets. While the troops were settling in for the night, marauders swarmed to Kreshchatik from all parts of the city. The Germans on Kreshchatik, bellowing and punching, broke up the crowd. Then they set about their own plundering. Each man carried or hauled off something, as in a huge disturbed anthill.

The Bessarabka market came to life after dinner. Women turned out to sell boiled potatoes or hot patties stuffed with peas, though they did not really know what prices to demand. They preferred to barter their goods, on this principle: Give me a package of *makhorka* shag, and you can eat as much as you like.

Two barbershops opened; and the expectations of the enterprising barbers were fully justified, for the shops soon filled with German officers.

All this proceeded cheerfully. There was almost a holiday spirit about it. It was a bright, sunny day, conducive to good spirits.

The keys of the locked apartments were kept by the house superintendents. Accompanied by the superintendents or janitors, the Germans made the rounds of the apartments, opening them and taking whatever they wanted. Furniture and feather beds were carted off to the barracks. The janitors also took their share.

None of this property was returned, despite the order from the commandant. Weapons and radios were duly turned in, however. After the first few had been turned in, other people, seeing this and probably frightened, followed suit. Gas masks were especially numerous. They were turned in at No. 27, at the café opposite the commandant's, and were already piled in heaps up to the ceiling.

The employees of Radio Kiev were the first to be summoned (from the list kept in the personnel department). The Radio Committee was situated on the corner of Kreshchatik and Institute Street. The newly appointed German chief of the radio station stepped out on the platform, looked the men over, and began in a rather unusual manner:

"Jews, rise!"

There was a deep silence. No one rose; only some heads stirred.

"Jews, rise!" repeated the chief, louder, and reddening with anger.

Still no one rose.

"*Zhidy,* up!" he roared, clutching his pistol.

Some musicians then stood up in various parts of the hall, violinists and cellists, joined by a few technicians and editors. With hanging heads, they made for the exit in single file.

The chief waited until the door had closed behind the last one and then announced in broken Russian that the world should hear the voice of free Kiev, that it was urgent to restore the radio station in record time, and that everybody was expected to return to work tomorrow. Those who did not would be considered saboteurs. The time had come for peaceful, creative work.

Subdued and puzzled, the radio employees arose to go their ways; and just then the first explosion came.

It was 4 P.M. on September 24.

The building of the commandant's office, with the Children's World store on the first floor, exploded. The explosion was so powerful that windows shattered not only on Kreshchatik, but along the parallel Pushkin and Meringovsky Streets as well. Glass from every floor fell on the heads of Germans and passersby, and many were hurt.

A column of fire and smoke rose over Proreznaya Street; and immediately crowds filled the street, some fleeing from the explosion and others hurrying toward it for a better view. The Germans were confused for a moment, but then threw a cordon around the burning building and proceeded to seize anyone on the street or in the courtyards.

A lanky redheaded fellow was dragged out and beaten terribly. The rumor went around that he was a partisan, that he had delivered a radio to the Children's World store, but that it had turned out to be a bomb.

Those arrested were shoved into the cinema nearby, and the place soon filled up with wounded, beaten and bloody people.

At that moment there was a second and equally powerful explosion amid the ruins of the same building. This brought the walls down and turned the commandant's headquarters into a heap of rubble. The whole of Kreshchatik was filled with dust and smoke.

The third explosion gutted the building across the way, the one with various German offices and the café stuffed with gas masks.

The Germans now fled from the cinema, shouting, "Run for your lives! Kreshchatik is blowing up!" They ran in all directions, followed by the people they had arrested, including the lanky redhead.

Incredible panic ensued, for Kreshchatik really was blowing up.

Burst followed burst at intervals, up and down Kreshchatik, and it was impossible to gauge the next one. The explosions continued all night, spreading to the adjacent streets. The circus blew up; its battered cupola was hurled clear across the street. Next to the circus, the Continental Hotel burned; it was occupied by the German staff headquarters.

No one will ever know how many Germans perished in those explosions and flames, nor how much equipment and how many documents they lost, for no statistics were ever published about it.

The weather was dry, and this helped spread a fire that could well be compared with Moscow's great fire of 1812. Many cases of bottled fuel had been stored in the garrets, and these kept blowing up with characteristic booms from time to time, drenching the buildings with fresh streams of fire. This really finished Kreshchatik.

The Germans, who had entered so triumphantly and established themselves so comfortably, were now rushing about Kreshchatik like rats in a trap. They understood nothing, knew nothing, not even where to run. The people, some with bundles of belongings and some without, ran toward the park along the Dnieper, toward Vladimir Heights or to Shevchenko Boulevard. Many were left homeless.

The Germans cordoned off the entire center of the city. The fire had already spread to Pushkin and Meringovsky Streets, and to Proreznaya, Institute, Karl Marx, Friedrich Engels and Passage Streets, which cross Kreshchatik. One had the impression that the entire city was being blown up.

Tunneling for a subway had begun in Kiev before the war, and now rumors spread that it had not been a subway, but that monstrous mines had been placed under the whole of Kiev. Even people far from Kreshchatik fled their homes, for no one knew where the next explosion would come.

The Germans rushed long hoses to Kiev by plane, stretched them all the way from the Dnieper across Pioneer Park and began driving water through them with mighty pumps, but the water never reached Kreshchatik. In the underbrush of the park someone cut the hoses.

Strong air currents formed over the great bonfire in the heart of Kiev. They sucked up burning debris, papers and glowing embers, which showered now on Bessarabka, now on Pechersk. Germans, police and janitors climbed up on all the roofs, heaped sand on the burning debris and stamped out the embers that fell. The homeless slept in air-raid shelter trenches at the stadium.

The Germans could not even remove the bodies of their men, for they were burned to ashes, together with all they had plundered.

After fighting the fire for several days, the Germans gave up. They withdrew from the fiery furnace and watched the blaze from a distance.

Kreshchatik, completely deserted, went on burning. A roof or a wall fell thunderously now and then, hurling a fresh cloud of embers and torches into the sky. The city was filled with the odor of smoke and at night was lit by a red glare. The glare, it was said, could be seen for hundreds of miles.

The explosions did not subside until September 28. The heart of the fire continued for two weeks, and the cordons of tommy gunners were never removed in all that time.

When the cordons were removed and the Germans entered the area, they found that there were no longer any streets. The fallen buildings on both sides had heaped up great barriers. Months were needed to clear passageways. The hot rubble continued to smoke for a long time, wisps of smoke stealing through the ruins even in December—something I saw myself.

To my mind, the dynamiting and burning of Kreshchatik ought to go down as a tragic and heroic page in the history of the war. One should remember what Kreshchatik meant to Kiev. Its destruction might be compared to razing the center of Moscow, the part circled by the Sadovaya Ring, or Leningrad's Nevsky Prospekt with everything surrounding it, or, say, the heart of Paris to the *grands boulevards*. This was the first strictly planned operation of its kind in history. It was after Kreshchatik that the Germans established the rule, Examine every house and tag it "No mines."

No capital in Europe received the Hitlerites as Kiev did. The city could not be further defended, and it was left; it appeared to be at the mercy of the enemy; but it burned itself down under the enemy's nose and carried many of his men to the grave. They entered the city as they were accustomed to entering West European capitals, preparing to feast and be merry. Instead they were dealt such a blow that the very ground burned under their feet.

Many things are still unclear about the Kreshchatik epic. There are many rumors and legends: about the unknown hero who broke into the lobby of the Continental Hotel, carrying a bomb, detonated it there, and himself perished in the explosion; about another who blew up the Shantser Cinema when it was filled with Germans during a performance; and about others. It is difficult to verify such stories. The Germans said nothing about them and executed no one publicly, though evidently most of the underground group responsible for the extraordinary Kreshchatik operation perished.[1]

CHAPTER VI

THE ORDER

On the morning of September 28 we had an unexpected visitor—Ivan Svinchenko, of the village of Litvinovka. He was on his way home, his army unit having been encircled.

Ivan was kind, simple and ignorant, a hard worker and the father of a large family. When he used to come to market in town, he usually spent the night with Grandfather and Grandmother, never forgetting to bring some trifle for me from the village. I was shy with him, perhaps because of his speech defect. He had a breathless way of choking on his words and sometimes one could only make out a sound like "balabala."

He turned up very ragged and dirty this time. He had already managed to change from his uniform into civilian rags. Here is what had happened to him.

His unit had left Kiev and crossed to Darnitsa, on the left bank of the Dnieper. The men followed the country roads and circled through the woods. They were bombed and strafed and badly mauled. When they lost contact with their command, the men began to shout that they ought to break up and go home.

Deep in the woods they came upon some partisans, who were well equipped. They had stores of ammunition and food and plenty of weapons. Warning the soldiers of what would happen to them if the Germans caught them, they urged the soldiers to join the partisan detachment. Ivan, however, had grown homesick.

"So I waited, balabala, until night time, and ran away," he explained.

He had been making his way for many days through the fields and woods. There were many others like him everywhere.

Grandmother fed Ivan, sighing sympathetically as he told his story. Grandfather started out to take a walk, but came pounding back along the porch and burst into the room:

"Here's news!" he said. "Not a Jew will be left in Kiev by tomorrow. Let them go. They'll be shipped out. They've put up an order about it outside."

We ran outdoors. There was a notice pasted to a fence. It was printed on bad wrapping paper. There was no heading and no signature.

> All Jews of the city of Kiev and its environs must appear on the corner of Melnikov and Dokhturov Streets (beside the cemetery) at 8 A.M. on September 29, 1941. They must bring their documents, money, valuables, warm clothing, etc.
>
> Jews who fail to obey this order and are found elsewhere will be shot.
>
> All who enter the apartments left by Jews and take their property will be shot.[1]

The same text was repeated in Ukrainian below, and once again, in smaller print, in German. The notice was thus a three-story affair. I read it through twice and felt strangely chilled. It was cold and windy on that day, besides, and the street was deserted. I was too troubled to go home, and wandered to the bazaar instead.

Many Jews lived and worked in a cluster of clay huts, small barns and cowsheds huddled around a kitchen garden two doors from our house. I peeped in and found them in the grip of a quiet panic, rushing from hovel to hovel, assembling their bundles.

Similar notices had been posted in other spots. I stopped to read them again, but felt there was something about them I could not understand. For one thing, there was neither a Melnikov nor a Dokhturov Street in Kiev. But the city had a Melnik Street and a Degtyarev Street. The notice had evidently been composed by Germans with the aid of incompetent translators. Those streets were near the Russian and Jewish cemeteries at Lukyanovka. They were also near the Lukyanovka freight yard station.

Which meant that they were to be sent off by train. Where to?

Shurka Matsa would have to go, but what about his mother? She was a Russian. He would have to go by himself. I felt sorry for him and sorry to part with him.

The Kurenevka militia precinct, where my father had once served, now belonged to the *Polizei*. They had put a portrait of Hitler in the window. Hitler looked out at me sternly, almost ominously. He wore an elaborate visored cap, drawn down over his forehead.

I could not, of course, miss such an event as the deportation of the Jews from Kiev, and ran out into the street.

59

They came out when it was still dark. Perhaps they hoped to be first to board the train and to find seats. With their wailing children, their old and their sick, the Jewish tenants of the kitchen garden spilled out into the street, weeping and quarreling among themselves. They carried rope-tied bundles, battered wooden suitcases, patched carpetbags and carpentry toolboxes. The old women wore strings of onions around their necks—their provisions for the trip.

In normal circumstances the crippled, the sick and the aged stay at home and are unseen. But they all had to emerge now, and I was shaken to find that there were so many sick and unfortunate people in the world.

There was another factor, too. The able-bodied men had been drafted into the army. All who could be evacuated, who had had money or could go off with their factories or other enterprises, had certainly gone. Those who were left constituted the real poor described by Sholom Aleichem. They were now limping and crawling into the streets.

"What's all this for?" I wondered. "It's cruel and unjust, and I pity Shurka Matsa. Why are they chasing him out like a dog?"

Feverishly I scurried from group to group, listening to the talk. The closer I came to Podol, the more people I saw in the streets. They stood watching and sighing at the gates and house entrances.

A great crowd was ascending Glubochitsa toward Luk-yanovka, a sea of heads. These were the Jews of Podol on the march. Ah, Podol, Podol![2] People were talking on all sides. "Where are they taking us? How are we going to get there?" One group could say nothing but, "The ghetto, the ghetto!" A distraught elderly woman approached: "Dear people, this means death!" The old women broke into wailing. It was said that the *Karaim*[3] had passed somewhere (I had never heard the word before, but realized that they must have been some sort of sect)—old men in loose garments reaching to their heels. They had spent the night in their *Karaim* synagogue. In the morning they had come out chanting, "Children, we are going to our deaths! Prepare yourselves! Let us meet death bravely, as Christ did."

Some were indignant. Why should anyone start a panic like that? It was already known, however, that a woman had poisoned her children and herself rather than go. A girl had jumped from a window near the Opera House. Her body lay covered on the sidewalk.

Suddenly there was a great troubled stir. People were chattering on all sides, saying that Melnik Street had been cut off. One could pass through the cordon there, but not return.

This frightened me. Tired and dizzy, I was afraid I would not manage to get out of the crowd and would be driven off with them. I pushed hard against the people, made my way through, and got out. Then I took the long way home through streets that were empty now except for a few latecomers who were almost running to catch up.

When I came home I saw Grandfather in the middle of the yard. He stood there with a finger raised, straining to hear the sound of firing far away.

"D'you know what they're doing?" he said, shaken. "They're shooting them."

I heard it distinctly now: the even ra-ta-ta of a machine gun from Babi Yar.

This was calm, unhurried firing, as on a shooting range. Our Babi Yar adjoined the cemetery. One had only to cross the ravine to get to Lukyanovka.

Grandfather looked puzzled and frightened.

61

"Those shots could be coming from the shooting range," I suggested.

"What shooting range?" he snapped. "The whole of Kurenevka is talking about it. Victor Makedon came back after seeing his wife off. He barely saved himself. Mother of God, Queen of Heaven, what are we coming to!"

We entered the house, but could not sit still, for we heard firing and more firing. Grandfather went to Makedon's house to learn what he could. The place was full of people listening to the young fellow (he had married just before the war) tell how passports had been examined and thrown onto a bonfire. He had managed to shout, "I'm a Russian." Whereupon they had torn his wife from him and led her off to Babi Yar. He had been chased away by a *Polizei*.

It was cold outside. Yesterday's piercing wind had not abated. I kept running out to hear what people were saying. Grandmother brought me my coat and hat and paused to listen too. It seemed to me she was crying. I turned to look at her more closely. She was crossing herself, facing Babi Yar and muttering "Ahfath! Whoart in Heaven—"

The firing stopped after dark, but resumed in the morning. In Kurenevka it was said that 35,000 had been shot on the first day and that the rest were waiting their turn.

Grandmother came back from the neighbors with news. A fourteen-year-old boy, the son of the stableman, had come running back to the kitchen garden and was telling of the horrors he had been through. He said that everybody was being undressed, that people were being lined up in front of pits, one packed closely behind the other, so that one bullet could kill many. He said that the bodies were stacked in a layer, covered with dirt, and then a fresh layer of bodies was laid on them. Many of those shot were still alive, so that the ground kept moving; some had even managed to crawl out. That was what he had done—crawled out and run away.

"We've got to hide him," said Mama. "In the shelter."

"Child," Grandmother told me, "run as quickly as you can. Bring him. We'll give him food and hide him."

I ran to the vegetable garden, but was too late. A cart, drawn by a bony nag, stood at the gate. A German sat in the cart, holding a whip. A second soldier with a gun under his arm was leading the white-faced boy through the gate. He was not leading him, actually, for the two were walking side by side.

They reached the cart and climbed in from opposite sides, the soldier even moving the hay to make the boy comfortable. He dropped his gun on the hay, while the youngster stretched out, leaning on his elbow. His large eyes met mine indifferently, unseeingly.

The soldier behind the horse waved his whip and clicked his tongue. The cart moved off as simply, as prosaically, as if they were going out to the meadow for hay.

Several people escaped directly from the Babi Yar pits, and I shall relate the story told by one of them. I wrote it down myself from her words. She was Dina Mironovna Pronicheva, an actress at the Kiev Puppet Theater and the mother of two children. I shall give her story exactly as she told it, without adding anything.

CHAPTER VII

BABI YAR

She went out to read the order, read it quickly and left. Nobody was inclined to spend much time in front of that notice or to start conversations there.

But in every home the discussions and conjectures continued all day and into the night. Her parents were old and feeble; just before the Germans arrived, her mother had returned from the hospital, where she had undergone an operation. They all wondered how she would manage to make the trip. The old folks were sure that everyone would be put on trains at Lukyanovka and sent to Soviet territory.

Dina's husband was a Russian. Her surname was Russian, and she did not look Jewish at all. After talking, conjecturing and thinking it over, they decided that the old folks would go, that Dina would see them to the train, but that she would stay behind with the children and let come what may.

Her father was a glazier and lived with her mother at 27 Turgenev Street. Dina and her children lived nearby at 41 Vorovsky.

She came home late and tried to fall asleep, but could not. She lay awake all night. There was a constant running and thudding of boots in the yard. They were trying to catch a girl who lived in this house. She had run up to the attic, then come down by the fire escape. "There she is!" men shouted.

Just before the Germans had entered Kiev this girl had said, "They'll never enter the city. If they do, I'll pour kerosene all over this building and set it afire."

Remembering this, and afraid that the girl really would set the house on fire, the janitor's wife had told the Germans about it; and this night they had come to seize her.

It was a tense, harrowing night. Dina could not stop trembling. She never learned whether the girl had been caught or not.

At dawn Dina washed, combed her hair, took her identification papers and went to her parents' apartment on Turgenev Street. The streets were exceptionally crowded. People were hurrying and intent, carrying belongings.

Dina reached her parents' apartment shortly after six. The whole house was astir. Those about to depart were saying good-bye to neighbors, promising to write, and turning over apartments, property and keys to them.

Her parents could not carry much; they had no valuables and took only food and essentials. Dina slung the knapsack over her shoulder, and they emerged shortly after seven.

Many people were moving along Turgenev Street, but Artem Street was packed solid. People loaded down with bundles, some pushing baby carriages, barrows or handcarts; horse-drawn baggage carts, and, at rare intervals, even trucks —all these came to a standstill, moved a short distance, then stopped again.

The loud voices merged into a din, the din of the crowd. The scene was reminiscent of a demonstration, when the streets are similarly packed; but there were no banners here, no bands and no celebration.

It was strange about the trucks. Where did they get them? Here and there the tenants of an entire apartment house evidently had chipped in and hired a truck. Now they clung close to their trucks or carts. The sick and feeble lay among the bundles and satchels, and clusters of children sat among them. As many as two and three infants were packed into a single baby carriage.

Many had come to see these people off. Friends, neighbors, relatives, Russian and Ukrainian, helped to carry the bundles or assist the sick; some carried the latter on their backs.

The procession was a slow one and Artem Street was long. German soldiers stood in a gateway, watching the crowd. They called to Dina, motioning that they wanted their floors washed:

"Komm waschen!"

She waved them away. This droning procession, this "demonstration" of pushing, of chatter and of wailing children, went on and on to the point of stupor. Dina was wearing a short fur coat and began to feel warm.

They did not reach the cemetery until the afternoon. She remembers that on the right were the long brick wall and gates of the Jewish cemetery. The street was blocked here with a barrier of barbed wire and antitank obstructions; a passage had been left through the middle. A row of Germans with badges on their chests stood there, and also Ukrainian *Polizei* in black uniforms with gray sleeve cuffs.

A very tall and energetic man in an embroidered shirt stood giving orders at the entrance. He had a large, drooping Cossack moustache and was altogether a striking figure. The crowd poured by him into the passage, but no one came back

except for an occasional empty cart rumbling the other way, with its vociferous driver. These drivers had already dumped their loads somewhere and were pushing against the crowd, shouting and brandishing their whips. This intensified the crowding and cursing.

It was all completely incomprehensible. Dina left her parents at the cemetery gates and went on ahead to see what was happening.

Like many others, she still thought there was a train up ahead. She heard firing nearby, and a plane circled low overhead. Everybody around her was anxious and panicky. She heard snatches of conversation.

"It's the war, the war! They're going to evacuate us to a safer place."

"But why only the Jews?"

An addled old woman offered the incredible suggestion:

"Because the Jews are kindred to the Germans. That's why they decided to evacuate us first."

More and more alarmed, Dina pushed through the crowd and finally saw that those ahead of her were being required to lay down their bundles. Clothing, knapsacks and suitcases were heaped on the left, and all food on the right. The Germans then sent the people on, batch by batch. They sent off one group, waited a moment, let another pass, counting the people off, counting . . . stop! The people were let through mostly in groups of ten. This started more talk, arguments and noise.

"Don't you see? Our things will go by baggage car. We'll sort them out at our destination."

"How will we sort them out there, with so many things? We'll simply have to divide them evenly among us."

Dina's flesh crawled. There was nothing like a station or a railroad anywhere around. Though she did not know what was happening, her heart told her this was no evacuation. Anything, but not an evacuation.

The bursts of machine-gun fire nearby seemed strangest of all. She was still unable to imagine that they could be shooting people. In the first place, there were so many of them. Such things don't happen. And then—why?

One can safely assume that most of the people there felt like Dina; they sensed there was something wrong but clung to the idea that "they're evacuating us," for the following reason: The old people had related many times how the Germans had behaved when they occupied the Ukraine in 1918. They had not troubled the Jews then but treated them fairly well; probably, some thought, because of the similarity between Yiddish and German.

"There are all sorts of Germans," said the old people, "but in general they're cultured and decent, quite decent."

There was another, very recent instance. Two days before, some people on Vorovsky Street had seized the apartment of an evacuated Jewish family. Whereupon the family's relatives, who had stayed behind, went to the nearest German headquarters to complain. An officer turned up, sternly ordered the intruders out of the apartment and bowed politely to the Jews: "There you are, all is in order." This had happened only the day before yesterday. People had seen it happen and promptly spread the story. And Germans were known to be very consistent and logical.

But if this was not deportation, what was it? What was happening here?

Dina said that at that moment she felt only brute fear and dizziness, a state beyond compare.

The people were being stripped of their warm clothes. A soldier approached Dina and deftly whipped off her coat without a word.

70

At this point she turned back, found her parents and told them what she had seen.

"Daughter, we don't need your help any longer," said her father. "Go now."

She made her way back to the barrier. Many people had gathered here, trying to get permission to go back. The crowds kept rolling in toward them. As before, the moustached man in the embroidered shirt was shouting orders. Dina pushed her way to his side and told him that she had come to see her people off, that she had children in the city, that he should let her go back.

He asked for her passport. When she handed it to him, he glanced at the line marked "Nationality."

"Why, you're a Jewess, a *zhidovka!*" he shouted. "Get back there!"

At this point Dina finally realized: This was an execution.

Feverishly she tore her passport into bits and threw them underfoot, right and left. She returned to her parents, but told them nothing, so as not to alarm them prematurely.

Though her coat was gone, she felt she was suffocating now. There were too many people around, a solid steaming mass. Lost children were wailing on all sides. Some people sat on their bundles, eating. "How can they eat?" she wondered. "Don't they realize yet what's happening?"

Now fresh commands were shouted; all who were seated were brought to their feet and moved on; those behind pushed forward, and a fantastic queue took form. The people set down one kind of belongings on one side, another kind on the other side. There was more crushing, more lining up. Dina lost her parents in the chaos but caught sight of them in a group farther ahead. The line in front of her came to a halt.

They stood waiting. She craned her neck to see where her father and mother had been taken. A huge German approached and said:

"Come to bed with me. I'll let you go."

She eyed him as she would a madman, and he went away. Finally it was her group's turn.

The talking subsided now. Everyone was quiet as though stunned, and they trudged on in silence for a long time. They were flanked by lines of fascists, and ahead they saw files of soldiers with dogs on leashes. Behind her Dina heard someone moan:

"Help me, children, I am blind."

She put her arm around the old man and walked on at his side.

"Where could they be taking us, Father?" she asked.

"My child," he answered, "we are going to pay our final debt to God."

At that instant they entered the long passage formed by the files of soldiers and dogs. This was a narrow corridor, only about five feet wide. The soldiers stood shoulder to shoulder, their sleeves rolled up. All were armed with rubber truncheons or big sticks.

They rained blows upon the people running this gauntlet.

It was impossible to hide, impossible to dodge. Furious blows, drawing blood at once, descended on heads, shoulders and backs from right and left. *"Schnell, schnell!"* shouted the soldiers, laughing heartily, obviously enjoying themselves and trying to hit hardest at sensitive places.

Everyone cried out; the women screamed. As in a film, Dina saw, directly in front of her, a young man she knew from her street, an intelligent boy who had always been well dressed. Now he was sobbing. She saw people fall. The dogs were set on them at once. One man got up with a cry, but others remained where they lay. The crowd was pressed over them, treading on the bodies, stamping them into the earth.

Dina was in a daze now. She walked on woodenly, her head high, never bending. She guessed she was injured, but barely felt or realized anything. Only one thought pulsated in her mind: "Don't fall, don't fall."

The maddened people emerged into a space cordoned off by the troops. This was a level, grass-covered field, littered everywhere with underwear, shoes and clothing.

Ukrainian *Polizei* (not local men but, judging by their accents, from the Western Ukraine) seized the people coarsely, beat them and shouted:

"Undress! Quick! Quick!"

Those who dallied were forcibly stripped, kicked, beaten with brass knuckles and clubs by the *Polizei*, with drunken viciousness and in a strange sadistic frenzy.

This was obviously done to prevent the crowd from regaining its senses. Many of the naked were streaked with blood.

Dina heard her mother call to her from the side where the naked were being led away. She saw her waving:

"Dina! You don't look like one. Save yourself!"

Dina turned determinedly to a *Polizei*, demanding to see the commandant. She said that she had come to the cemetery to see someone off, that she had been caught up in the crowd by accident.

He demanded her papers, and she reached for her purse, but he took it from her and examined the contents himself: money, her labor record booklet, her trade union card, but nothing to indicate her nationality. Her surname Pronicheva convinced the *Polizei*. He did not return her purse, but pointed to a hillock at the side, where a group of people sat.

"Wait up there. We'll shoot the Jews and let you go."

Dina went to the hillock and sat down. Everyone here was silent, stunned. Only an old woman in a knitted wool kerchief complained to Dina that she had been seeing her daughter-in-law off and got into all this trouble.

Everybody on the mound had come to see someone off.

Thus they sat while the nightmare unfolded in front of them as on a stage. Group after group of screaming, beaten persons emerged from the gauntlet of soldiers. The *Polizei* fell upon them, struck them, stripped them, and so on endlessly.

Dina says that some of the victims were laughing hysterically and that she saw several turn gray as they undressed and were marched off to be shot.

The naked were lined up in small groups and led toward a narrow passage in a high earth wall. What lay beyond could not be seen, but the sound of shooting came from there.

Mothers clung to their children, and now and then a German or a *Polizei* lost his temper, snatched a child from its mother, strode to the earth wall, swung it in the air and hurled it over the top like a log of wood.

Dina sat riveted to the spot, her head drawn in, afraid to look at her neighbors, who were growing more and more numerous. She no longer responded to the screams and the shooting.

It began to grow dark.

Suddenly an open car drove up, carrying a tall, well-knit, elegant officer carrying a riding crop. He seemed to be in command. His interpreter stood at his side.

"Who are these?" he asked a *Polizei* through his interpreter. There were about 50 people on the hillock now.

"These are our people," replied the *Polizei*. "We weren't sure whether to release them."

"Shoot them! Shoot them right away!" stormed the officer. "If just one of them gets away and spreads the story, not a Jew will come here tomorrow."

The interpreter conveyed all this conscientiously to the *Polizei* while the people on the hillock listened.

"Get going! Move! Get up!" shouted the *Polizei*.

They staggered to their feet as though drunk. It was already late, and this was perhaps why nothing was done to undress this group. Instead, they were led through the passage in the sand wall just as they were.

Dina walked in the second batch of ten. Coming through the passage, they emerged on the brow of a deep sand quarry with almost sheer walls. All were herded to the left, single file, along a very narrow ledge.

The wall rose on the left, and the quarry fell away on the right. The ledge, evidently cut specially for the executions, was so narrow that the victims instinctively leaned against the sand wall so as not to fall in.

Dina glanced down and grew dizzy. The quarry was fearfully deep. Below lay a sea of bloody bodies. She caught sight of light machine guns strung out on the opposite side of the quarry, and also of German soldiers. They had lit a campfire and seemed to be cooking something.

When the file of victims had occupied the ledge, one of the Germans moved away from the fire, took his place at a machine gun and began shooting.

Dina felt rather than saw the bodies fall as the line of fire rapidly approached. The thought flashed through her mind: "Now I . . . Now . . ." Without waiting for the bullet, she hurled herself from the ledge with her hands clenched.

She seemed to fall for an eternity. The ledge was really high. As she hit the bottom she felt neither the impact nor the pain. Warm blood splashed over her, and blood covered her face. It was as if she had fallen into a bath of blood. She lay with her eyes closed, her arms outspread.

There were muffled sounds all around and beneath her. Many of the victims were still alive. The entire mass of bodies was perceptibly stirring, settling deeper and tighter because of the motions of those being buried alive.

The soldiers emerged on the brow of the quarry and raked the pit with their flashlights, shooting with revolvers at any who seemed alive. Even after these scattered shots someone kept moaning near Dina.

Then she grew aware of footsteps, stepping directly on the bodies. The Germans had come down. They were bending over corpses, taking things from them, and shooting at whatever moved.

Wading through the dead, too, was the *Polizei* who had examined her documents and taken her purse. She recognized his voice.

An SS man stumbled on Dina and thought her suspicious for some reason. He turned his flashlight on her, raised her up and struck her savagely, but she hung limp, showing no sign of life. He kicked her in the breast and trod on her right hand until it crunched, but he moved on without shooting.

Within minutes she heard a voice above:

"Come on, shovel away!"

She heard the ringing of shovels and the thudding of sand on the bodies. The sounds came closer, and the sand finally descended on her.

It rose rapidly around her, but she did not stir, not until it dribbled into her mouth. She lay face upward, inhaling sand and choking until, losing control, she began to thrash about in wild horror, ready to be shot rather than buried alive.

She began to dig her way out of the dirt with her good left hand. Still choking and about to cough, she used the remains of her strength to suppress her coughing. She breathed easier. Finally she managed to crawl out from under the sand.

The men on the edge of the quarry had stopped shoveling. Having covered the bodies lightly with sand, they were evidently satisfied and had withdrawn. Dina's eyes were full of sand. It was pitch dark, and the stench was heavy.

Dina looked about for the nearest sand wall, moved toward it very, very slowly and cautiously, gained her feet and began to dig footholds into the wall with her left hand. She inched her way up, every second in peril of falling.

Her hand found a shrub at the top. She clutched it convulsively, and when she hauled herself over the edge she heard a hushed voice, and nearly fell back in terror.

"Auntie! Don't be afraid. I'm alive too!"

It was a boy in an undershirt and shorts. He had crawled out as she had and stood before her trembling.

"Shush!" she hissed. "Crawl after me."

They moved ahead on all fours, without making a sound.

Crawling on and on, slowly, painfully, they reached a precipice and then another. They turned and crawled on, evidently all night, for it was beginning to get light. Then they hid in a clump of bushes.

This was at the edge of a deep ravine, and there were Germans nearby, sorting out the clothing and stacking it. Dogs fidgeted on their leashes. Sometimes trucks came for the clothing, but more often flat horse-drawn carts.

At dawn they saw an old woman running, with a six-year-old boy running behind her, crying, "Grandma, I'm afraid!" She tried to wave him away from her. Two German soldiers soon overtook them and shot them, first the old woman and then the child.

Germans talking loudly passed now below, now above; and the shooting never stopped. It was so continuous that Dina felt it had never stopped, that it had gone on all night. She and the boy lay huddled together in the bushes, dozing off and then waking. He said his name was Motya, that none of his family was left, that he had fallen off the ledge with his father during the shooting. Dina looked at his frightened face and could not help longing to adopt him if she survived.

Her hallucinations began toward evening. She saw her father, mother and sister. They stood around her in white shrouds, laughing and capering about. When she came to, she found Motya whimpering over her:

"Don't die, Auntie! Don't leave me alone."

With an effort she realized where she was. It was dark now, so that they could emerge from the bushes and crawl on. During the day she had tried to memorize the way to the wide meadow and grove in the distance. She had moments of forgetfulness now and then and tried to rise, but Motya clung to her and pulled her to the ground.

She must have lost consciousness too, for at one point she fell into a gully. They had had nothing to eat or drink for more than 24 hours, but were neither hungry nor thirsty.

They crawled on another night, until it began to grow light. There were shrubs ahead, and Motya crawled on to reconnoiter. They had done this many times. If all was well, he was to rock the bushes. Instead he screamed:

"Don't crawl ahead, Auntie! Germans!"

Shots rang out, and the little boy was killed on the spot.

Fortunately, the Germans could not understand Motya's cry, and Dina crawled back along the sand. Her hands mindlessly dug a pit, then filled it with sand until there was a neat little mound. She was imagining that she was burying her companion Motya, and she burst into tears. She was half crazed.

When daylight came she found herself sitting, rocking to and fro, on a highway. There were fences on the left, and something like an alleyway between them. She crawled toward the opening, found it to be a garbage dump, and pushed into the thick of it, covering herself with rags and paper and pulling an old discarded basket over her head so that she could breathe beneath it.

She lay very still. Some Germans passed nearby and stood for a while, smoking.

Two green tomatoes lay in a kitchen garden just in front of her, but she would have had to crawl into the open to reach them. It was only then that she became thirsty, and fresh agony began. She tried to think of other things and closed her eyes tightly, telling herself not to think of thirst, but the two tomatoes were still there, drawing her on like a magnet. But she still stayed in the garbage.

Only when it was dark did she crawl out; she found the tomatoes, devoured them and crawled away on her belly. She had been crawling for so long now that she felt she had forgotten how to walk.

She wormed along for a long time, falling into a trench that contained barbed wire. Toward morning she saw a house and a shed behind it. She would try to get into the shed, she decided. It was not locked, but a dog in the yard barked the instant she was inside. Other dogs in the neighborhood took up the cry. The din grew so loud that it seemed to her there were hundreds of dogs. A sleepy woman came out and shouted, "Quiet, Ryabko!"

She peered into the shed and saw Dina. She looked sullen, and when she asked Dina who she was and what she was doing there, Dina began to lie, saying she had come from the trenches, that she had lost her way and had decided to spend the night in the shed. She even asked the way to the commandant's office in the city.

"But where were you?"

"At Belaya Tserkov [a town southwest of Kiev]."

"Belaya Tserkov? Well, well!"

Dina looked frightful, of course. She was covered with dirt and clots of blood. She had lost her shoes in the quarry, and her stockings were torn.

The neighbors came out now, and Dina was soon surrounded.

There must have been Germans near, for an officer turned up almost at once.

He looked Dina over and nodded, *"Komm!"*

He walked down a path, and she followed. He said nothing, only looking around now and then to see that she was still there. She walked hunched over, with her arms folded across her breast. She was cold; her right hand ached —it was bloody; and her feet hurt—they were badly cut.

They entered a one-story brick house, where some 20 German soldiers were breakfasting, drinking coffee from tin cups. Dina was about to take a seat in a corner, but the officer barked at her and she sat down on the floor.

Soon the Germans began to gather up their rifles and leave. Only one man, an orderly, stayed behind. Clearing the table, he looked at her and pointed to a chair as if to say, "Sit down. It'll be all right."

She got up from the floor and sat down on the chair. The soldier glanced at the window and handed her a cloth, indicating that she should wipe the glass. It was a big window, almost as big as the wall, composed of many rectangular panes, like a French window. Looking out, Dina saw that she had been crawling round and round Babi Yar and had come back to the same place from which she had fled.

The soldier was talking quietly to her now. He did not know that Dina understood every word he was saying, and he did his best to make her comprehend.

"Try to understand at least a little! My superiors are gone. I've given you that cloth so that you can run away. Wipe the window and choose a place to run to. Try to understand, *Dummkopf,* stupid!"

There was a note of sympathy in his voice, and Dina felt that what he was saying did not sound like a provocation. But in the state she was in she could not trust anyone, and she kept shaking her head as if she didn't understand.

The disgusted soldier thrust a broom into her hands and sent her off to sweep the neighboring hut, where she found herself alone. She began sweeping and was indeed about to run, when she heard noise and weeping. An officer entered, leading two girls of fifteen or sixteen.

They were crying, sobbing, rolling on the ground and trying to kiss his boots, begging him to make them do anything he wanted, but not to shoot them. Both wore braids and the same kind of neat black dress.

"We're from an orphanage!" they shrilled. "We don't know our nationality. We were brought there as babies."

The officer watched them thrash about, then stepped back and told them and Dina to follow him.

They emerged on the same field where the people had

been made to undress. It was littered with clothes and shoes, as before. Beyond the clothes, to one side, sat 30 or 40 old men, women and sick people. They were probably the remnants, flushed out of their apartments.

An old woman lay paralyzed, wrapped in a blanket.

Dina and the girls were placed among these people. The girls wept softly.

They sat below a ledge on which a sentry with a sub-machine gun trudged to and fro.

Dina kept watching him out of the corner of her eye, watching him go back and forth, back and forth. He noticed this finally, grew nervous and suddenly shouted in German:

"What are you watching me for? Don't look at me! I can't do *any*thing for you. I have children, too."

She reflected that for some of the Germans it was not easy, either.

A girl in an army blouse and trench coat sat down beside her, noticed that she was shivering with cold, and threw a fold of her coat over her.

They talked quietly. The girl's name was Lyuba. She was nineteen, had served in the army, and her unit had been surrounded.

A truckload of Soviet prisoners of war drove up. Each one of them had a shovel. The old people stirred with horror. Were they to be buried alive? But one of the prisoners looked at them from a distance and said, "You're in luck."

They were ordered to stand and were herded into the back of the truck in which the prisoners had arrived. Two soldiers lifted the old woman in like a log, and hands reached out to take her.

It was a high-sided open truck. One German sat in the cab, another sat at the back of the truck, and four *Polizei* stood at the sides.

Where were they being taken?

It was hard to discover any logic in what had been happening. Some people had been forcibly stripped, others not; some had been killed off; some were still being brought to the field, while others were being hauled away from it.

The truck reached Melnik Street where there was a large trucking establishment. Behind a row of garages and workshops was a big courtyard. When one of the gates was opened to let in the truck, the yard was seen to be jammed with people. Crushed together like sardines, screaming and choking, they spilled forward as the gates opened. This was where the crowds from the streets had been herded during the night. This was where they had sat for several days, awaiting their turn to be shot.

The paralyzed old lady in the blanket was lifted off the truck and shoved into the garage. The Germans closed the gates with difficulty, to the sound of shouting and screams, then talked earnestly among themselves. Dina understood what they were saying and tried to guess what they would do next.

The truck began backing out of the gateway. The German in the rear of the truck jumped down. Now there were only four *Polizei* left, two in the cab and two at the sides. These two were not at the rear, but in the middle. Dina and Lyuba began to whisper that they had to jump. Let them shoot; sudden death would be better than waiting their turn.

The truck was moving fast now. Lyuba again threw a fold of her trench coat over Dina to protect her from the wind. Winding through the streets, the truck barreled into the Shulyavka section, near the Brest-Litovsk highway.

Hidden behind Lyuba's coat, Dina swung over the tailgate and jumped while the truck was speeding along. She rolled over and over on the pavement, was bruised and bloodied, but no one on the truck noticed her go.

Perhaps no one really wanted to.

Passersby surrounded her. She began mumbling that she had been riding in a truck, that she had wanted to get off at the bazaar, but that the driver hadn't understood, so she had decided to jump. Some of the people believed her and some did not, but she saw humane eyes all around her. Quickly the people carried her into a backyard.

Half an hour later she was at the home of her sister-in-law, a Polish woman. The family kept heating water all night, soaking the slip off her back where it had become firmly pasted to her wounds.[1]

A CHAPTER OF RECOLLECTIONS

We were three friends. We were the Three Musketeers. We were a three-man tank crew. We were also the Arctic pilots Chkalov, Baidukov and Belyakov. We had one thing in common—we all had been abandoned by our fathers and were being raised by our mothers.

Bolik Kaminsky was the oldest, and, when he cuffed us we got back at him by calling him "Bolyambat—Bolya Commander," but we were very fond of him. He was a tall, thin boy with a delicate complexion, like a girl's. He had seen the war film *Chapayev* 25 times, *Shchors* 20 times, *If War Breaks Out Tomorrow* 17 times and *Bogdan Khmelnitsky* 10 times.

All of us had war fever, but Bolik was the worst. He was so infatuated that he could talk about war for hours on end. Even a game of chess was war to him: The rooks were cannon, the knights machine-gun carts, the bishops machine guns, and the queen a dive-bomber.

We set up a machine-gun nest in the attic of the wood-shed, just as Chapayev had done in a belfry. We stuck a pole out of the dormer window and fired away: "Y-y-y-y!"

Bolik entered a factory vocational school and began to look down on us after he became a member of the working class; but then real war broke out, he was ordered to dig trenches on the outskirts of the city, and he disappeared.

Shurka Krysan was the same age as I. He was puny, nimble, enterprising, and he would have gone through fire and water for the sake of the gang. Shurka displayed prodigies of hero-ism in the street battles that our end of the street regularly fought with the neighboring "Tanners," but he got pummeled more than anyone else, too.

His favorite film was *If War Breaks Out Tomorrow,* and his favorite song was the one that began with those words.

Everybody called him "Shurka Matsa," and I always called him that too, because, after all, you have to call a fellow something; but in my naïveté I had no idea that *matsa*—matzo—was a Jewish holiday food; in the simplicity of my heart I thought that Shurka had got his nickname be-cause he spoke so quickly and seemed to be clicking his tongue: tsa-tsa-tsa.

There was nothing that interested us less in those days than our origins or nationalities. We all went to Ukrainian school; our native language was Ukrainian. Only later did I realize that we were hybrids—half-Polish, half-Jewish and half-Ukrainian. We were all friends with a little girl who lived on the same street and who also did not have a father. Her name was Lyalya Engstrem. I was especially fond of her, only she wouldn't play war for anything.

To be fair I must say that they used to tease me too,

very seldom, true, but when they did they hurt me to the quick. They would call me "Semerik-tru-tu-tu."

One fine summer day Shurka Matsa and I set off for the meadow to go swimming. There was a small lake there called "Kovbanka," which means "frog pond" in the Kurenevka dialect.

When we reached the meadow we found trucks driving over it and Red Army soldiers running about; antiaircraft guns covered with green branches stood there, and barrage balloons were being inflated. Right by our Kovbanka two Red Army men were sunning themselves.

"Hey there, brats, beat it, it's dangerous here," they said.

We took offense and sulked, but we did not go away. We started swimming to the other side and back, showing off. On the way back I tired. I started gasping for air and flailed my arms helplessly. Everything began to turn green, and I saw a Red Army soldier on shore looking at me curiously. But at that moment I felt bottom under my feet and, swaying, emerged onto land. I looked back. There was no sign of Shurka's head above the water.

The soldier plunged into the water just as he was, breeches and all. The water rippled, and he came up dragging Shurka, who had turned green. He lifted Shurka onto shore like a kitten and shook him, so that the water would run out of his belly.

"What a tribe," he said. "Now beat it home, or I'll march you off to the militia station."

We beat it so fast that the reeds swished. Then we crouched in a hole and began to share our impressions.

"Yes," said Shurka, "he got in my way. I'd dived down and was walking to shore along the bottom."

Airplanes appeared overhead, about 30 of them. The

antiaircraft guns swung skyward. The shots deafened us, and then for some reason every time there was a shot our faces hit the ground. There was absolutely no place to hide in the meadow. We pressed against each other in our hole and listened to fragments or bullets or whatever they were, falling right beside us: *Shpok, shpok, shpok!*

As I lay there completely exposed beneath the blue sky, which was being slashed by roaring planes with black crosses on them, for the first time in my life I physically experienced my own vulnerability: the helplessness of my puny body, into which one of those *shpoks* could sink as if into pudding, and that would be the end.

The planes flew past. The antiaircraft gunners had not hit them, nor had they hit anything. Thousands of white leaflets fluttered in the air. Clearly, the wind was not carrying them over the city; they were coming right toward us, onto the meadow. We jumped up and ran after them, trying to catch them. They were all the same, with *"BEAT UP THE JEW-POLITICAL OFFICER, TAKE A BRICK AND SMASH IT IN HIS FACE"* printed on them in capital letters. An explanation in small type said that this was the password for surrender. When you saw a German soldier you were to say these words clearly and loudly.

"Red Army men," the leaflet urged, "the Red Army is smashed, the Jew-Bolshevist commissars' power in Russia has ended. Arrest your commanders and commissars; throw down your arms and surrender. Good conditions await you. You will all go to your homes to work peacefully. When coming to surrender bring with you a change of underwear, soap, a mess kit and a spoon."

I sensed that something was wrong and turned around. Shurka was sitting in the grass very pale and with fear in his eyes.

"Tolik," he said, "that means me. According to them I'm a Jew."

All this time I was dying of frustration. If I'd been a bit older I'd have volunteered for the army or, like Bolik, at least have gone off to dig trenches, and then, who knows, I might have remained to fight in them.

Suddenly the news spread through our end of the street: Bolik had come back. I rushed over to his house. His mother was fussing around him. He was eating potatoes, choking on them as he told his story:

"We were digging a ditch, a big long one, across a whole field. There were thousands of people, all sorts of professors, girls. They were dishing kasha out of caldrons when a 'Messer' (Messerschmitt) came over and started machine-gunning—I saw that my professor was lying on the ground and there weren't any lenses in his glasses. I hid in the hay."

In a little while German tanks appeared and everybody scattered. Bolik walked through woods and fields, taking shelter from the "Messers" in swamps. He trembled when he talked about them; he hated the Germans so much it made him stutter.

"He flies straight at you, takes aim and then he's after you, he wants to kill you—and nothing will help, you can shout, cry, fall to the ground, it's all no use. Fellows, I'll tell you a secret. Now we'll get hold of a machine gun, we'll set it up in the attic, and when they come this way, we'll give it to them: 'Y-y-y-y-y-y!' "

His mother, Auntie Nina, wept with joy because he was alive; she washed him, dressed him up in a clean suit and gave him money for the movies. The two of us, Bolik and I, went to the movie theater on Kreshchatik to see *St. Jorgen's Day*. We laughed till we cried at Igor Ilynsky's antics, although we could hear the sounds of sirens and explosions outside; shows were not stopped during air raids.

After the show we went outside, bought ourselves ice cream and loafed around on Kreshchatik. We felt good, and we didn't know a thing: that Kiev was already doomed, that we were seeing Kreshchatik for the last time, that the very next day Bolik would be evacuated with what was left of the vocational school and would disappear again without even saying good-bye.

Meanwhile loudspeakers were shouting up and down Kreshchatik, "Kiev speaking, Soviet Kiev speaking! Do you hear, Homeland? Kiev is and will remain Soviet!" Moscow replied to Kiev, "You have resurrected the immortal heroic traditions of the Great October Revolution and the Civil War. You are not alone. The Red Army is with you; our entire Soviet people is with you."

Going home, we were walking against a flood of troops, evidently retreating. The Red Army men were tired and dusty. Women had poured out onto the sidewalk and were watching with folded arms, sighing, blowing their noses, crying softly. A worn old man with a can stood crying near a telegraph pole. He was saying to a soldier boy who was playing "Polechka" (a Ukrainian folksong), "Come back to us, boys, come back."

People cried a great deal as they watched our retreating troops.

The grass on our square was crowded with tired soldiers, sitting or lying down. One soldier was cleaning a Maxim machine gun, and we sat down near him and watched attentively.

"Boys, if I give you a ruble will you bring me some milk?" he asked.

We ran off to my grandmother. She oh-ed and ah-ed, refused the ruble and gave us a pitcher of milk. The men held out their cups and we filled them, but it was only a drop in the ocean.

My grandfather was carting a load of bread down the street. Bread wasn't being sold in the stores anymore; it was being rationed according to lists of names. Each family had made itself a sack and written the family name on it in indelible pencil. The store clerks filled the sacks, and my grandfather had taken on the job of delivering them in his handcart. We were bursting with a desire to do something, so we rushed over and pushed the cart; we knocked on doors and emptied the sacks. It was a complicated matter to maneuver the cart among the troops marching along the street.

"Well, boys, all is lost, eh?" said Grandfather. "They're surrendering Kiev."

We were indignant.

"Oho, Grandfather, there's going to be some battle yet! Wait and see!"

"Battle?" Grandfather waved his hand. "Take a look at them. How can they fight?"

Tired, starved little horses pulled army carts, guns and ordinary wagons. The soldiers were caked with dirt, unshaven and covered with wounds. Some, whose feet were bruised and bleeding, were walking barefoot and had their shoes slung across their shoulders. They walked, bending under the weight of their knapsacks, bedrolls and weapons, and their mess kits clinked.

"Oh, unhappy Russian soldiers," my grandfather muttered, taking off his cap.

The Author Speaking

This chapter of recollections does not make the slightest claim to present the broad picture. It merely offers a few sidelights that help to explain some of the events and also the character of the small boy I am writing about. There was a great deal that that boy did not see and even more that he did not understand. He was only twelve years old.

It is easier now, from the vantage point of the years, to understand who was who and what was what, to rejoice, fret or wax indignant over why things happened thus and not so. But I am describing not how things should have been, but how they were. At least how my hero saw them. Stalingrad, the fall of Berlin and all the rest were still to come. The powerful avalanche of fascism was advancing, and no one seemed to know how it could be stopped or whether it could be stopped at all. Bombs and "Beat up the Jew-Political Officer" leaflets poured down, the defense of Kiev had lasted for 83 days, partisans were getting supplies and driving off to the forest in carts, Ivan Svinchenko had abandoned his arms and was on his way home, Red Army soldiers with bloody feet were walking barefoot, Grandfather Semerik was waiting for the Germans' arrival, Bolik wanted to fire a machine gun. And there in the midst of all this was I—a very small gnat. I would advise the impatient reader who is all ready with conclusions and generalizations to refrain from drawing them, so as not to find himself in the same position as Grandfather Semerik.

You'd do better to listen to what comes next.

CHAPTER IX

A CHAPTER OF DOCUMENTS

ORDER

Residents (all persons) are forbidden to appear on the streets from 6 P.M. to 5 A.M. German time.

Violators of this order may be shot.

COMMANDANT OF THE CITY OF KIEV. [1]

From a notice:

All men between the ages of 15 and 60 must report at the housing administration of their district. . . .[2]

Headline of feature article in the newspaper:

"THE JEW IS THE GREATEST ENEMY OF THE PEOPLE." [3]

Nonresidents are strictly forbidden to enter Kiev. Anyone who arrived in Kiev after September 20 must leave the city immediately. Anyone who wishes to remain in the city for valid reasons must obtain permission to do so from the passes department at No. 8 Comintern Street.

Anyone who stays in the city without a permit after October 15, 1941, will be liable to severe punishment.

COMMANDANT OF THE CITY. [4]

From an article entitled "The Tasks of the Ukrainian Intelligentsia":

Our task is to restore the Ukrainian national culture that the Jew-Bolsheviks destroyed. [5]

Commandant's notices:

As a repressive measure in connection with today's act of sabotage, 100 residents of the city of Kiev were shot.

This is a warning.

Every resident of Kiev is responsible for every act of sabotage.

Kiev, October 22, 1941.

COMMANDANT OF THE CITY. [6]

ORDER

All pigeons in the city and in the suburbs must be destroyed immediately.

Anyone who still has pigeons after October 26 will be SHOT as a saboteur.

EBERHARD,

COMMANDANT OF THE CITY. [7]

Every issue of the newspaper carried this appeal at the top:

THE FUEHRER OF THE GERMAN PEOPLE
HAS SAID:

"Millions of German farmers and workers fulfill their duties the very best they can."
Ukrainians, fulfill your duty too and work diligently! [8]

The Fuehrer was quoted as having said on October 3, 1941:
"We are putting the entire continent at the service of our fight against Bolshevism."
Ukrainians, your place is at Germany's side in the fight for a better Europe! [9]

Commandant's notice:
Instances of arson and sabotage spreading in Kiev compel me to take decisive measures.
Therefore 300 residents of Kiev were shot today. A much larger number of residents of Kiev will be shot for each new instance of arson or sabotage.
All residents are obliged to inform the German police immediately of anything suspicious.
I will maintain order and calm in Kiev whatever the cost and by all possible means.
Kiev, November 2, 1941.

EBERHARD,

MAJOR-GENERAL AND COMMANDANT OF THE CITY. [10]

Order of Lieutenant-General Bayer, November 6, 1941:
All felt boots in the possession of the population, including children's felt boots, are subject to immediate requisition. The wearing of felt boots is for-

97

bidden and will be punished on a par with bearing arms. [11]

Notice of the city commissar:

In accordance with an agreement with the *Stadt-kommandant*, the population of Kiev is informed that civilians may appear in the streets only from 5 A.M. to 5:30 P.M.

COMMISSAR OF THE CITY. [12]

Commandant's notice:

Communications facilities in Kiev (telephone, telegraph and cable lines) have been damaged maliciously. Because saboteurs can no longer be tolerated, 400 MEN HAVE BEEN SHOT IN THE CITY, which should serve as a warning to the population.

Once again I demand that anything suspicious be reported to the German troops or the German police, so that the criminals may be punished according to their desserts.

Kiev, November 29, 1941.

EBERHARD,

MAJOR-GENERAL AND COMMANDANT OF THE CITY. [13]

ON GERMAN TIME

One hundred hostages, 300 hostages, 400 hostages. This had already become a war declared against an entire city.

Hostages were seized at night, from sections cordoned off at random, and the number taken was exactly as stated in the notices. At the end of this narrative I shall describe how mass graves were opened up and the hostages' bodies were found. Once hostages were seized on Kreshchatik in the daytime, right on the sidewalk.

Kreshchatik was still smoking, but pedestrians were permitted on it. By some miracle, at the very beginning of Kreshchatik one small block and the Duma building had survived; the Duma building was on Kalinin Square and looked like an opera theater. Now that building belatedly exploded and burst into flames. The fascists began to seize everybody on Kreshchatik they could lay their hands on; they put them in trucks and sent them off to Babi Yar.

In Kurenevka, right above Babi Yar, there is the large Pavlov Psychiatric Hospital. Its buildings are spread out in the lovely Kirillov grove, where a little old church stands, always locked. We kids, however, used to get inside it, climb all over it, right up to the cupolas, and look at the Vrubel murals there, which few people know about.

On October 14 a German detachment arrived at this little church; the detachment was headed by a doctor and brought something that no one had ever seen before—death trucks. Groups of 60 or 70 patients were forced into the trucks, the engines were turned on for about fifteen minutes, and the bodies of the asphyxiated were dumped into a pit. This went on for several days; the work was done calmly and methodically, without haste, and the hour-long lunch break was never skipped. After what had happened at Babi Yar, the destruction of a big hospital passed unnoticed, as if it were an everyday affair. Indeed, everything under the sun is relative.

The fascists hunted Gypsies as if they were game. I have never come across anything official concerning this, yet in the Ukraine the Gypsies were subject to the same immediate extermination as the Jews.

Passports had decisive importance. They were checked in the streets and during house searches. Next in importance was appearance. Persons with dark hair and eyes and long noses were better off not showing themselves in the streets. Whole tribes of Gypsies were taken to Babi Yar, and they did not seem to know what was happening to them until the last minute.

A German soldier came over to Ratuyev, the elderly janitor at our school, and ordered him to take a shovel and follow him. They went to the Park of Culture, where another soldier was guarding a Jewish girl. The old man was ordered to dig a pit. When the pit was ready, the girl was shoved into it, but she began to scream and to try to climb out. The soldier began to beat her on the head with the shovel and to pile dirt into the pit. But the girl kept getting up, so he began to beat her on the head again. They filled up the pit at last and stamped on it. The old man thought that the same thing would happen to him, but they let him go.

The curfew was not a mere formality. Shots rang out all night long. With her own eyes Grandmother saw a murdered woman on Bessarabka Street. She lay, glassy-eyed, across the sidewalk, and everybody walked around her. People said that a patrol had shot her during the night and left her there for everybody to see.

Quite a few people were sent to Babi Yar because of their pigeons. This was because the order went into effect on the very next day, and many people did not even get to see it in the newspaper. At first orders were printed in three languages: Russian, Ukrainian and German; then in two: in Ukrainian in big type and in German in small type. Then the other way around: in German in big type and in Ukrainian in very small type. What was most important for each day was concentrated in these orders and notices; life and death depended on them, and after the tragedy with the pigeons the only question anybody asked was, "What is the latest order?" People bought newspapers just to see the orders.

Communists and activists began to be arrested, and at the first denunciation, without any evidence. Notices with the following message were put up: Anyone who tells the German authorities about Jews, partisans or important Bolshevik officials in hiding or about Communists who did not show up for registration will receive 10,000 rubles in cash, food products or a cow.

"Jews *kaputt,* Gypsies too; and then Ukrainians, then

101

come you" became the most popular saying. Grandmother heard it at the market and came home and told it to Grandfather with a gloomy smile. Grandfather didn't say anything; he just blinked. It really looked as if things would come to that.

THE BOOKS ARE
BURNED

"Come on, now, hand over all your honor citations," Grandfather said. "All portraits, all Soviet books! Marusya, get to work! If you want to live."

My school citations had portraits of Lenin on the left and of Stalin on the right. Grandfather, who had never been interested in books before, now took it on himself to throw whole bundles of them into the stove. At first my mother resisted, then she gave up.

It was cold, and the books got the stove well heated. All that was left, I remember, was the collected works of Pushkin. Grandfather wasn't certain about him. Pushkin was a *moskal,* a Russian, but he had lived a long time ago, and neither the Bolsheviks nor the Germans had condemned him.

The books produced a lot of ashes, and the flue got stopped up. My mother took a shovel, cleaned it and raked out the ashes. Her face was expressionless, and she worked intently. I said:

"Don't take it to heart. Some day we'll have lots of books again."

"Never have idiots spared books," she said. "Never. The Alexandria Library burned, the Inquisition bonfires burned, Radishchev's books were burned, Hitler burned books in the streets. If you live, remember this: When books are burned it means things are bad, it means that violence, ignorance and fear are everywhere. And what is happening now? When a gang of degenerates burns books in the streets it is horrible, true, but it's not the worst thing that can happen. When each person in each house begins to burn his books, shaking with fear—"

I have never forgotten that speech of hers. Perhaps she used slightly different words, but I have conveyed their substance accurately—about the Alexandria Library and the Inquisition, both of which I thus learned about concretely, for a bridge led straight from them to our stove.

An army unit moved into the school, and for several hours they threw desks, laboratory equipment, globes and books out the windows. They went to our district library and threw books right out into the garden. Books were lying about in the streets, trampled on as if they were garbage.

When the unit was transferred and vacated the school, I went over to take a look. They had turned the entire ground floor into a stable. My feet sank into a layer of straw and manure which covered our classroom floor; and iron hooks for tying up the horses were nailed into the walls. In the upstairs classrooms there were bunks filled with straw. Bandages were lying around on the floor, together with magazine pictures of naked women. In the yard outside they had dug a long ditch and had fitted poles over it. This was their toilet, in the open and visible to everyone.

The mountain of discarded books had already been badly damaged by the rain. The books on top were soggy and their pages were stuck together. I climbed on top of the heap and began to dig into it. The books underneath were wet, slimy and warm. They were rotting.

I sat on top of the heap, huddled against the wind, and I looked through them. I discovered Hugo's *Bug-Jargal* and lost myself in it. I could not tear myself away, and when it got dark I took the book home.

The next day I took a sack along and started collecting books. I selected the least damaged ones, with the most solid covers. I brought them home and dumped them in the shed, in the far corner behind the stack of firewood. I thought up a story to tell Grandfather: "We don't have much wood; these books will dry, and we can use them for fuel." He reflected. On the one hand, these were certainly books, but, on the other, they did not belong to us—we had only gathered them for fuel. "All right, you're a smart boy," he praised me.

We had no more kerosene. The electric bulbs hung lifelessly from the ceiling. So I cut some wood into tapers, fitted them into the split end of a stick and put a match to one of them. This wasn't bad at all. It burned away as you read, adjusting it now and then with one hand. When a taper burned out, you flicked it off and lit the next one; it smelled nice and even gave some warmth. I had made myself a place on the stove, which was nearly cold because my grandmother had become very saving of wood. The tomcat Titus would join me and we'd keep each other warm while I read. How many books I read then! But when I finished a book Grandfather took it away for fuel.

I read late into the night, as long as the bundle of tapers

lasted. My mother would come out, cracking her knuckles, and look at me strangely.

"Why aren't you asleep?" I'd ask angrily.

"A car is blowing its horn outside; I can't fall asleep," she'd reply.

HUNGER

And now a strange situation set in. The stores stayed as they were, all smashed up; nothing was being sold anywhere except at the market, but even if the stores had opened, what was one to buy with?

Before the war bread had cost 90 kopeks a kilogram (about two and a half pounds) in the stores. Now homemade bread was sometimes sold for 90 rubles a kilogram at the market.

This was as much money as my mother used to get for a whole month's work. But now we had no money left at all.

Grandfather and Grandmother decided to sell a few of their things. They rummaged through their belongings, looking for something to sell, but everything was old rubbish. Grandmother took some stuff to the market and stood there two days in a row—but what was the use? Nobody was buying, everybody was selling.

Grandmother and Mother scraped up all our reserves, every handful of cereal and every dry crust they could find, and they discussed and computed how much we needed to eat a day; they invented potato-peel patties and pea cakes, which they baked in a saucepan without fat.

And economy began. This word was new to me, and I liked it. In my nook on the stove I had a secret box in which I started my own economy. I did not eat all that Grandmother gave me, especially the dry biscuits—I hid some, anticipating a time when there would be nothing left at all and I'd delight everybody with my secret store.

Near our house grew an old, spreading hazelnut tree. Every autumn in the past Grandmother used to gather a basketful of nuts and save them for Christmas. Now this basket became our emergency supply and our hope.

Grandfather and I climbed over the fence and started to dig in the collective-farm vegetable garden. Once in a great while we'd find a potato that had been missed. I used to squeal with joy when I found a potato.

We combed the garden on the square and gathered half a sackful of horse chestnuts. Horse chestnuts are acrid and bitter, but if you dry them and roast them they are all right —they even taste good when you are hungry; it's all a matter of what you're used to. At that time I was reading Sholokhov's *The Quiet Don*. As I read I gnawed on the horse chestnuts, which we had dried on the stove. For me *The Quiet Don* has always been associated with the taste of those chestnuts. So many years have gone by; I have reread the book, I have taken exams on it and have seen the film, yet the taste of horse chestnuts is still there!

As Mother was washing one morning, she said:

"I don't know what's wrong. I can feel my whole skull."

I touched my face; the thin skin was stretched so tightly over the bones that you could study anatomy from my face. I ran my fingers over it, and it was terrifying. Hungry, hungry. The worm of hunger bored all day long. What could I find to eat? At night I dreamed of meals, but I had a strong will and I ate hardly anything except chestnuts. Grandmother washed potato peels (in Kiev they are called *lush-paiki*) and put them through a grater to make patties. They were bittersweet, but at least they were real food. In the closet was a flat brick on which pans were placed. A hundred times I mistook it for a loaf of bread and then I threw that brick out; I simply could not stand to see it in the closet.

Suddenly a rumor spread that the Kurenevka neighborhood council was opening a dining room for starving children. Mother ran there to apply, and then I was given a card for it. I went there the first time with Lyalya Engstrem.

The dining room was in the former kindergarten, on Bondar Lane. We lined up in front of a window, and each of us was given a bowl of hot, real millet soup. We took our bowls to a table and sat down, feeling like millionaires in a restaurant, and while we ate we were happy; I savored every spoonful, although the soup contained nothing but water and millet. Children sat all around, eating quietly; nobody made any noise. Some licked their bowls with embarrassment.

We began going there for that bowl every day, as if we were going for something miraculous, and I went there punctually all winter long. I tried to arrive at closing time because at the end of the day the thickest part of the soup was left at the bottom of the caldron, I watched anxiously to see whether the lady would dip the ladle way down.

Lyalya Engstrem's mother had been a forelady at the cannery, a friend of my mother's, and Lyalya and I, when we were small tots, were inseparable. Later we went to different schools, but now this dining room had made us close friends again. Lyalya's mother was a Party member; she had been evacuated and had left Lyalya behind with an aunt, who taught German.

One day after we left the dining room, we went over to

Lyalya's house. On the table I saw a loaf of genuine fresh bread, a jar of jam and paper bags of groceries.

I was literally dumbfounded.

"They're issued to us," Lyalya said.

"Where?"

I was all ready to run and shout, "Grandmother, they're issuing things, and we're not getting any. Hurry!"

Lyalya showed me a notice. It said that *Volksdeutschen* were to report at such a store on such a day at such a time and bring with them paper bags, sacks and jars.

"What does *Volksdeutschen* mean?

"It means Germans who live in other countries—almost Germans."

"But you're not Germans, are you?"

"No, we are Finns. And Finns are an Aryan nation, *Volksdeutschen*. My aunt told me that I shall go to the school for *Volksdeutschen* so I can become an interpreter like her."

"So that's how you've managed," I muttered, not yet quite understanding this complex matter. Lyalya had been Lyalya, my friend; we had shared everything half and half; and now she was an Aryan nation and I was rubbish.

Suddenly I burned with furious, hungry anger. So for us the stores were not open; we fed on horse chestnuts, while *they* were really living!

"So that's it," I said darkly. *"Volksdeutschen.* And you still have the nerve to go to the dining room for the hungry?"

I left, slamming the door so hard that I felt ashamed of myself. But I was filled with a hatred for her that lasted many years, though somewhere deep in my heart I realized that it wasn't Lyalya's fault. What had Lyalya to do with it?

I BECOME
A BUSINESSMAN

By now everybody knew that Shurka Matsa was staying in the house and not going out anywhere; his mother was hiding him. When he finally risked going outside he came running to me first thing. I didn't recognize him: skinny as a stray kitten, nearly blue, fiercely hungry, with eyes that shone like lamps. Over at his house, they were obviously on their last legs.

"Come on to the market to sell matches. Come with me. I'm afraid to go by myself." He shook a basket of boxes in front of my face. "My mother said for you not to call me Matsa; my name is Krysan. Alexander Krysan."

"All right," I said. "We'll call you 'Alexander, president of the dead rats [krysy].' "

He smiled pathetically, and I ran to Grandmother:

"Give me some matches. We're going to the market!"

Grandmother had about fifteen boxes of matches, and after some hesitation, she gave us ten. After all, one could keep a· fire burning, or use hot coals, or run to a neighbor for a light; matches weren't essential.

It was very cold. Shurka shivered in his light coat and kept looking around apprehensively, as if he were in a zoo and the cages were open.

The market was nearly empty. We knew the price of matches—ten rubles a box. We set up our matches in attractive stacks on a bare bench and waited. Next to us a woman was selling saccharin. The saccharin was in small packets like headache powders from a pharmacy, but at that time no one knew what saccharin was. The woman called out, praising her wares; she said saccharin was sweet, better than sugar, and that one packet was enough for four glasses of tea. The devil knows where it came from and where it went later, but all through the war I saw only saccharin, never sugar.

Somebody bought a box of matches from me. I received a crisp ten-ruble bill—and I was lost. I had money. Money! Real money with which I could now buy enough saccharin for four whole glasses of tea! Shurka stood there, frozen and dejected, but I, I was feverish, I passionately desired people to buy more from me, more and more. For the next box of matches I was given a German mark, and now at last we could inspect German money. The rate of exchange was ten Soviet rubles for one German mark. The mark was small—half the size of a ruble—and brown, with eagles and swastikas on it.

We managed to sell all our matches before dark, and we had money. Our teeth chattered with excitement. We looked greedily at the heaps of potatoes, three in a heap, and at the flour, which was sold by the glass. We each bought two and half pounds of bread and a packet of saccharin.

That evening we had a holiday at our house. Everybody drank tea with crystals of saccharin and ate bread. I was simply bursting with modest pride. I already knew what I was going to do the next day. I was going to sell nuts.

Shurka had nothing more to sell, so I went by myself. I picked a price at random—three rubles a nut—and people began to buy from me. Not often, but they bought. My old friend and subsequent enemy Vovka Babarik came over to me, gravely put down a three-ruble bill, and selected a nut. A minute later he came back:

"Change it. It's rotten."

"How do I know you didn't have a rotten nut in your pocket?" I said, because I trembled over each ruble.

"Look, it's your nut!" He pushed the two halves under my nose. The nut was moldy inside.

"It's not too bad to eat!" I tried to squirm out of it, defending my little basket of nuts with shaking hands.

"Change it, Semerik-bloodsucker, or give me back my three rubles!"

"I won't! What's bought is sold!" I cried in desperation, although deep down somewhere I felt like a heel.

He raised his arm threateningly. I was ready for this and ducked under the bench. He was after me—I raced down the aisles, ducking under tables, holding tightly to my little basket, ready to run as far as Podol if necessary but not to give back the three rubles. Vovka tired of chasing me. He stopped and looked at me contemptuously:

"Ugh, Semerik-tru-tu-tu," he said with hatred. "Worm, we'll meet again."

We were indeed destined to meet again one day.

Nowadays one had to walk cautiously in the street, but I was blazing with happiness because I had got three rubles for nothing.

Once upon a time we had been friends, though he was

a little older than I. Our enmity began when I let his birds go free. He was an ardent bird catcher. I used to go to his house and help him. I'd inspect the goldfinches, siskins and tomtits. Then I'd pester him to let them go, saying, "It's all right to catch them, lock them up in your cages for a while and then let them go. But you keep them locked up here until they die. It's pitiful." But for him, the thought of letting them go was pitiful. One fine summer day he hung the cages up on the trees in the garden. I came over and found that he was off somewhere. I opened all the cages, and for two weeks after that he tried to catch me in the street to beat me up.

I did not have many nuts left when Shurka came running.

"I got some paper! Do you want half?"

He had a basketful of cigarette papers.

"A man stole them and didn't know what to do with them. He's giving them away, ten for a ruble, and we'll sell them for a ruble each! He's given them to me on credit meanwhile. I figured there are lots of smokers, and they'll buy them!"

I took half from him at once and felt myself to be a great merchant. It is very easy to be a merchant. You stand there and shout, "Cigarette paper! One ruble! One ruble!"

The papers came in little booklets with 100 strips in each; you tore one off and rolled yourself a cigarette. But those damned Kurenevka smokers had grown accustomed to rolling cigarettes from the *Ukrainskoye slovo,* and business was slow. I built a house out of the booklets, with the colorful labels on the outside. A lady passed by with a little boy. When the child saw the house his mouth fell open:

"Mama, buy it!"

She looked, hesitated. I stood there and prayed that she

would buy it. The boy thought that the booklets would be just as pretty on the inside. He would be disappointed, but I didn't care—I needed that ruble.

"Oh, it's a waste of money!" the mother said and took the child's arm.

With hatred I watched her walk away.

On the first day Shurka and I each sold only about ten booklets, but just with what we got for them we each bought almost a quarter of a pound of bread and ate it right there in the garden; again I felt proud that I could earn my own keep.

"We can sell newspapers, or shine shoes," Shurka reflected. His eyes burned with a feverish, hungry brilliance.

And we did do all this, staying at the market from morning to night. Grandfather was right. A new life had begun for me, a new life indeed.

BOLIK
COMES BACK
AGAIN

Water does not flow under a stone that stands still. To be a good trader you have to hustle. We divided the market into spheres of operation, and each of us did the best he could on his half, scurrying up and down the aisles and meeting buyers at the gates.

"Cigarette papers, cheaper than mushrooms—take the whole hash, whoever has the cash. Uncle, buy a paper! Ugh, skinflint!"

Business was terrible. We could hardly scrape together enough for a slice of bread, but I still went to the dining room for bowls of soup, so I was no longer dying of starvation.

One day I was whining at the gates in my usual manner when I saw a tattered, strangely familiar figure walking down the street, swaying.

"Shurka," I yelled across the entire marketplace, "Bolik has come back!"

It was indeed Bolik. Lord, he could hardly drag himself along. And what he looked like—terribly thin and bruised and up to his eyes in dirt.

He had left the city with other evacuees just before the Germans entered. The train had to be abandoned when it was bombed. He had nine lives, that devil, like Titus; no matter how far he was taken, he always came home again.

We went home with him. Auntie Nina wept and fussed over him, and no wonder—an only son, her darling! Her darling ate potatoes with dry biscuits soaked in water; he shivered and trembled as he told how bombs fell on their train and how everything burst into flames, and then everything came to a standstill because there were German tanks up ahead. He got off the train and started home, walking back along the tracks.

He had slept in haystacks, had been fed by kindhearted women in the countryside, and here he was.

"Why didn't you bring a machine gun?" I asked.

Bolik waved a hand.

"Fellows, we're going to look for the partisans. If we can't find them, the three of us will form our own detachment!"

We burst out laughing. Just look at him; his body might be drooping but his spirits were as high as ever—our warlike Bolik! So everything was all right, and off we went to roam about.

The rails on the embankment were already turning orange with rust. Empty cartridge cases lay on the ground between the rails. The three of us got excited and started walking along the embankment, our eyes glued to the ground underfoot. Bolik found the first whole cartridge clip. Then we found two full machine-gun belts in the bushes. We literally went mad with joy; we rushed about the embankment, pick-

118

ing up cartridges. They were all Soviet cartridges. Our men had obviously left them after defending this spot. But there was not a single rifle.

"A machine gun, a machine gun!" Bolik prayed.

We did not find a machine gun either, and if my grandmother had known this she would have said that God was protecting us.

But we collected every single cartridge and, according to all the adventure-story rules, we buried them, on the southern slope of the embankment, counting 20 footsteps from a big rock.

KHARKOV
IS CAPTURED

The newsstand that used to be so colorful, all plastered with newspapers and posters, was now smashed, dirty and missing its window glass. The newsstand lady had put up a piece of plywood for protection against the wind, and she sat alone, like a spider, over a heap of *Ukrainskoye slovo.*

As always, she was pleased to see us and counted out 100 newspapers for us at a discount.

"What's new there?" Shurka inquired in a businesslike manner.

"Well, Kharkov has been captured. There are successes outside Leningrad. We've been hearing about these 'successes' for three months now."

We ran off to the marketplace, yelling:

"Today's newspaper! Kharkov captured! Nothing but successes outside Leningrad! Read all about it, whoever can read!"

But the marketplace was empty except for a few trades-women, who were not interested in the written word. We managed to sell only a few papers.

We hurried on to the next stage—marching down the

street. Shurka took the left side, and I took the right, and we pestered everybody we met all the way to the streetcar depot opposite Babi Yar. There we had a stroke of luck. A crowd had gathered in the hope that a freight car might come out; when one did, people rushed onto the platforms and the driver collected money and took them to Podol or to Pushcha-Voditsa, wherever he was going.

People reacted in various ways as they bought our newspapers. Some had satisfied smiles, some were impenetrably grave and some were angry. One man, wearing a good coat and carrying a briefcase said:

"Now it's finished! Soon we'll hear about Moscow, and the war will be over!"

A woman sighed bitterly:

"A fortune-teller in Podol says the war will end when the potato plants blossom."

"I think it will be sooner," the man said.

People threw angry looks at him, but no one argued. They were afraid.

I was very hungry. I used to get dizzy often, and a breeze could have knocked me over, as the saying goes. The package of newspapers was heavy, my arms were tired, my feet burned.

Shurka was still bombarding the streetcar depot gates, but I sat down on some stone steps and began to think. Before the war I had visited Moscow with my mother. I remembered it well. So the Germans would soon take Moscow; they'd ride in the subway and walk on Okhotny Row. They'd probably blow up the Mausoleum. They'd put up an order and start shooting Jews, Gypsies and hostages. Then the potato plants would blossom, and Hitler's reign would take over the earth forever, I could see this picture so vividly that I went all cold inside.

Newspapers, you see, are a special kind of business. Unless you sell them all, you cannot make anything on them, and you must sell them today. The goods don't keep, so to speak. So run, run; money won't walk into your hands, you have to go out and get it for yourself. But I did not have the strength to get up. I sat on the icy steps until I was frozen to the marrow, watching with agonizing hope every passerby in the distance who could possibly be a buyer.

Shurka and I saw a huge crowd. It was moving from Podol, jamming all of Kirillovskaya; it was a dark avalanche, like a natural disaster. There was something ominous about it, but we did not immediately realize this and rushed toward it with our newspapers.

Only then did we notice the guards. They were leading prisoners of war. There were a great many prisoners. They moved in a disorderly mob, tripping and bumping into one another like a herd of cattle being driven to slaughter. As a matter of fact, this is what people used to say then—not prisoners are being "led," but prisoners are being "driven."

They were dirty, unshaven, and their eyes seemed absolutely insane. Army greatcoats hung in tatters on many of them. Some had their feet wrapped in rags, others were barefoot. Some were carrying packs. Rustling and stamping filled the air; the men plodded on, staring straight ahead with expressionless eyes; only very, very rarely did someone peer avidly at me and Shurka, and the dandified guards clicked their iron-studded boots and called to each other in German.

Frightened faces appeared at windows and gateways.

A few days later an escaped prisoner hid in our house. He talked all night long. He came from Saratov and his first name was Vasily, but I don't remember his last name. The next chapter is based on the story he told us.

CHAPTER XVI

DARNITSA

Encircled units of the Southwestern Front had tried to break out of Kiev by way of Darnitsa, but they were all shot down or taken prisoner.

A huge area was ringed with barbed wire, and about 60,000 prisoners were driven into it; additional new groups were constantly being shoved in.

Vasily was in one of the first groups. They were driven through the gates and left to themselves. At the entrance, however, the Germans picked out commanders, political officers and Jews, the ones they managed to discover, and put them into a separate compound, so there was a sort of "camp within a camp." This smaller compound was given a stronger guard.

The huge crowds of men sat, slept, walked around, waiting for something to happen. They were not given anything to eat.

After a while they started to pull up the grass and to dig for roots. They drank water from puddles. In a few days there was no more grass left. The camp had become a barren expanse.

The nights were cold. The freezing men, slowly losing their resemblance to human beings, huddled together. One man put his head on another man's lap, that other man put his head on the next man's lap, and so on, until a tight cluster was formed. In the morning, when the cluster began to move and crawl apart, a few were always left on the spot, men who had died in the night.

Finally the Germans set up caldrons and began to cook beets—they got the beets right on the other side of the fence. All around were large collective-farm fields of unharvested beets and potatoes.

Each prisoner was entitled to one scoop of beet slop a day. The prisoners, weak from starvation, were forced into a line with sticks and shouts and then were made to crawl on hands and knees to the caldron. The purpose of this was to "control the approach to the caldrons."

The commanders, political officers and Jews in the inner compound were not given anything at all. They clawed up the earth and ate everything that could possibly be eaten. On the fifth or sixth day they chewed their belts and shoes. By the eighth or ninth day some had died, and the rest were half crazed.

"There we were," Vasily said, "walking about and watching them; we were hungry and savage ourselves, but the ones behind the fence there had no reason left at all. We couldn't bring ourselves to look at them. A guard with a submachine gun saw to it that no one threw anything over to them."

The rumor that this camp existed spread instantly. Women began to come to Darnitsa from Kiev and from the countryside to look for their men. Long lines of them walked along the roads, carrying bags and parcels that they hoped to pass on to the prisoners.

At first there was some confusion, and policy was inconsistent. Sometimes when a woman found her husband he was released, sometimes he was not. Then they completely stopped releasing prisoners.

Parcels were accepted for the prisoners, but first the guards brought the parcels to their booth and took the best things. Sometimes they took everything. Therefore the women deliberately brought just potatoes, carrots or moldy bread. They tried to throw things over the fence themselves, but the guards would yell out and shoot.

The guards never gave the parcels to the persons they were intended for. They simply came out of the booth and shouted, "Bread, bread!" and threw it on the ground. The mob lunged forward and fell upon it—the starving men fought and tried to pull the bread away from each other, while the guards stood there laughing. Correspondents came and filmed these scenes. (Later I myself saw photographs of Darnitsa in German magazines—horrible, barefoot, unshaven men—with captions reading, "The Russian soldier Ivan. It is with soldiers like these that the Soviets want to defend their disintegrating state.")

Soon the guards got tired of this kind of entertainment. They began to vary it. They brought baskets out of the booth and yelled, "Bread! Bread!"—and then they announced that anyone who touched the bread before the order was given would be killed. The mob stood motionless. After talking and smoking for a while, the guards would turn around and go away. At that the prisoners rushed for the bread, but the guards turned around and fired their submachine guns. Dozens of bodies were left lying on the ground; the mob fell back. This game would go on for hours, until the Germans gave their permission to take the bread.

"I fell upon it like everybody else," Vasily said. "You don't use your head there. You see bread and you go for it, you don't think that you may be killed. Only when you see bodies on the ground does it penetrate. We'd fall back, stand, wait, our eyes on that sweet bread."

One of the guards, a sergeant-major named Bitzer, was an ardent hunter. He'd come out with a small-bore rifle and go hunting in the camp. He was an excellent marksman. He'd shoot at a sparrow somewhere and then turn around instantly and shoot at a prisoner. One shot at the sparrow, one at the prisoner, and he'd get them both every time. Sometimes this Bitzer shot 20 or 30 prisoners in a single day, so when he went hunting everyone tried to hide.

Vasily lost count of the days. He admitted that he survived because he used to go to the garbage dump outside the German kitchen. A crowd swarmed there, looking for potato peels, onion peels and the like. The Germans took photographs of this too, and laughed, "Russians are pigs."

Later some sort of order was introduced. They began to make the prisoners work. At six in the morning they banged on a rail and crowds of prisoners poured out of the barracks and got into formation; noncoms selected men for work crews and took them off to fill in ditches, repair roads or clear away debris. A crew never came back with all its men. Those who were too starved to stand up or who worked poorly or tried to escape were shot. Sometimes 100 men left in the morning and ten came back.

The prisoners wrote notes, wrapped them around stones and threw them over the fence. The women, who hovered around the camp all day long, picked up the notes and carried them all over the Ukraine. The contents of the notes were always the same: "I am in Darnitsa, bring me some potatoes, get documents, try to get me out." And an address.

These notes were passed from hand to hand. Women walked around the marketplace shouting, "Anybody here from Ivankovo? Take a note!" If there was no one from Ivankovo, the note would be passed on to Demidovo, and from there to Dymer, and so on until it got to the right address.

This improvised mail operated without a hitch. There wasn't a soul who threw away a note or was too lazy to deliver one.

I myself often passed on notes—some of them were so greasy and worn that I had to retrace them in ink.

When relatives, wives and mothers got such notes, they naturally hurried to Darnitsa, but they by no means always found the note-writers alive, and if they did find them, what could they do?[1]

Vasily used to go to work; he buried the dead near the barbed wire, and here he and a man from Kiev picked out a suitable spot. They got themselves a strip of iron, crept out of the barrack during the night and began to dig a tunnel under the wire.

They threw dirt on each other so as to be less noticeable. They had chosen a spot that the searchlight did not reach very well.

Of course, they were conspicuous anyway, especially after they got through the first row of barbed wire and found themselves on plowed-up earth.

"I shook like a madman," Vasily related. "I knew I had to move carefully, but I rushed. Then I saw that I could get through—my shirt tore, the skin came off my back, but I pushed through and set off as fast as I could go! I looked back—my partner wasn't there. I was thinking that he had broader shoulders and must have got stuck. Then they started firing."

I am telling this as Vasily told it. His comrade died. Apparently he could not get through the hole, lost time and was noticed. The guards probably concluded that only one man had tried to escape, or maybe they did not feel like pursuing or searching in the dark field. Vasily heard them laugh and swear as he got farther and farther away.

At last he reached the potato field. The top soil was already frozen. Vasily dug into the earth with his fingernails, pulling out potatoes and chewing them, together with the dirt. He knew he had to keep going and going, but first he had to eat his fill. Then he did another stupid thing. He rose to his full height and started running. He could not remember how long he ran and wandered about; he hid in a hole and covered himself with potato plant leaves.

He spent two days and nights in the fields, like a wild animal, avoiding the villages and filling himself on potatoes and beets—he could not have wished for a finer feast.

He wandered onto a battlefield. Dead bodies were rotting, and shells and rifles lay on the ground. Someone had already done some looting here. The corpses were without boots, the pockets of their clothes were turned inside out, and some had been stripped. Vasily found some clothes that fitted him and armed himself with a pistol. In the forest he came across a black horse with an injured leg. He caught it, mounted it and continued on his way. He saw a two-wheeled army cart in a ravine. He harnessed the horse to it and drove on in the cart.

Finally he ventured into a village. The women fed him

and gave him civilian clothing. He looked at himself in a mirror and saw an emaciated, ragged old man with a beard.

The women advised him to go off, not to remain in those parts. The fascists were still scouring the area, hunting for prisoners. His unfortunate comrade had told him a great deal about his family in Kiev, and Vasily remembered the address. He decided that he might pass unnoticed in a big city.

He was afraid to drive on the highways, so he wandered along the country lanes for a long time until he hit the Dnieper River. He drove along the river and was thinking of abandoning the horse and cart when he saw a ferry. He paid for the crossing with his pistol, for which he would not have any use in Kiev.

Fortune looked after him. He did not see a single German all the way to Kiev. He grew bolder, and he realized that the Germans traveled in groups, army units or whole armies along certain roads, while the land as a whole was empty, and there was still room in it for a man to save himself. He rode boldly into Kiev. There were so many old men driving carts then that no one paid any attention to him. He went to the address and found that the house had burned down. It was on Kreshchatik.

Vasily drove through the whole city as if he had business to attend to, and when he reached Kurenevka he did not know what to do next. He saw my grandmother inside the gates and asked if she'd let him in for the night. Grandmother told me to open the gates.

BEAUTIFUL, SPACIOUS, BELOVED LAND

It was all Grandfather's idea and, I think, a good one. Vasily must not remain in the city, but must go off to some out-of-the-way village, where, incidentally, a man, especially one with a horse, was worth his weight in gold. I went along to show him the way.

There used to be a lot of life on the Dymer highway, but now we drove along it without meeting a soul, and the clatter of the army cart's huge wheels, which were as big as I was, rang out loudly in the forest.

Here and there straw, horse manure and yellowed scraps of newspaper had been trampled into the cobblestones. Grass was growing among the cobbles and had sprouted shoots. Once upon a time people used to pass here, but that was long ago, and those people had vanished, become extinct. Now there was only myself, Vasily and the black horse.

It felt as if it was still peacetime. Spacious, everlasting. Tall, tall old pine trees soared into the sky, rustling quietly up there in the blue height, calm and wise.

I lay on my back in the hay and watched the treetops float by. Sometimes I caught sight of a red squirrel or a brightly colored woodpecker, and I seemed to think about everything at once: that the world was wide, that Vasily was right—the gray-green locusts kept to the highways and to centers such as our city, where the devil knows what was happening, where there was Babi Yar, Darnitsa, orders, hunger, Aryans, *Volksdeutschen,* bookburning, while all around here it was like millions of years ago, with the tops of the pine trees rustling softly, and a huge, abundant land stretched out under the sky—neither Aryan nor Jewish nor Gypsy land, simply land for man, just that, for man.

When we passed Pushcha-Voditsa, from the top of a hill we could see for 40 miles on our right. Below, the blue Dnieper meandered through its valley, and there was not a steamship or even a rowboat to be seen on it. No people, no people, nothing but fields as far as the eye could see, and this bright ribbon of highway, overgrown with grass and as straight as if it had been drawn with a ruler—it seemed to lead into the sky.

Two crosses stood by the roadside amid some beautiful bushes—simple wooden crosses with German helmets on them. Someone had put flowers on the mounds, but they had long ago withered and dried up.

Vasily dozed all the time; sometimes he fell asleep, and then the lame black horse, which was obviously sick and tired of limping into the unknown, slowed down more and more until he stopped altogether. Then Vasily woke up, gave him a lash on the belly, and the horse started pulling energetically and willingly, shaking his head vigorously as if to say, "Now it's all clear, now I understand perfectly!"

The first village on our route was Petrivtsa, and we went through it like Martians or ghosts. Women and children came running to their fences and watched us in amazement and astonishment, and the entire village watched until we reached the fields again and vanished onto the lifeless highway.

By noon our livers had become mixed up with our spleens from the pitching and tossing we got on the cobblestones, so we told our black horse to go along the side of the road. He didn't like this very much; he stopped watching the road and kept looking sideways, no doubt praying to his god that Vasily would fall asleep again—and when he did, he turned joyfully back onto the cobblestones. But he did not take into account that the shaking would awaken Vasily. After dragging along for another five miles or so, the black horse, perplexed, offended and contrary, went on strike. We unharnessed him, hobbled him and let him go off and graze by himself. Meanwhile we munched dry biscuits, spread some hay under a wild rose bush, laid a torn raincoat and a no less torn quilted jacket on top of the hay and lay down for a nap, since we were not in any hurry. And I had one of the best naps in my life.

After the crosses with the helmets we saw another reminder of the war: picturesque ruins of a bridge across the Irpen River, near the village of Demidovo. There wasn't any village; just ashes and dazzling white tile stoves with their chimneys pointing into the sky like index fingers.

The Irpen is not much of a river, but it is very swift. When the German troops crossed it they built a brushwood road across a branch of the river, but they themselves broke it up so badly that we nearly sank our heavy cart as we crossed. However, when we finally drove into the burned village and turned off the cobblestone road onto a dirt road, our destination was near at hand.

I liked the army cart very much. It had a retractable step, handles on the sides, door handles like those of a truck, and boxes under the seat. Everything in it had been well thought out, except for one detail. Its wheels did not coincide with the ruts in the dirt roads. The distance between the wheels of all farm wagons is the same. God help you if yours are different; if they are, you'd better not try to drive over our roads. Besides, our roads are usually dried mud with deep ruts, in which the wagon runs as if it is on tracks; or liquid mud, in which you sink right up to the hubs if you get out of the ruts; or, finally, simply two deep ditches across a meadow, with puddles and frogs in them. Nothing but ruts.

One wheel of our cart was in the rut. The other bounced desperately, jumping and lurching over bumps, ridges and holes, so that we drove along lopsided, nearly turning over. Three miles of this sort of ride turned us inside out and was three times as hard as all the rest of the distance we had traveled that day.

Ivan Svinchenko lived at the far end of Litvinovka, on the other side of the dam, which was graced with a burned down windmill. There was a whole street of Svinchenkos there, and Ivan's sister Gapka took me in.

Gapka lived in a very low hut that had almost grown into the soil; it had tiny little windows and a thatched roof with holes in the rotting straw. Inside it was like a cave, its uneven dirt floor covered with rags, straw dolls and crawling children and kittens. A crooked stove with the paint peeling off stood in the middle, and near it was a sort of dais with rags thrown over it; this was called the "floor," and everybody slept on it in a heap. The air in the hut was strange and stifling to anyone unaccustomed to it.

Gapka's husband was missing in the war, and she had been left with a bunch of children. Her neighbor on the other side of the wall had children, too. In general there were children everywhere; they crawled all over the hut and the yard, like roaches—bare-bellied, dirty, with runny noses, in torn shirts and dresses. On the stove sat a mysterious old man and old woman, who frightened me at first; they were the patriarchs of the Svinchenko tribe. The old man was so skinny that he seemed transparent, and he coughed and cleared his throat all the time. The old woman would slip off the stove and drag her feet heavily across the yard; she could barely walk, yet she was always trying to be useful. She was hunchbacked and bent double, so that she looked at the ground she walked. Back at home Mother had told me that Gapka was a very hard worker and that the ancient grandfather and grandmother were wonderful people who all their lives had done nothing but good for others. Yet at first I could not free myself from a sinister impression.

After Gapka had asked us all about our life in the city and ah-ed and oh-ed about it, she began telling us about her own life.

The Germans had passed through once and had never been seen here since. And everyone started to live as best he knew how. There were unharvested collective-farm fields all around. Everyone went out, picked out a patch for himself and threshed grain and dug up potatoes and beets. There was nowhere to sell all this, so it remained here. "It's not enough to say that we all have plenty to eat," Gapka said. There were stores for the winter, the cellars were bursting, and the attics were filled with apples and pears. Why, it was exactly as if there were no war at all, as if no misfortune had befallen people roundabout. The old women said, "This is how it is before the end of the world."

In the evenings friends gathered around a torch of burning tapers; they distilled their own liquor and munched sunflower seeds until they were in a stupor. In the daytime the clang of chains was heard in every yard. Everyone was threshing grain, and women, girls and old men swung the chains, winnowed the grain and pounded it between stones.

Gapka boiled up a huge pot of potatoes, emptied it onto the dinner table, and the whole family, I along with them, sat around the table and peeled potatoes, dipping them in salt and washing them down with sour milk. I ate my fill, I ate until my head started going around and around and I was swaying as if drunk; by the time I got to my apple I could only peck at it listlessly.

Ivan Svinchenko himself took Vasily into his hut. The very next day Vasily drove out to the fields to haul potatoes, and that was the last anyone saw of him until Sunday. There were indeed very few men and horses in Litvinovka, and nobody set a high value on potatoes; so Vasily was paid half a load for each delivery from the fields—he got one out of every two sacks. He emptied this great wealth into Svinchenko's yard and was up to his ears in work. Meanwhile I loafed.

The Svinchenko children took me to a field where there were many shell holes, with the tail of a mine protruding from nearly every one of them. The mines had wings and made pretty good toy windmills. We climbed all over the long, dark collective-farm stables and sheds, looking for hidden hens' nests; we found eggs and drank them down on the spot. We put on all the warm clothing we could find, put coals into "censers" made out of tin cans, mounted horses and rode them into the night pasture. I rode a black horse. In the field was a crippled tank with black-and-white crosses on its armor; it had been stripped inside, but it had seats, and the hatches worked. While the horses grazed, we played war. Some of us climbed into the tank, others fired at it with stones. The noise inside was so loud it made your ears ring.

At last Ivan and Vasily loaded the cart and we set out. They were going to the city, and I was going back home. My share was a sack of potatoes, half a sack of grain and a few other things. All day long I tramped on foot, walking way ahead on the empty highway, thinking, thinking all the time, brimming over with strange, conflicting emotions. I arrived home as the savior of the family, in a sense.

CHAPTER XVIII

NIGHT

When we came to Olya's this time, Marusya did not even let us into the house, and Grandmother and I sat a while at Grabarev's, resting before we started back for home.

"Oh, Lord," Grandmother worried. "Now what will I say to Olya? It's highway robbery!"

"They are doing wrong," Grabarev remarked phlegmatically. "They'll be sorry for it some day."

"Olya put her sweat into this house, and they've seized it like robbers!"

"This too will pass," Grabarev said, "Don't take it to heart. Thousands of people are dying, and you are worrying about a house."

Grabarev was planing a board. He was making a coffin to order. He had decided that this was the most profitable trade nowadays.

"This will all pass, Marfa Yefimovna," he repeated. "Olya will come home and Marusya will be thrown out and will answer for this."

"The law is on her side now."

"That won't always be so."

"Do you think our army will come back?"

Grabarev shrugged, "If I knew that . . ."

"You know," Grandmother said suddenly.

"I know exactly what everybody else knows. That Moscow has not been captured, for instance, and behind Moscow, Marfa Yefimovna, is a big Russia."

We hardly paid any attention to the distant thunder. There was so much thundering and shooting going on all around then. All we heard was an explosion somewhere.

We started home. Grandmother walked deep in thought, then she said:

"No, Grabarev didn't stay behind in Kiev for nothing. God save him."

We came to our favorite spot, and the Lavra lay before us. It was burning.

The Lavra's main belfry shone with a bright orange light, as if it were illuminated, yet there was little smoke. There was no more Cathedral of the Assumption—there was nothing but a heap of stones, with the remains of frescoed walls protruding from it. All the museums and the whole walled town were burning.

Grandmother sat down right where she was standing. People came running from there, from the Lavra, and everybody was saying that the Cathedral of the Assumption had been blown up. Many ancient manuscripts and books had been kept in it. The wind carried the burning pages, and they came down like rain and set fire to everything. But no one knew who had blown it up, who had needed to do this.

It was November 3, 1941, when I saw the Lavra burning.

It had a profound effect on my grandmother. She sat there for a long time, crossing herself now and then. With difficulty I persuaded her to come away. Something seemed to have snapped inside her.

Only after she got home did she begin to come to herself. She started fussing over the stove as usual and said, as she ladled out the soup, "Ah, my child, you'll see so much. Some people don't see as much in their whole lives. May God save you."[1]

The day the sailors were driven to Babi Yar it was very cold, even snowing, I think. Rumor had it that these were sailors from the Dnieper fleet. Their hands were tied with wire, but apparently not everyone's, for some raised clenched fists over their heads. They walked in silence (perhaps they would be shot if they called out); every so often a clenched fist went up, as if a man were stretching or squaring his shoulders.

Many were barefoot, some were naked to the waist, and some wore nothing but underpants. The ones in front were especially horrifying—they walked in a solid row, looking straight ahead; they seemed to be made of granite. They didn't shout or fight back until they reached the Yar. As they were being shot they shouted, "Long live Stalin!" "Long live the Red Army!" "Long live Communism!"

The report in the newspaper that I was selling on November 23 was a strange one (it did not contain the customary fanfare and raptures):

FURTHER SUCCESSES AT THE BEND OF THE DONETS RIVER AND ON THE CENTRAL SECTOR OF THE EASTERN FRONT.

THE ENEMY'S UNSUCCESSFUL ATTEMPTS TO BREAK THROUGH AROUND LENINGRAD.

THE FUEHRER'S HEADQUARTERS, NOVEMBER 21.
The high command of the armed forces states:
Further successes were achieved in battles at the bend of the Donets River and on the central sector of the Eastern Front.

The enemy's attempts to break through around Leningrad were repulsed by German artillery. [2]

An excerpt from an article in the same issue of this newspaper, with the rather inexpressive headline, "The Nature of the War in the East," read:

The Bolshevist army has been routed in the main. The Germans have taken millions of prisoners of war. As many have been killed, and what the Bolsheviks are still sending to the front is just cannon fodder. War is not won by numbers or by adherence to tactical forms; it is won by spiritual depth, for it is not matter and mass that win but spirit and man. And from this standpoint there is no one and nothing in the world that can compare with Germany, and therefore Germany is invincible.

It was on this day, I think, that I felt—too early in my life—the first pulse beat of manhood. I was sitting unhappy and angry under a large awning on the marketplace, with the wind somehow managing to blow from all sides at once. My hands and feet were icy; my shoe polish had frozen, damn it, and I no longer had any hope of a customer because it was getting dark. The last of the marketwomen were leaving and it was getting close to curfew time. I wasn't making any more money shining shoes than I had made selling cigarette papers or newspapers, yet I didn't give it up. I kept hoping for something.

Then I looked around me in surprise, and the dusty gray curtain dropped from the world. I saw that my grandfather was a fool. That there was violence in the world. Blood. Hunger. Death. And for some reason I was sitting here under an awning with my brushes, in the heart of this black world. Who had done this and why? There was nothing at all to look forward to. Winter. Night.

With numbed hands I began to gather up my belongings. I heard the sound of hoofs. A column of Cossacks was riding across the square. I didn't even pay much attention to them, though I had never seen anything like them before—mustachioed and red-faced, with stripes on their trousers and richly ornamented sabers. It was as if they had stepped out of olden times, or out of a historical film about the Revolution. Had Commandant Eberhard summoned help?

I hurried home because it was fast growing dark. The Cossacks' horses had filled the air with the stench of stables. Dogs were barking in the yards. At Babi Yar the machine guns were firing.

CHAPTER XIX

"MAN EATS TO LIVE AND LIVES TO EAT"

The books I read told about love and suffering, heroic deeds and voyages, great discoveries and ideas. But for some reason they rarely said anything about where the food came from every day for loving, suffering, traveling and learning. The heroes of most books seemed to draw nourishment from the sky. Probably they had dined first, before accomplishing things more deserving of attention. But just a moment. How did they get their food? Where did their dinners come from?

Wherever I looked, most people in real life were preoccupied simply with what to eat, what to wear, where to live. Many of them were concerned entirely with this, to the exclusion of everything else, so hard did they find these things to come by.

A wise man once said, "Man eats to live." Another added sardonically, "and lives to eat."

In page after page, books described the lusty feats of various kings and musketeers, matters unquestionably worthy of attention, and I read of them with about the same curiosity I felt in reading about the labors of Hercules. But I must admit that I had a far warmer spot for Sholom Aleichem, whose characters struggled so desperately for a slice of bread, who made ink for sale, and so forth. With boundless affection and gratitude, I read and reread every line of Taras Shevchenko[1] where he describes a mother who gathers another's wheat on the estate, beds her babies between the furrows and gives them a cloth dipped in poppyseed oil to suck on so they won't whimper. And how well I understood the whole depth and complexity of the problem of Gogol's overcoat!

My God, but we need to eat every day; after all, we need to eat to live! I saved by passing up breakfast, figuring I'd have more for dinner if I went without breakfast; and if I passed up dinner, there would be more to eat tomorrow.

But then Grandmother noticed that my hands and feet were swelling. She and Mother ate hardly anything at all, giving their morsels to me.

I had to lay my hands on something to eat. Every day my head throbbed with the thought, "How can I get something to eat? What will I eat today? What else can I swallow that's digestible?" I walked about, narrowly examining the pantry, the barn, the cellar, the yard.

Our school's old mathematics teacher, Balatyuk, starved to death. He had been trying to work as a janitor in his last days. The factories opened, and the workers were paid 200 rubles a month. A loaf of bread cost 120 rubles at the bazaar, a glass of millet 20 rubles, ten potatoes 35 rubles and a pound of lard 700 rubles.

When Zhorka Gorokhovsky's father, a fitter for the Food Industry Machinery Trust, went off to the war (never to return), he left all his tools behind. His workshop in the shed became Zhorka's. The place was heaped to the ceiling with metal junk, all of it highly useful and irreplaceable—broken clock mechanisms, spokes from bicycle wheels, parts from a cannon, bits of harness, magnets, bedsprings, boxes and boxes of small scrap, washers, nuts and God knows what else. This came about because Zhorka had one rule in life. Whatever piece of metal he saw on the ground—a bolt, a piece of wire, a horseshoe—he would pick up and promptly take home to his treasure chest.

I had shared a school desk with him for four years and was very fond of him, because he was a serious fellow who felt that man lived not by bread alone—he had to have iron too! And Zhorka was really smart. He knew how to make cigarette lighters from bits of copper pipe and empty cartridge cases. His younger brother Kolka and I used to sit open-mouthed and respectfully watch him perform his rites with a soldering iron.

Kolka was the complete opposite of his older brother: a carefree loafer, an incipient tramp and a mischief-maker. And he was fond of breaking things. If he found a light bulb, it was foredoomed to be shattered on the pavement. A fire extinguisher had to be turned on the instant it was sighted.

There was plenty of material for this. Directly behind the shed stood the big building of the Antiaircraft and Civilian Defense School, which the fascists took over for a barracks and from which, true to form, they spent two hours throwing instruments, books and study aids through the windows so as not to clutter their lives.

My first antifascist act was connected with this particular building and with Kolka. The Germans dug their usual latrine trench on the school grounds in such a way that they squatted there, newspapers in hand, with their backs to

149

us. So we got hold of a good slingshot, selected some rough-edged nuts with toothed flanges from one of Zhorka's boxes, stole up to the fence and, having singled out the fattest behind, opened fire. As Zhorka told the story afterwards, a mighty roar issued from the "reading room," and the German lost no time in scaling the fence and looking for us—to share his impressions, no doubt.

Later, the troops departed and a dining room for the aged was opened in the school building. Hundreds of old people shuffled in with their crutches, pots and spoons. The management had issued meal tickets to the dying, the bloated and the solitary. They crowded, trembling and bickering, around the distribution window to receive a splash of soup each, and then sat down immediately at the small tables to slurp it, savor it, smack their lips, poke one another and spill soup on their beards.

Kolka and I wandered glumly among the tables, almost hating these oldsters and eyeing their bowls, which they jealously shielded with their hands.

The cook suddenly called to us, "Want to carry water to the vat, boys? I'll give you some soup."

With what approached a squeal of joy, we grabbed the biggest pot by its two handles and staggered to the hand pump. We carried water until closing time, fawning on the cooks and peering into their eyes. Finally they gave us each a plate of soup, filled to the brim. Proud and happy, we took a long time to eat the soup, stretching out our pleasure and praying that they would need water tomorrow too and the next day and the day after that.

My grandfather tried to get a meal ticket, but they turned him down, saying he was able to work. He then

carried on so about it that they hired him as night watchman at the dining room. He took his greatcoat and a pillow
and set off for his first watch, and I went with him. I was
hatching a bold plan.

While Grandfather remonstrated with the cooks and dish-
washers because they hadn't left him any soup, I sat meekly
in a corner. The doors slammed and everyone went
home. Grandfather barred the front door, came back and
set about making himself a bed out of benches, grumbling
all the while, "The damned cutthroats fill their own pails
to the top, the vipers!"

I decided to start with the second floor. This building
had long corridors, hidden nooks, stairways and scads of
doors to lecture halls and classrooms, and there was no one
in the whole vast building but Grandfather and me.

The walls of the lecture halls were lined with planks
laid across sawhorses, the floor was littered with straw,
bandages and bits of paper, and there was a heavy scent
of soldiery. I began feverishly to rummage in the straw, to
crawl under the benches and tables. Nothing but cigarette
butts and magazines.

The photos in the magazines, on glossy paper, were
excellent: German soldiers standing on a hill and looking
at the cathedrals of ancient Smolensk; smiling people in
folk costumes proffering bread and salt to a general; a
typical Russian beauty with a luxurious braid, who might
have stepped out of a Russian folk chorus, bathing naked
in a small wooden tub in front of a log wall, with the cap-
tion, "Russian Bath."

I painstakingly gathered unfinished, flattened cigarette
butts and put them in my pocket. I was so hungry my

vision blurred. Pirates had once chewed tobacco, so I started chewing the butts, but they were bitter and scorched my tongue, so I spat them out with all my might.

In the tenth or twelfth room I finally found a bread roll. It was about half the size of my palm and moldy, but white bread! I began gnawing at once, without scraping off the mold; in order not to lose a single crumb, I broke the roll up on a window sill, drooling, put the fragments in my mouth, and sucked them until they turned into a paste, which I shifted with my tongue, swooning at the taste and in no hurry to swallow. My body tingled all over.

Enlivened by success, I moved on to the chemistry laboratory. Here there were so many shelves, glass vials and gauges that the Germans had apparently grown too lazy even to throw out and had merely smashed everything and drained the alcohol from the burners.

My eyes popped. There were so many unfamiliar objects —racks of test tubes, jars of chemicals—and I, understanding not a word of the labels, kept opening the jars, emptying them and sniffing. No, there was nothing that looked edible.

A metal wall locker, broken open, contained flasks labeled "Yperite," "Lewisite" and so on, and I started to contemplate them. The lewisite had an uninviting red color, but the yperite, or mustard gas, looked like black coffee, and I began to imagine it really was coffee, with sugar. I quivered inside, so great was my craving for coffee. I imagined removing the glass stopper and tasting the contents. Suddenly it wasn't real yperite at all, only simulated, a classroom mock-up that someone had simply filled with coffee to show the students what mustard gas looked like. That could be after all, couldn't it? And even without sugar, coffee was nourishing. With great effort, I put the flask back in place.

I opened the door to the next classroom and froze. A blood-caked figure without legs or arms was set up on a table in the middle of the room. My first thought was that the fascists had used the place for torture. But I immediately spotted anatomical charts on the walls. This was the anatomy classroom.

The head and chest of the model on the table were riddled with bullets, and the charts on the walls, especially around the eyes, had also come under heavy fire. The soldiers had obviously taken target practice on them with pistols.

A shattered piano stood in the recreation room. It seemed to have been hit with something heavy—sledge hammers or axes. The top was smashed and the keys hung out or lay about on the floor like broken teeth. They must have hated that piano terribly to hurt it so.

My catch from the third floor was poorer: a twisted black crust, no bigger than half my little finger. On the landing outside I found a mysterious staircase spiraling to the ceiling. I went right up, lifted the trapdoor with my head and found myself in a tower littered with dusty boxes, fire buckets and sheets of iron. The wind hooted through the broken windows. I climbed atop a box and looked out.

Below me lay streets and clusters of roofs. No smoke came from the chimneys, since there was no wood: menacing orders had been printed about turning in all firewood and coal reserves. We had no reserves, and Grandmother lit the stove only once every three days. There was not a soul to be seen on the grounds of the Tsepi Gallya Plant. The place seemed to have died. The little hurrying figures of passersby on the streets were few and far between, as though the city had been stricken with plague. Far away I saw a straight column of soldiers probably coming from the bath house. They were marching along a sidewalk in a long gray-green rectangle, every last one of them carrying an identical rolled newspaper packet, and they were singing, in the same very precise and earnest way they did their work, a song that went like this:

> *Ai-li, ai-la. Ai-la!*
> *Ai-li, ai-la. Ai-la!*
> *Ai-li, ai-la. Ai-la!*
> *Ho-ho, ho-ho, ha-ha-ha . . .*

It was getting dark, and my main objective still lay ahead, so I slid off the boxes and ran down. Grandfather was already snoring on the benches, his greatcoat under him. I slipped into the kitchen.

It was filled with a faint scent of soup, but the stove was quite cold and piled high with huge pots and skillets, all clean and dry. I ran my hands over the tables, climbed under them and inspected every corner. But there was nothing, not even a crumb. Never in my life had I seen such a bare and spotless kitchen, empty except for that smell, which was driving me out of my mind.

Trying to find at least a grain of cereal, I crawled about on all fours, studying the cracks in the floor. Everything was swept clean! I couldn't believe it and began my search all over again. Something had burned on the side of one of the pots and not all of it had been scoured off. I scratched off the burned stuff and chewed it, not even knowing what it was. One of the frying pans looked to me as if it had not been wiped thoroughly. I sniffed—and it smelled of fried onions. Oh, those damned viper cutthroats! For themselves they charged up the soup with onions and sunflower seed oil! I wanted the onion-flavored soup so badly I whined. I began licking the pan, imagining or perhaps really tasting onion and oil, whined and licked again.

"ENEMIES"

The newspaper *Ukrainskoye slovo* closed down in December. So did the literary almanac *Litavry*, which had evidently blurted out something wrong. The explanation:

> TO OUR WORTHY READERS!
> Henceforth the Ukrainian newspaper will appear in a new format and will be called *Novoye* [new] *Ukrainskoye slovo.* Extreme nationalists, together with Bolshevist-minded elements, tried to turn the national Ukrainian newspaper into an information agency for their treacherous purposes. All warnings from the German civil authorities to the effect that the newspaper must be neutral and exclusively serve the interests of the Ukrainian people went unheeded. An attempt was made to undermine trust between our German liberators and the Ukrainian people.
>
> The editorial staff has been purged of treacherous elements. [1]

Oh, that meaningful last line!

The newspaper got right down to business. It carried a vituperative article headed "Whisperers," about people who told malicious jokes. "These vile, simple-minded jokes and dark rumors," the newspaper wrote, "are spread by enemies and betrayers of the Ukrainian people, by malcontent Philistines and bigots. A determined public struggle must be waged against rumormongers, maligners and whisperers, and they must all be decisively punished."

Another article was called "The Dregs." It castigated loafers, those dregs who refused to go to work, living instead by unknown means, on various unsavory earnings, and contaminating society with their presence. These people had to be ferreted out and severely punished.

The newspaper was filled with screaming threats and nervous bluster. Half of its announcements were printed in German only. And its reports from "the Fuehrer's headquarters" grew terse and anxious: *"POWERFUL ATTACKS REPULSED AT BEND OF DONETS." "SOVIET ATTACKS REPULSED ON EASTERN FRONT."*

Mama said that in a German newspaper one had to know how to read between the lines, not the lines themselves. I was learning.

Grandfather saw a hanged man on Vladimir Hill. Powdered with snow and barefoot, he hung with his head twisted to one side and a black face. Either he had been badly beaten, or his face had turned black after death. There was a signboard announcing that he had made an attempt on a German's life. Grandfather was so terrified that even his beard shook as he told us about it.

The partisans exploded a mine at the German headquarters on Dzerzhinskaya. Everyone was seized, not only men, but old people, women and babies in arms. Word spread that more than 1,000 people were sent to Babi Yar. Commandant Eberhard was issuing no more announcements.

We were afraid to go into the streets now. The devil knew where the next explosion would hit, and then they would grab you.

"You skulk about all over the place!" Mother shouted at me. "You come home late. They'll pick you off like a rabbit! Don't you dare go out!" Keeping German time was a nuisance. We had no radio, and the wall clock ran when the spirit moved it. So before going into the street, Grandmother would call on the neighbors to find out the time or look over the fence for passersby and ask them what time it was.

There was all kinds of talk. They were shooting saboteurs at Babi Yar; they were shooting Ukrainian nationalists, shooting blackout violators, shooting loafers, shooting rumormongers, shooting partisans—enemies and more enemies. The machine gun in the ravine chattered every day from morning till evening.

"What is this?" Mother asked, listening. "What has civilization come to?"

"The enemy has come! Quiet!" answered Grandmother.

"But in two years' time they will have shot so many 'enemies' that there'll be nobody left. Then they'll have their ideal: no people, no enemies, clean and quiet."

"That's true, daughter. It's written in the scriptures, 'And then the enemy will devour himself.' "

"Does our side know that? The Germans didn't take Moscow, they've already been stopped! Perhaps our side will soon take up the offensive."

"Ah, daughter, we'll be dead before that day comes."

THE WOUNDED
ON THE STAIRWAY

I had to go to the hospital and I feared the sight of the men I would see there. I dumped the rolls out of my box, broke a couple of boiled potatoes into pieces, wrapped them in a separate parcel and put this in a basket Grandmother had prepared. This basket was a fabulous treasure. It contained a jar of jelly, a cup of milk and even a pat of butter. I had forgotten how these things tasted. To me they were like precious stones: beautiful, but not for eating.

At the bazaar I hopped onto an empty truck and squatted in a corner, hoping the driver wouldn't look out the rear window. He didn't, and he drove so fast I was rocked like a *vanka-vstanka* (a doll weighted at its base that always recovers its standing position), but he made a turn at the streetcar depot, and I had to bail out. I had jumped on and off those trucks, like a cat, many a time. The main thing was to catch them at a turn, and, if you had to jump off at full tilt, to push away from the truck with all your might in order to counter the speed. I had learned this to perfection after banging the pavement with my snout.

I climbed onto a freight streetcar at the yard and squatted in a corner of the platform. When the conductor came along collecting fares, I turned away and pretended not to see him and he passed me by. Where would I be getting money to pay him?

I jumped off at Podol and started down St. Andrew Hill. There were beggars at every step. Some whined and wheedled, others silently held out the stumps of their missing limbs. Quiet, mannerly old men and women in spectacles or pince-nez stood by—various professors and teachers, like our late mathematician. Some sat in such a way that you could not tell whether they were alive or had already grown cold. These beggars had multiplied at a fearful rate and were always knocking on doors—burned-out families, nursing mothers, refugees, starvelings.

The frost was bitter, and passersby trudged somberly, crouching against the wind, worried, ragged, in rotting overcoats and incredible boots. A whole city of beggars—that's what it was!

St. Andrew's Church on its high hill looked as if it were soaring over Podol. Built by Rastrelli, it was a sweeping, airy blue-and-white structure. It, too, was besieged by beggars. Services were under way, and I pushed my way inside, stood a while, listened and looked at the paintings by famous masters on the walls. It was luxurious inside, gold and more gold. In ludicrous contrast, a ragged, hungry, sniffing crowd of women worshipers pounded their heads on the icy stone floor.

I could not stand this for long and went up to the gallery. From there I had a bird's-eye view of the Dnieper, Trukhanov Island and remote Darnitsa on the left bank of the river. This was a good place to lean on the parapet and think.

A German officer who had made his way up the slope through the snow was photographing the church from a special angle below, and I, something of a photograper myself, watched him pick his vantage point with skill. I was his only human figure and would have to end up in the middle of his viewfinder.

I did not go away, but looked at him steadily, thinking, "You'll click that shutter, then develop the film, make prints and send them home to your family, so they can see what you have conquered. You photograph everything as if you owned it. You won that right with a gun. What business have you with St. Andrew's Church, with Kiev? Only that you shot your way in. Killing. Taking over like a bandit. Some people build things, laboring by the sweat of their brow, and then there are always the bandits, unable from birth to create anything, but able to shoot. It is you, only you, the shooters, who are the real, the true enemies. From now on, and to the end of my life I shall hate you and your gun-toting bogeymen. Maybe I'll die of hunger or from your bullets, but I'll die despising you as the most loathsome creatures on this earth."

I walked away, choking with impotent rage and grief, coming to myself only on Bogdan Khmelnitsky Square, which just then was being crossed by a weird column of ski troopers. They had absolutely no ability on skis and kept stamping, slipping and tangling with one another. Their clamor filled the whole square, and they looked rather wretched, with sullen, angry faces. They were evidently being compelled to learn this tricky business. Their officer kept yelling and losing his temper at them. They crawled up Vladimir Hill very slowly. I would have liked very much to watch them break their necks, but I was late already, so I only glanced briefly at them.

The passenger streetcars were running in the center of the city. People stood in the wind waiting for a car. Among them was a scrawny German in a fatigue cap, trench coat, boots and woolen earmuffs. He was frozen and turning blue. His hand were shaking and could not find his pockets. His whole body jerked as if on hinges. He kicked one foot with the other, rubbed his face with his hands, and then suddenly started dancing, flinging his legs out like a wooden clown. It looked as if he were about to emit a piercing scream, unable to stand the stinging frost any longer.

The idea that he was absurd could never have entered his head, because the only people around were the local populace, and to the Germans this was the same as being in a void. In our presence, as if in seclusion, they nonchalantly let their pants down, picked their noses and flipped the snot away with two fingers, or openly passed water.

Two trucks trundled from the gates of St. Sophia Cathedral carrying something covered with canvas. They were carrying out some fresh booty. I'll be damned if every tenth word the Germans uttered wasn't "culture": "the thousand-year German culture," "the cultural renewal of the world," "all human culture depends upon the success of German arms," and so on. The things that can be done with words! It's enough to drive you mad! This culture of theirs, it seemed, consisted in cleaning out the museums, using manuscripts from the Academy library for wrapping paper, and firing their pistols at statues, mirrors, tombstones and anything else that could serve as a target. This was what renewal of culture meant.

Then there was "humanism." German humanism was the greatest in the world, the German army was the most humane, and everything it did was only for the sake of German humanism. No, not just humanism, but German humanism, the most noble, intelligent and purposeful form of the common run of flimsy, ineffective and hence inimical humanism, for which there was only one place—Babi Yar.

I had to grasp these concepts of "culture" and "humanism" with all their subtleties very early, because every day I had to hide from them, lest I become their beneficiary.

When the streetcar arrived, the crowd pushed in through the back door while the German got on at the front. Streetcars were segregated: the back was for the natives, the front for Aryans. In the past, when reading about Mister Twister (an American villain in a Soviet children's poem) and Uncle Tom's cabin, I had never dreamed I would have to ride a streetcar this way.

Stores and restaurants drifted past the streetcar windows, displaying big, conspicuous signs: "For Germans only" and "Ukrainians keep out." The billboard outside the Opera House was in German. Across the street, the swastika flew over the Academy of Sciences building. It was the city commandant's office now and the main office of the *Polizei*. In full accord with *German* culture and *German* humanism.

The fire on Kreshchatik had reached up to the indoor Bessarabka market and stopped. The square, therefore, was in an appalling state of ruin on one side, while the other side sparkled with signs and show windows, its sidewalk filled with pedestrians, mostly German officers and ladies. It was unsettling and a little scary to walk among them, as though you had barged in where you didn't belong. And I'll tell you why.

Sleek, clean-shaven, with chests out and visored caps down over their eyes, the officers walked along without ever noticing the inhabitants. If they did happen to glance at them, it was in an unseeing, distant way, as if they were in a livestock pen on some kind of business—a little rebuilding here, a boost in revenues there, a bit of rearranging somewhere else. And if a close, searching stare ever did settle on you, woe to you. It meant that you had caught attention through some irregularity and could be marked for the scrap heap; so God save you from such attention from the wielders of power.

But the ladies were magnificent. In furs from head to foot, their bearing regal, they walked their beautiful, well-fed police dogs on leashes. Later in life, no matter how much I tried to reason with myself, I could never rid my soul of the cold hostility I felt for this beast, which is said to be so intelligent and so loyal to humans.

German shepherd dogs forever remain fascist shepherds, as far as I'm concerned. I can't help it.

I moved on. At the indoor market there was a big queue of about 2,000 people waiting to buy bread with their ration cards. The cards had been issued at the approach of winter: two pounds of bread a week for workers, a half pound a week for others.

Grandfather, Grandmother, Mother and I had received four half-pound cards. One day I fought my way through the line and brought home almost a whole loaf of fresh bread.

We had never seen such bread before. It was terribly crumbly and dry, its crust almost separate, and sprinkled with millet husks. It had been baked of ersatz flour made up of corn cobs, millet chaff, barley, sometimes even horse chestnuts. It was gritty and had a slightly bittersweet taste. It gave you heartburn, but, of course, I treasured it. I divided my half pound into seven parts—which meant about an ounce a day—and never laid a finger on the next day's ration.

Grandfather and I could not forgive ourselves for gathering so few horse chestnuts before the snow came. We could have scoured the other parks, after all. The city council had published exhortations to use horse chestnuts for food, explaining about all the calories, protein and starch they contained. We had been eating horse chestnuts for a long time.

Now Grandfather fell ill. Finding doctors was complicated and difficult. How Grandmother and Mother searched for a doctor, and what it cost them, would make a long story in itself. Grandfather was found to have gallstones and was taken to the October Hospital, beyond the Bessarabka market, for an operation. There was a strange story about this hospital. Most hospitals were being used as barracks, the patients having been shot. But for some reason the October Hospital was left unmolested. It stayed open until the summer of 1942, when it was finally closed. Stranger still, it had some wounded Red Army men left over from Soviet times, and the fascists for some reason didn't touch them.

The hospital kept going by using up its old supplies, but there was no food. Once a day a half quart of hot water with occasional grains of floating cereal in it was issued to the patients. The civilian patients lived on food packages, the army wounded on what they could beg. I was the one who brought Grandfather's food packages, and this came to be a nightmare for me.

I was surrounded by the wounded as I entered the building. They didn't shove, shout or grab, but only looked at me silently, craning their necks. I made my way through them, took a hospital gown out of the cloakroom and went up the stairs.

On the spacious, luxurious second floor, the walls were

167

lined with the wounded—wasting away, skeletal, with crutches and bandaged heads, never saying a word, only looking at me with feverish, half-crazed eyes. Now and then one of them timidly extended a hand, palm upward. I unwrapped my bundle and placed microscopic pieces of crust and potato in the hands around me, feeling wretched, the little benefactor of these grown men. And when I reached Grandfather's ward at last he immediately guessed what I had done and howled, "What are you giving away, idiot? Feel rich, do you? Don't you dare give those scoundrels anything; they'll die anyway, and here I am, dying myself!"

I didn't know what to do. Grandfather really did look like a living corpse. He had already had his operation, and a tube had been run through his abdomen with a bottle attached to the end. He was so feeble he could barely move. But he cursed like a healthy man, clutched the basket, put the food into his night table drawer, slammed it shut and laid his hand over it as an extra safeguard.

The next cot was occupied by a soldier who had lost his legs. His emaciated face, overgrown with a heavy black beard, looked like the face of Christ on Grandmother's icons.

"You've got a mean grandfather there, boy," he said faintly, moving only his eyes. "He's quarreled with the whole ward already. Come closer, I have something to tell you."

I moved closer, sorry that I had not one crumb left for him.

"Gather some fallen leaves," he said. "Dry them out well, roll them up between your hands and bring them here. I'm dying for a smoke."

I nodded. Leaves, at least, were something I could get.

"Cherry leaves are best," he said wearily. "The cherry tree."

At home I dug about in the snow for a long time, scraping up the blackened, frozen leaves. Then I picked out the cherry leaves, dried them on top of the stove and rolled them up. But when I went to the hospital with another parcel two days later I learned that the legless man had died. I can't express how sorry I was. If only I had known, I would have delivered those leaves sooner.

My little sack of leaves was greedily accepted by other wounded men, and later I brought them lots more. I don't know what happened to those men when the hospital was closed.

BUSINESS BECOMES DANGEROUS

I began my usual working day by dressing as warmly as I could, taking my bag and going to the corner of Kirillov-skaya and Syretskaya Streets, where ten or so entrepreneurs like myself were already lounging about. It was there that the streetcar carrying peat to the cannery would make a turn, and we would swarm over its platforms like a horde of locusts, tossing peat overboard, then collecting and dividing it up.

A flatcar turned up this time, and a conductor in his greatcoat and felt boots was perched on the front apron. We, of course, went into the attack. Suddenly we saw that the car was loaded not with peat, but with beets. Good God! We fell on them like wolf cubs. Being frozen, they clattered on the pavement and bounced like pingpong balls. I took a firm hold and started throwing, farther than all the others, and kept it up until the conductor's greatcoat loomed over me. I just barely slipped out of his hands.

As I was running back a fight broke out in the street,

and many of the boys lay on the ground. The sight of the beets had driven them wild, and they had forgotten all about dividing up the loot.

I swore with outrage because I had thrown off more beets than any one else. I jumped into the fight, grabbed a bunch of beets from some little boy and shoved it under my shirt. But at this point someone fetched me such a blow that I saw stars and was momentarily blinded. I fell, tripped up by someone, but shielded my face with my arms. My assailants kicked me in the side, trying to make me turn over so they could take the beets away. I don't know what would have happened if a second streetcar hadn't turned up, also laden with beets.

This time I was cagey. I ran on ahead. When all the others were hanging on, and the cursing conductor came running over to the beet pile to chase them off, I jumped onto the front apron he had deserted.

Those platform cars had nasty little rungs, no bigger than a man's palm, and instead of railings there was only a thin iron bar welded to the side. I clutched this, stood with one felt boot on a rung, reached over with all my might, and snatched one beet after another, stuffing them under my shirt. But at that instant my boot slipped. I was left hanging, holding the iron bar with both hands. I could see the steel-gray streetcar wheel rush along the steel-gray rail after my dragging boot. I could not feel my hands— they were numb from the icy bar—and I had not a drop of strength left to pull myself up. High overhead I saw the conductor, who had come back. I let out a thin, short yell, "Help!"

He saw my plight at once, caught me by the arms and hauled me onto the apron. Then he reached for the trolley rope overhead and disengaged the trolley from the power line. The car coasted a short way and stopped.

I sprang to the pavement and ran as I had never run before. The motorman and conductor shouted and cursed, but I ran all the way home without looking back. I flew into our shed, latched the door and sat down on a box to recover. Then I entered the cottage and solemnly laid three beets on the table in front of Grandmother. She clapped her hands in wonder.

DEATH

Grandfather was brought home from the hospital just before Easter. Before the war, Grandmother used to celebrate Easter "as well as anyone." Her preparations would begin while it was still winter. Gradually, as cheaply as possible, we used to accumulate flour, raisins, packets of dye, and onion skins. Grandmother spent hours at the bazaar haggling over every kopek. At home she sternly kept watch to see that no one dared touch the stores of Easter provisions. It was Lent, besides, and we all ate very meagerly. Though Mama and I were godless, we did not want to hurt Grandmother, and obeyed her in everything. She smoked the ham herself, fried the homemade sausage, cooked a special holiday "brew"—a compote—baked cheesecakes and, of course, boiled eggs. I was entrusted with the job of mashing poppy seeds and sugar with a ladle, for which I was allowed to lick the ladle afterward. The little packets of dye were opened and the eggs were dyed bright, cheerful colors. Some of them were boiled with onion skins, and turned a dark orange.

Grandmother had an array of crockery forms in the pantry for her Easter cakes. She baked two big cakes, each the size of a suckling pig, for home consumption, and a whole brood of little ones, no bigger than a cup, to take along on visits and give to the poor. Vanilla was used in the Easter cakes, and when they were in the oven the cottage had a fragrance that would make you swoon.

Grandmother would go off to the all-night vigil with her basket, while we, hungry but honest, went to bed. She would return at dawn, solemn, radiant, unworldly, and wake us up with holiday greetings. Everything was sparkling clean in the cottage. The walls were newly whitewashed, clean curtains were up and fresh strips of rug lay on the well-scoured floor. A holiday through and through—an extraordinary holiday.

The table, spread to full length, was laden with flowers and food. But only an ill-bred boor would throw himself on the food at once. It was necessary first to wash in a large basin with silver coins glittering at the bottom, then to put on freshly laundered or new clothes. Grandmother then solemnly seated each of us around the table at a strictly assigned place and recited a fervent Paternoster.

"Christ is risen!" exclaimed Grandfather, joyfully licking his lips.

"He is risen indeed!" Grandmother happily responded, her eyes welling as she cast a last look over the table. It hadn't been easy, but she had indeed done as well as anyone. And finally, she gave the go-ahead: "God be with us! May we be happy!"

With these solemnities over, the good life began.

And now Grandmother had decided to bake some Easter cakes again, come what may. She was willing to do without all the rest, but she clung to the cakes as if salvation depended on them. Grandfather was still very weak after

returning from the hospital, so Mama made a long bartering trip from which she brought back some grain and
potatoes.

First, the grain had to be ground. Some people on the
other side of the embankment had a little mill and would
let you grind your grain for a glass or two of flour. Grandmother and I went there together.

The little mill stood in a shed and consisted of two cir-
cular cross sections of a log, one on top of the other. The
upper one had to be turned with a handle, while you poured
your grain through a hole in the middle. The rubbing sur-
faces of the wheels were inlaid with metal studs so that the
grain would be crushed and ground into flour.

Grandmother and I, standing on either side of the mill,
gripped the handles. The two of us could barely turn the
heavy log sections. Grandmother poured her grain in the
smallest doses, almost in pinches, but it was still very heavy
work. We labored for half a day, to the point of exhaustion,
and then rested, soaking wet. There was a strong draft in
the shed, and Grandmother was afraid I would catch cold.

Numbed by a biting wind, we barely managed to drag
ourselves home. Grandmother started sifting the flour, and
sifted out a pinch of razor-sharp metal shavings—fragments
from the grinding metal of the mill. I got a magnet, ran it
through all the flour and fished out many more fragments.
Grandmother grieved because our homemade flour would
not produce white Easter cakes, but gray loaves; however
she mixed it anyway, and then went to bed. In the night,
she grew feverish and started demanding white flour, raisins
and butter.

The next day Mother ran all over, hunting for a doctor.
A little old man turned up and wrote a prescription, for
which we paid him two glasses of flour.

"But I don't know where you'll get this filled," he said.

"What are we to do, then?" my mother asked.

"What can I do?" he fumed. "First, get the place warm enough so you can't see your breath. Then give her some hot milk. And she needs food; she's completely exhausted."

Mother boiled some herbs for Grandmother, then ran all over town until she found someone to fill the prescription. But Grandmother was getting worse. She could hardly breathe, and kept wailing, "It's hot! Give me air!"

We took turns sitting and fanning her with a newspaper, but she felt best when we simply blew on her. Now and then she recovered her senses and worried about the Easter cakes. Mother baked them, but they turned out black and sticky, and sand grated in our teeth. Grandmother took one look and broke out crying.

My godmother Lyaksandra and her blind husband Mikolai came to see us. They were surprisingly kind and gentle old people, the kindest I've seen in all my life. Grandfather and Grandmother had been friends with them since their childhood. At one time they had had a son, just one. Grandmother told me he was a wonderful fellow. He became one of the first Young Communists in Kurenevka and was sent to organize the Young Communist League in one of the villages, where he was killed. This happened in 1919. Mikolai went blind after that. "He cried his eyes out," Grandmother said, but it was a sickness, of course, that blinded him. Neither Lyaksandra nor Mikolai knew anything at all about politics. All they knew was that their only son Kolya was a good boy; so they could never understand why he had been killed, or who would have wanted to do it.

Mikolai and Grandfather had once worked together,

but Mikolai was quite feeble and helpless now. He had a sparse tuft of gray hair, and wore a pair of spectacles on his nose—I'm not sure why. The right lens was dark blue and the left one was gone, so Mikolai had replaced it with a disk of thin plywood.

Godmother Lyaksandra had been with Grandmother at my christening. She was a cleaning woman. Early in the morning she used to come out on the square, bringing Mikolai along. She would set to work with a broom, after handing her husband a rake. And he, blind as he was, would drag the rake along the ground very neatly and methodically, never missing a single twig or scrap of paper.

They would work like that for many hours because it was a big square, but when they were through it looked splendid—every inch furrowed by the rake, like a freshly planted garden in springtime.

They were Belorussians but had lived in Kiev almost all their lives, though without learning either Russian or Ukrainian.

"Misfortunes never come singly, but always in pairs," sighed Lyaksandra, sitting down on Grandmother's bed. "Cheer up, Marfushka; you're still young, you haven't yet seen the best of life."

"You will, you'll see it yet!" Mikolai soothed Grandmother tenderly as he fanned her vigorously with a newspaper.

It was hard to tell if Grandmother heard them. Her breathing was raspy, her coloring a waxen yellow, her face shiny. Suddenly we heard the quiet but unmistakable sound of glass cracking. The medicine vial on the night table beside the bed had cracked just above the middle, on a perfectly straight line. Lyaksandra's mouth fell open, and there was terror in her eyes. Grandmother turned her head and looked at the vial in an odd, pensive way.

"This is all we need!" I muttered, diving for the vial. "Nothing spilled; I'll pour it into something else right away."

I had heard about this omen: When a glass broke without apparent reason, it meant someone would die. Why did that damned little piece of junk have to break just then?

I carried the vial quickly to the kitchen.

Mother, her friend Lena Gimpel and Grandfather were sitting there, discussing what the whole city was talking about. The Germans were shipping people to Germany for work.

"And they're right," said Grandfather, tapping the newspaper with his finger. "Here there's a famine, but there people can eat their fill and make some money. You'll see!"

It was all convincingly explained in the newspaper: Under Soviet rule children wanted to do nothing but study to be engineers and professors, whereas the chief form of training was, after all, labor. By going off to Germany, the young people would learn to work and would have some time abroad. The trip to Germany was necessary for the sake of a happy future.

" 'It always happens,' " Grandfather read gravely, " 'that one generation must make great sacrifices in order to provide its progeny—its children and grandchildren—with a better life.' Hear that? A better life for children and grandchildren!"

"Oh Lord," said Lena Gimpel. "We know all about that 'better life.' "

Lena's husband, an X-ray technician, had gone to the front like everybody else, leaving her with a child. She was always desperately hungry and as ill-tempered as a thousand devils. She seemed to enjoy taunting Grandfather.

"You fool, you don't understand anything!" shouted Grandfather. "It's not their better life that matters—it's that the young people today must be taught to work. There are far too many smart ones; they do nothing but read books, and who's left to do the work? The Germans are right, work is the best training!"

"It's just that they need manpower—need to recruit as many workers as they can," Mother remarked, "and they ought to say as much."

"They can't," said Lena. "Nobody would go if they did, so they have to glorify it. *Pfui,* I wish they'd choke to death, the hyenas!"

"Fool, what are you saying!" Grandfather raised his hands in fright. "You want to go to Babi Yar?"

"That's right. Watch out, be careful with that kind of talk," Mother said, lowering her voice.

"What damnable times, it's Dante's inferno!" Lena said, seething with hate. "They say they've brought you freedom, but you haven't the right to say anything; you weigh every word, afraid of your own shadow; you don't trust anyone, everybody's a potential informer and provocateur. At night I feel like screaming. My nerves are giving out. Sometimes I think, 'Let them drag me to Babi Yar. I despise it all—everything!' "

We took turns watching at Grandmother's bedside all night. She was gasping for breath, sweating and thrashing about. Morning came, frigid, sparkling, rosy sunlight tinting the snow, icicles over the window and the whole room colored pink. And suddenly Grandmother got better and started to breathe easily and deeply, sinking back on her pillow in relief.

"The crisis is over!" Mother exclaimed, turning a beaming face toward me. "All's well. Ah, my God!"

181

I ran to the window and shouted to Grandfather, who was outside, "Grandmother is well!"

But when I turned back I saw Mother was strangely still, watching Grandmother's face. It was growing steadily whiter, and Grandmother's breathing became uneven and feeble—and then she stopped breathing altogether.

"She's dying!" Mother screamed. "Money! Bring some money, the five-kopek coins! Quick!"

Grandmother had kept some old silver half-ruble and copper five-kopek coins in a box stuffed with buttons and thread, and she had told us to cover her eyes with the five-kopek pieces when she died. I rushed for the box as though it held our salvation. I brought the coins and held them out to Mother, but she went on crying, shaking Grandmother, stroking her shoulders, until finally she snatched the coins from me and laid them on Grandmother's eyes. That was all.

Grandmother had an unfamiliar, stern and very solemn look, with those dark, tarnished five-kopek coins on her eyes.

We had no money for a coffin. Grandfather took his saw and plane, selected a few old boards from the shed and knocked together a clumsy and not altogether proper coffin. It was supposed to be painted brown, but Grandfather had no brown paint. Instead, he found a can of blue bedstead enamel. He hesitated, pondered, then painted the coffin sky-blue and put it in the yard to dry. Never in my life had I seen a sky-blue coffin.

The house, of course, filled up with neighbors—old women—who provided the due amount of keening, extolled the virtues of the deceased and vied with one another to point out the skirts and slippers she had given them without

Grandfather's knowledge. They shoved these reproachfully under his nose.

"That's the sort of wife you had, Semerik! And you bullied her all her life!"

Candles burned, a deacon said prayers, and Mother sobbed constantly, wandering indoors and out, "I'll never get over this." And Lena kept soothing her, "There, there, we all die some day." It all seemed so senseless and useless to me. The old women with their strained wailing were unpleasant, their voices drove into my ears like pins, and I roamed hither and yon, all tense and jittery.

But at this point the priest appeared with his choristers, and Grandmother was laid in her coffin. At full length she didn't quite fit; and the coffin wasn't completely dry—the paint came off. Godmother Lyaksandra scurried about anxiously. "We need men, men to do the carrying!" But there weren't enough men. The coffin was lifted at last and clumsily carried out the door, with a bit of tilting. A ribbon with some Church Slavonic writing lay on Grandmother's brow, and she held one of the two little wooden crosses that had been kept beside the icon.

Grandfather, hatless and worried, put his shoulder to the coffin with the others, and blind Mikolai took his place behind him, his cane under his arm. They had put newspapers against the coffin to keep the paint off their shoulders. Two gonfalons were unfurled, the priests began a nasal chant, the choristers gave voice, everyone moved toward the open gate, and Grandmother's coffin drifted along solemnly, above it all.

"Stay here and look after the house," Mother ordered, her face swollen with tears, and suddenly aged and ugly.

I watched the procession move on, closed the gate and gathered up a few fir twigs fallen from the wreath. It had become quiet. And that was when I started to choke, when it all came home to me.

"We all die," Lena had said. Grandfather would die, Mother would die, Titus the tomcat would die. I looked at my finger, spread them, looked again at my spread fingers and realized that sooner or later they would be no more. Death is the most terrifying thing in the world. It's such a horror when someone dies, even when someone very old dies of illness—a natural, normal death. Isn't this horror enough? Do people have to invent more and more ways for making death, to set up these damned Babi Yars?

Hardly able to stand up, I staggered into the cottage. It was depressing inside: tracked with mud and littered. Up-ended stools lay around the bare, bowlegged table, and the stale odor of incense hung in the air. Titus the cat watched me closely with yellow eyes from the stovetop.

HITLER'S BIRTHDAY

A child came into the world one April day, the twentieth, to be exact. He was properly ruddy, weighed about seven and a half pounds and was around 20 inches long. He stared with unthinking button eyes and stretched his mouth as if to yawn, arousing indescribable tenderness and compassion in his mother. She did not know as yet that she was holding in her arms the most gruesome monster ever born on earth.

Echoes of the event resounded in Kiev in April, 1942, in the following form:

NOTICE

By *Stadtkommissariat* order of 4/18/42, one pound of wheat flour per mouth will be issued to the population on the occasion of the Fuehrer's birthday.

The flour will be issued at bread counters on April 19 and 20 for coupon No. 16 of the bread ration cards.

MUNICIPAL ADMINISTRATION. [1]

At dawn, barely waiting for the end of the curfew, I sped to the bakery, outstripping other runners.

It turned out, however, that about one and a half thousand mouths had already lined up in the middle of the night, scorning the curfew. Though opening time was still a long way off, the queue was seething and rumbling. There was a fight at the door of the bakery, and the sweating, angry police could barely restrain the crowd.

I took my place at the end of the line and stood there gloomily, listening to the old wives' chatter about when the war would end; when the potatoes would sprout; how the Germans hadn't whipped the Russians but yet the Russians couldn't win either and so a peace would be signed somewhere along the Volga and we would perish under the Germans.

Even a blind man could see that I would have to stay in that line until evening. After taking note of my place in the line, I ran home for cigarettes and went back into business.

My friends had drifted apart. Bolik Kaminsky had been mobilized to rebuild the bridge across the Dnieper, where he was kept under guard and not allowed to go home. Shurka Matsa's mother had taken him away, no one knew where; they had found another apartment because in the old one they had been in constant terror that someone would give Shurka away. Even my old enemy Vovka Babarik was gone. His mother had sent him off to some out-of-the-way farm in the country to save him from having to go to Germany, so I no longer needed to fear his punches. As for Zhorka Gorokhovsky, his grandmother had found him a place as an acolyte at Priory Church. There, he wore a silly robe, handed the priest first the Gospels and then a censer and genuflected with his palms together. Kolka Gorokhovsky and I sold cigarettes together.

This was child's play. We took the streetcar to the huge Galitsky bazaar, sought out the Germans or Hungarians and asked them *"Zigaretten ist?"*

"Drei hundert ruble."

"Nein, nein! Zwei hundert!"

"Nein."

"Ja, ja! Hey, Soldat! Zwei hundert, bitte!"

"Weg!"

"Zwei hundert, you crook, you *kulak,* hear? *Zwei hundert?"*

"Zwei hundert fünfzig."

Speculators through and through, they sold any kind of junk, bargaining and wrangling. Finally they came across with a carton of 200 cigarettes for 200 rubles. But it was difficult.

This business had one subtlety to it. When bargaining with a German, you could not work with your tongue alone; you had to produce your money and shove it under his nose. The sight of it made him nervous, and he reached for it involuntarily. Once he had taken it the deal was closed.

We were badly stung the first time. When we opened the packs at home, we found fifteen cigarettes missing from each. The Germans had made holes in the packs and fished out the cigarettes with a piece of wire. After that we opened up each pack and checked the contents before buying. So you can see the wide range of the German mind: On the one hand they aimed at the conquest and cultural renovation of the whole world, and on the other they peeled the dirty underwear off the people they murdered and fished cigarettes out of a pack with a wire.

And so we ran about in Kurenevka from morning till

night, hanging around the bazaar, the streetcar yard, street corners, bridges and at factory gates when the shifts were changing—managing to sell a carton of cigarettes in about five days. Selling them singly, we got two rubles each. In five days I often netted as much as 200 rubles, enough for almost four pounds of bread.

So there I was at half past six in the morning, cruising along the queue and ranging over the bazaar, cheerfully calling, "Cigarettes here! Levantes and strong, top-grade Hunnias, two rubles apiece, cheaper than mushrooms! Have a cigarette, mister, they're good for the stomach."

At the same time I gathered cigarette butts, from which we extracted tobacco to sell.

The bakery opened at seven o'clock. It was impossible to see what was going on inside: a deadly crush, moans and shrieks. The first people to get their flour emerged tattered, bruised and soaking wet; but their faces were happy as they hugged their little bags of powdery, honest-to-goodness—not imaginary—white flour.

I checked on my place in line; I hadn't moved up, but there were as many behind me now as in front.

The women were saying some men had been shot in Dymer for listening to a shortwave radio; and the opera house was presenting *Swan Lake,* but there was a sign outside saying, "Ukrainians and dogs not allowed."

People whispered that the Germans had been stopped cold, that swarms of them had been laid out near Moscow, that they couldn't even take Tula and that a second front was expected in Europe. I listened eagerly, in order to re-tell the news at home. Oh, this wireless human telegraph! Why were we forbidden to listen to radios? News spread just the same.

At eight o'clock, a streetcar filled with German children appeared. Many Germans had come to Kiev with their families. Now they were sending their children to the Pushcha-Voditsa Sanatorium for the day. The children would return by streetcar in the evening. These streetcars were special. Each bore a portrait of Hitler on the front, along with swastika flags and wreaths of flowers.

I ran toward the streetcar to have a look at the German children. The windows were open, and the children sat inside, well dressed, rosy-cheeked, uninhibited, noisy, yelling, screaming, leaning out the windows—a menagerie. And suddenly spittle hit me in the face.

I hadn't expected it. But they, boys like myself, all wearing the same shirt *(Hitler Jugend?)*, went on clearing their throats and taking aim at me with a kind of cold contempt and hatred in their eyes. Little girls spat from a second streetcar hitched on behind. Their governesses said not a word to them; they just sat there in their furs (they worshipped those furs and never parted with them, even in summer). Dumbfounded, I watched the streetcar and its trailer trundle past me and down along the queue, with the passengers, like two cages of vicious, squealing monkeys, spitting on the people in line.

I went to the brook, my knees trembling. I laid my cigarettes on the ground, scrubbed myself for a long time, and cleaned my jacket. Something in my stomach or chest started sucking in a metallic way, as if someone had poured acid there, or reddish lewisite.

At eleven o'clock the *Polizei* finally had matters in hand. The doors, having lost their panes by now, were closed. People were let in ten at a time, but for some reason the queue did not move up at all. It was growing warm. At noon some German *Polizei* came by with two young men in hand, pushing them along in front. I could tell by the way they acted, brandishing their submachine guns, that those fellows did not have long to live. This sight was so common that it caused no comment in the crowd.

Cigarettes were not selling well. I reflected for a while, and decided to try something I had often resorted to before. At this time, children ran about in all the bazaars, carrying jars and singing, "Who wants cold water, who wants wa-ter?" I went home, got a can and mug, filled them at the pump and started down the queue, singing, "Who wants wa-ter?" at the top of my lungs. A mug went for 20 kopeks, a jug for 40. Soon my pocket was half full of change, but this change was nothing, just garbage. A German pfennig was worth ten kopeks, and it was only a miserable little aluminum disk, tarnished black. I turned my coins over to a tradeswoman for a crisp new mark. Fine, I thought, I hadn't wasted my time.

At four o'clock someone shouted at the queue to disband —there wasn't enough for everyone. That did it! The line disintegrated, and a new fight erupted at the door. Barely suppressing a howl of outrage, I hurled myself into the fray. The grown-ups traded blows; meanwhile I crawled forward among their legs, pushed people apart, slipped along snake-fashion, nearly knocking down a *Polizei*—and finally broke into the bakery. It was relatively uncrowded there. The salesclerks were casting terrified glances at the door, which groaned under the strain, and shouting, "That's all! We're closing!"

But they were still tearing off coupons and handing out paper bags.

Silently, with tears streaming, I pushed up to the counter, where some 30 people were jammed together. A ragged, red-faced old man waved his passport, and shouted plaintively, "I'm going to Germany tomorrow! It's stamped right here!"

"We'll serve only those going to Germany!" announced the manager. "All the rest, stop crowding and get out!"

A few more collected flour that way. Still quiet and tear-streaked, I pushed on stubbornly and found myself in front of a clerk. He looked at me and said, "Give him a bag."

"That's all, that's all! There's no more flour!" the manager declared.

The shelves were empty, powdered with flour, but not a single bag was left. I couldn't believe it, and, clinging to the counter, I combed those whitened shelves up and down with my eyes. Only a second ago I had seen little paper bags of flour standing there!

The *Polizei* started clearing the bakery. I walked out and drifted homeward in a daze, my mind still filled with the white paper bags acquired by the lucky ones, whom I hated one and all, except the very last ones, who were going to Germany. I could only pity them.

OFF TO GERMANY

One of the greatest national tragedies, after the Tatar yoke and the Turkish captivity, began on January 11, 1942, with the following newspaper announcement in two languages— German on top, Ukrainian below:

UKRAINIAN MEN AND WOMEN!
The *Bolshevik commissars* have destroyed your factories and jobs and have thereby deprived you of wages and bread.

Germany offers you an opportunity to do useful and well-paid work.

The first transport train will leave for Germany on January 28.

You will receive good supplies en route, in addition to hot meals in Kiev, Zdolbunov and Przemysl.

You will be well provided for in Germany and will find good living conditions. The pay will also be good: You will be paid in cash according to job scales and output.

Your families will be cared for, for as long as you are working in Germany.

193

Men and women workers of all trades—preferably metal workers—between the ages of 17 and 50 who wish to volunteer to go to Germany should appear at

THE LABOR EXCHANGE IN KIEV
daily from 8 A.M. to 3 P.M.

We expect Ukrainians to apply for work assignments in Germany without delay.

GENERAL-KOMMISSAR I. KWITZRAU,

S.A. BRIGADENFUEHRER [1]

The first trainload for Germany was ready ahead of time. It consisted entirely of volunteers, and it set off on January 22 to the blare of a band. The newspapers carried enthusiastic reports—smiling faces against a background of freight cars, and an interview with the chief of the train crew, who showed off a baggage car filled with sausage and ham for the journey. The headlines: "Real Patriots!" "Learn the Skills of Civilized Work!" "School of Life," "My Dream," "We'll Make Ourselves Useful There."

The second train left on February 25 and the third on February 27, their passengers mustered from those who were on the brink of starvation, who had nothing to lose and who were impressed by the words "good" and "well," repeated five times in the announcement, as well as by that fabulous baggage car full of sausage and ham.

Announcements in huge letters continued to appear throughout March:

GERMANY WANTS YOU!
Go to lovely Germany!

One hundred thousand Ukrainians are already employed in free Germany.

What about you? [2]

You should be glad of the chance to go to Germany. There, you, along with workers from other European countries, will help to win the war against the enemies of the whole world—the Jews and the Bolsheviks. [3]

Then the first letters from Germany arrived, with the impact of so many bombshells.

Almost everything but "hello" and "good-bye" had been cut away or thickly blacked out with India ink. A letter with a sentence the censors didn't understand was passed from hand to hand: "We are getting along wonderfully, almost as well as dear Polkan." "Polkan" in Ukrainian means "Fido."

Summonses were now being sent around to homes. The Labor Exchange was moved into the Art Institute building at the Hay Market, and it came to be the second most dreaded place after Babi Yar. Those who went there never came back. The place was filled with wailing and weeping. Passports were taken away and stamped with the word "Volunteer"; people were herded into a transfer camp where they waited weeks for shipment; and train after train pulled out of the station to the music of a band. Nothing was given to anyone, no "hot meals" in Zdolbunov or Przemysl. Fugitives from Germany reported that they were sent to factories to work twelve hours a day, were guarded like convicts and were given miserly pay, hardly enough for cigarettes.

Others told of being taken to special markets, where their prospective German masters, the *Bauern* (farmers), walked up and down the line, inspected teeth, felt muscles, made their selections and paid out five to fifteen marks for each man or woman. Work on the farms lasted from dawn

195

to dusk. And one could be beaten or killed for the slightest infraction, because slaves cost next to nothing, not nearly as much as a cow or horse; the livestock lived ten times better than the slaves. A woman in Germany, moreover, stood a good chance of ending up as a concubine if she wore the letters "OST."

An acquaintance of Mother's, a schoolteacher, received a brief notification that her daughter had thrown herself under a train. There were reports about others who had "tragically perished."

For Kiev and for all of the Ukraine, 1942 was the year of deportation into bondage.

Summonses were sent out in swarms. Those who failed to appear were arrested. There were raids on the bazaars, the public squares, the cinemas, the bath houses and even on people's homes. People were rounded up everywhere, hunted as Negroes had once been hunted in Africa.

A woman in Kurenevka cut off a finger with a hatchet. Another wrote the names of someone else's children in her passport and borrowed children from her neighbors when she appeared before the commission. Others falsified the dates of birth in their passports, abraded their skins with wire brushes and smeared kerosene or vinegar on the scrapes to produce sores, or offered bribes. The first exemption from Germany cost 3,000 rubles, and the price then went up to 15,000. The lower age limit for recruits dropped rapidly to sixteen, then to fifteen and finally to fourteen years.

On posters, in newspapers and in official orders Germany was never termed anything but "beautiful." Photos were published showing the lives of Ukrainians in beautiful Germany. There they were, distinguished in their suits and hats, flourishing canes, going to restaurants, cabarets

197

and the movies after work; here was a young fellow buying flowers in a German flower shop for his sweetheart; and there was his master's wife, affectionately and solicitously mending his shirt.

Here is an excerpt from the article entitled, "Reflections on the *Reichsmarschall's* [Goering's] Speech":

> With the exception of a few ridiculous letters from spoiled mama's boys, the Ukraine is receiving an enormous number of letters in which our workers express contentment. These are our own Ukrainians, who realize that the war has affected Germany's food supplies. These are our own Ukrainians, who do not look only into their own dinner pails. . . .
>
> At home in the Ukraine we may often hear complaints that Adolf Hitler is taking people away to work in Germany. But to secure final victory, Germany is not demanding any greater sacrifices from the Ukrainian people than the Germans themselves are making on a far, far greater scale.
>
> And so, brothers, I should like to talk to you quite honestly and frankly. I'm ashamed of all those who rail at Germany. When I read the *Reichsmarschall's* speech I was more ashamed than I had ever been in my whole life. [4]

Here are some passages from girls' letters which were cut out by censors and later discovered in German files:

> . . . If anyone lagged, paused or moved to one side, the police opened fire. The father of two children jumped off the moving train on the way from Kiev. The *Polizei* stopped the train, overtook the fleeing man, shot him in the back and killed him.

We were taken to the toilet under armed guard, and anyone who tried to escape was shot.

We were kept in the bath house until three in the afternoon. I stood there shivering, and toward the end, almost fainted. The men and women bathed together in the bath house. I was burning with embarrassment. Germans walked up to the naked girls, felt their breasts and hit them in sensitive parts. Anyone who cared to could come in and humiliate us. We are slaves, and they can do what they like with us. There is no food. Nor is there any hope of ever coming home. . . .

. . . I'm on the outskirts of Trier now, about 60 miles from France, living on my master's farm. You already know how I'm getting along. My boss has seventeen animals. I have to clean up twice a day. I feel nauseous when I clean the barn. My stomach hurts so badly I can't even cough. There are five pigs in the pigsty, and I have to clean that too. I can hardly see anything, my eyes water so as I clean. Then I have to clean the rooms, sixteen of them, and I have to do all the work. I don't sit down all day. When I go to bed, the night is gone before I know it. I walk around feeling as if I had taken a beating. . . . My mistress is a bitch. There's no woman's heart in her at all, just a stone. She doesn't do a thing herself, just shouts like a lunatic, the saliva flying from her mouth.

. . . As we walked by, people looked at us as though we were animals. Even the children held their noses and spat.

We were hoping someone would buy us soon. We Russian girls are pretty cheap in Germany—you can have your choice for five marks. We were bought by a factory owner on July 7, 1942. . . . At six o'clock we were led off to be fed. Mama, at home even the pigs wouldn't eat what they fed us, but we had to eat it. They cooked up a soup of radish greens and threw in a few potatoes. They don't give you bread with your meals in Germany. . . . They treat us like animals, dear Mama. . . . I don't think I'll ever get home, Mama. [5]

The Author Speaking

I am at a dead end. I am telling about what happened to me, what I saw with my own eyes, what the witnesses and the documents said; and now I am up against a dead end. What is this? How is one to explain it?

The dictatorship of dusky idiocy, terror, Babi Yars, slavery—a phantasmagoric return to the age of Herods and Neros. And on an unprecedented scale—a scale the Herods never dreamed of.

This happened in the twentieth century, the sixth millennium of civilization. It happened in the century of electricity, radio, the theory of relativity, the conquest of the skies by aviation and the invention of television. It happened on the very eve of the harnessing of atomic energy and man's conquest of space.

If it is possible in the twentieth century to use such a miracle as aviation for the slaughter of masses upon masses of people; if the world is putting more effort into the creation of lethal devices than into health; if pure slavery and racism are possible—and these things actually happened and continue to happen in the world—then the state of progress is not simply alarming; it is alarming in the highest degree.

Hitler was crushed, but fascism was not. Dark barbaric forces are smoldering in the world, threatening to break out.

Babi Yar

Primitive, degenerate ideas are at large, infectious as viruses; and carefully devised methods and systems for infecting enormous masses with these ideas continue to exist. Progress of science and technology without progress of conscience leads only to the result that slaves are not driven with ropes around their necks, but are shipped in modern sealed cars; and the fascist kills not with a simple club, but with a late-model submachine gun or with Cyclone B gas.

It is not my intention to be original, and what I am saying is common knowledge. But I should like to mention vigilance once again. I want especially to remind all the young, the healthy and the active, for whom this book is meant, of their responsibility for the fate of man. Comrades and friends! Brothers and sisters! Ladies and gentlemen! Please pause at your pursuits and recreations for a moment! Not all is well with the world!

Not all is well if in our age a handful of degenerates can herd multitudes to their deaths, and if these multitudes go along and sit quietly awaiting their turn to die. If enormous masses of people are plunged into slavery for life, and they become slaves without ever doing anything about it. If books that bring together the best of human reason through the millennia are banned, burned and thrown away. If a single small cylinder contains energy enough to reduce New York, Moscow, Paris or Berlin to ashes, and many such cylinders are accumulated and carried through the skies around the clock—and for what? Comrades and friends, brothers and sisters, ladies and gentlemen! CIVILIZATION IS IN DANGER!

NO BLESSED LAND

At the city line near Pushcha-Voditsa, across from the Abandon Sorrows Sanatorium, stood a massive column, erected to last forever, with a sign pointing the way to Dymer. Signposts like this, in German, stood all over the Ukraine. I laid my bundle of clothes under this sign, and Mother took leave of me because she was late for work at the school.

Once again I was setting out over my beloved, beautiful, blessed countryside; but now it looked different.

The Dymer highway, where the prisoner of war Vasily and I had once moved like Martians, was now alive with trucks, cars and people on foot. A guardhouse had been built at the roadside, and the *Polizei* stood near it. They stopped all peasants and traders who came by.

"*Oi,* why are you taking this away?" an old woman cried desperately, darting from *Polizei* to *Polizei*. "I've carried it 25 miles and traded my things for it! Please, dear people!"

One *Polizei* carried her sack into the shack. Another was already stopping an old man from some village, who was carrying two sacks, the smaller in front and the larger on his back. He was told to put them on the ground. He did so without a word.

"Good-bye, until we meet again!" the *Polizei* said sarcastically.

The old man turned and, without a word, walked back down the highway, just as deliberately as he had come.

This *Polizei* activity was due to an order that strictly proscribed carrying more than one day's food along the roads.

A truck stopped at the signpost, and I and other people scrambled aboard. Soon we were hurtling along the highway through the forest, but I could not feel even a trace of the sense of joy and peace I had once experienced here.

People were cutting down the woods, which showed many yawning gaps. Trucks and trailers were coming the other way, loaded with logs, long and straight as arrows. Germans, who were now stationed in the village of Petrivtsa, were riding around on horseback. People were working in the fields. The woods near Irpen were also being cut down, and stacks of logs stood beside the road, ready for removal.

Prisoners of war were building a bridge across the little river at Demidovo. They were muddy from head to foot; some had rags wrapped around their feet, and others were barefoot. Some were digging the still frozen ground and pushing barrows, while others, standing in the icy water up to their chests, passed logs along from hand to hand. On both banks machine-gunners sat in watchtowers, and foot soldiers patrolled with dogs.

The truck stopped at Dymer and everyone got off. The German driver collected 50 rubles a head, counted it efficiently and drove on. I headed for the fields.

The fields had not been cleared since last year; so there were rows of potatoes, never dug up and now spoiled, as well as rows of flattened and rotten wheat. And all the while there was such starvation in the city!

Everything on earth was fouled up.

For a long time Mother had been watching me grow skinnier and mangier. An X-ray machine had been set up at the polyclinic to check those destined for Germany. Mother took me there and managed to have me examined, and I was found to have symptoms of incipient tuberculosis.

Then Mother went to the bazaar and started begging collective farmers she knew to take me to the country for recuperation. Goncharenko, a kind woman from the village of Rykun (between Dymer and Litvinovka), agreed to take me in exchange for some old clothes. And so I went back to the country.

I was badly frightened myself. Tuberculosis was fatal under fascism and I did not in the least want to die. I wanted to outlive all this, to live a long time, far into old age.

Goncharenko received me well. She set a pitcher of milk, a saucer of honey and some freshly baked bread, warm from the oven, on the table before me. I ate until I could eat no more, but the craving in my mouth and throat did not go away.

Goncharenko regarded me thoughtfully, her chin on her palm, as I gobbled the chunks of bread. She told me that things were bad in the village: The Germans were demanding incredible taxes and threatening a general requisition. There had been an order to bring all horses and cows to the village square for a veterinary inspection; and when this was done, half of the animals, the best ones, were requisitioned. That's what inspection meant.

"Oh, it was awful!" she grimaced. "Women fell on the ground, clinging to their cows."

Goncharenko's cow was not taken. But they had issued her a booklet for milk deliveries, and every day she had to carry a big can of milk to the "creamery," where her booklet was stamped.

The German manager made his rounds in a *drozhky* with the *Polizei,* and never talked to anyone but the elders of the village. The *Polizei* were quartered in the Village Soviet Building. All the young people had been registered for deportation to Germany, including Goncharenko's eighteen-year-old daughter Shura. But her son Vasya wasn't old enough yet—he was under fourteen.

Vasya and I naturally found a common language at once. He showed me a crane's nest right outside on the barn roof, some mine fragments and some little pieces of explosive—TNT.

"Stop your loafing!" his mother said. "Take some bags and pick sorrel for borsch."

The wild sorrel had come up in thick clumps all over the field. We plucked its bright, juicy leaves, and I could not help popping some of them into my mouth. They were tasty, but so sour that a shiver ran down my spine.

Lying about in the field were yellow hunks of TNT, looking like Dutch cheese. They had flown all over the place when an ammunition dump blew up. We stuffed the sorrel into our bags for the borsch, and stuffed pieces of TNT under our shirts for our morale.

Having collected what we believed was enough TNT to make a few changes in the world, we built a bonfire, packed an empty can with TNT, planted a fuse from a grenade in it and threw the can into the fire. The can lay there a moment; then came a deafening explosion, and all that remained of the bonfire was a gray pit. We examined the destruction in detail and departed with a sense of a job well done.

Bare-bellied babies crawled about in Gapka's cottage, as before. An old woman, shaped like a pyramid, ground away at something in a mortar, and the grandfather snored and wheezed on the stovetop. I had crossed the fields to visit them in Litvinovka, but it would have been better if I had not.

Gapka was crying. Her hands were swollen and all her bones ached from work. It occurred to me that the serfs in Taras Shevchenko's time must have lived like Gapka—at the utter limits of poverty and despair.

Litvinovka's "luck" had been illusory and short-lived. The Germans soon appointed village authorities and extortion began in earnest. Everything people had reaped and threshed for themselves, or so they had thought, had to be turned in. A fantastic tax was levied on every homestead. Gapka could only clutch her head in despair. She had to plow, and to do so she needed a horse (where was she to get one?), a plow, a harrow and grain; and even then she would have to sow more than two men could.

"I never saw anything like this on the collective farm," Gapka lamented. "I used to curse the collective farm. We thought it was misery, but it wasn't at all! This is misery! This'll be the end of us, all of us! Oh, where are our collective farms?"

"The day of judgment has come!" the old woman muttered, crossing herself over the mortar. "May the Lord have mercy on us!"

I was thinking that if there really were a God, He shouldn't be prayed to, but punched in the nose for everything He had contrived. Only there was no God. It was all done by people.

Goncharenko had been wailing and lamenting over Shura since morning, as though her daughter were dead. She sat rocking on her bed in a black dress, her face bloated, chanting in a low, strangely unnatural voice, "Oh, my baby girl, my very own. I'll never, never see you again."

There was wailing in all the cottages. The *Polizei* had gathered outside the Village Soviet Building, and the band was tuning up. Vasya and I wandered around this sobbing, howling, chanting village like a pair of lost souls.

I was already stronger and well tanned. Vasya and I, like grown men, carried manure to the field and then did the plowing and harrowing. I had learned how to harness and hobble a horse, and to ride at full gallop. My jacket and trousers were faded and threadbare, and I was indistinguishable from Vasya in every respect but one: Although Goncharenko fed us alike, Vasya ate to contentment, but I could never get my fill. My craving for food persisted in my mouth and throat, but I was ashamed to keep asking for seconds. Most enticing was the honey, which Goncharenko kept in the pantry under lock and key, seldom to be served.

The *Polizei* came around to the cottages, flushing out deportees. This, like fat on a fire, brought the wailing to a new pitch. Shura slung a suitcase and a sack, tied together, over her shoulder and went to the square, her mother running after her. And there, my God, what a scene! The whole village was milling about, and the deportees were being formed into a column. The *Polizei* barked "Get going!" and the band, made up of invalids, blared forth. Women ran along beside the column, shrieking and sobbing, clinging to their daughters' necks; the *Polizei* pried them away, and some women fell to the ground; the Germans brought up the rear, laughing. And the band kept playing a march, so jolly that my hair stood on end.

The procession stretched out across the fields toward Demidovo, everybody running after it. But I stayed behind.

The band music faded away gradually, until all at once the silence was complete. I walked slowly to the cottage and suddenly saw that the door to the pantry was half open, and the lock and key lay nearby on a bench.

I entered the cottage and sat down by the window for a while, still trembling over the spectacle I had just seen. Then, as if in a fog, I got up, found a spoon and stole into the pantry.

The jar was covered with cheesecloth and oilcloth, which I carefully turned back. I began to scoop out and devour the honey by the spoonful. I gasped, swallowed one spoonful after another, and vaguely told myself to stop after the next—no, the next—no, the next. Goncharenko was walking all the way to Demidovo, wailing, and here I was being an out-and-out rat to her; but I had to have the honey to save myself from tuberculosis: This was how I salved my conscience.

CHAPTER XXVII

THE LEARNED
ARE ENEMIES

Mama was ordered to go back to teaching, and she did not refuse, because this would save her from being sent to Germany. The *Arbeitskarte* (labor card) was introduced on March 1, and soon became more important than a passport. It was stamped at the bearer's place of work each week. Documents were checked on the streets, and those who had no *Arbeitskarte* or who had not kept the stamps up to date were seized on the spot for deportation to Germany.

The teachers gathered at the school and proceeded to fill out questionnaires. The first in line was an instructor, formerly a very quiet, humble man with a spotless record, who loudly and proudly proclaimed, "I was a Petlura man against the Bolsheviks!" [1] He probably thought he would be appointed principal; but another was chosen—most likely someone with even more to recommend him.

The building needed a cleaning after its occupancy by the Germans. Teachers scraped out dung, repaired broken desks, fitted panels into the windows, and then went from house to house registering the children of school age. There could be no thought of school until spring because there was no fuel for heat. But a directive appeared to prepare for classes in the first four grades, which included children up to eleven. Older children were being put to work.

> The number of teachers for the reduced school programs must be limited. . . . All members of school administrative agencies instituted by the Bolsheviks and all teachers of upper grades are discharged. . . . Teachers who have cooperated with the Communist Party in any way are discharged. No pensions will be paid.
>
> The use of study plans, textbooks, students' and teachers' libraries dating from the Bolshevik regime, and politically tendentious study aids (films, maps, pictures) is forbidden, and such articles must be surrendered. Instruction will be improvised until the new study plans and textbooks are ready. It will be confined to reading, writing, arithmetic, physical culture, games, industrial and manual labor. The language of instruction will be Ukrainian and, where necessary, Polish. The Russian language will no longer be taught. [2]

Copies of *Novoye Ukrainskoye slovo*, dated May 14, 1942, were then distributed to the teachers so that they could study and absorb an article entitled, "The Schools." I repeat: This newspaper and the orders posted on the fences were more important than ever; one had to watch them steadily, never missing a word, lest one land in trouble unwittingly.

Mother and Lena Gimpel read the article together, slowly, with frequent pauses; and I listened in an effort to improve my mind. The article opened with an epigraph:

"WHAT IS NECESSARY TO DO HENCE-FORTH IS TO CHANGE OUR UPBRINGING.

TODAY WE SUFFER FROM EXCESSIVE EDU-
CATION. KNOWLEDGE ALONE IS PRIZED,
BUT THOSE WHO ARE TOO CLEVER ARE
THE ENEMIES OF ACTION. WHAT WE NEED
IS INSTINCT AND WILL."
—From Adolf Hitler's speech of April 27, 1923.

The article itself said:

. . . Taking our example from the entire life of
our liberators and particularly from their schools,
we shall make every effort to impart to our children
the qualities necessary for the regeneration of our
people, without which their further progress is impossible. Foremost among these qualities are love of
labor and ability to work, strength of character and
lofty morality. . . . The fundamentals of science are
very important, but they are not everything, nor are
they the chief thing at all. . . . To work! We wish the
free Ukrainian schools and the free Ukrainian teachers every success. The example and help of our
German friends will guarantee this. [3]

"So this is what we've come to," said Lena. "The twentieth
century needs workers with some education, but not too
much. Slaves must know how to sign their names, read
orders and count. Those who are too clever have always
been the enemies of dictatorships."

"I'm not going to teach," Mother said.

"They'll force you to."

"No they won't! Let them send me to Germany. Where
can I find a job in a hurry?"

"It's incredible!" Lena exclaimed, bewildered, twisting
the newspaper in her hands. "Here it is in black and white,

213

in all seriousness. After the Renaissance, after all the philosophers, the great scientists and writers, it is finally discovered that too much education is an evil. Go to work, children. For regeneration and progress."

"What about me?" I asked. "I've been through four grades already."

"You're educated now, so go and shine shoes, go sell cigarettes. By the way," Lena continued, "there's an order out, forbidding children to trade in the street. Go and read it, you're educated enough."

"Did you hear that?" Mother said.

"Oh, they can't stop me," I said.

Mother, having heard that a scrubwoman-messenger was needed at the Sport Plant, quickly resigned from the school and went to work at the plant. Classes for grades one through four began in May. The children studied the German language and learned German songs.

I sometimes walked past the windows and heard them singing about the cuckoo and the donkey: *"Der Kuckuck und der Esel . . ."*

But the schools had given the city council lists of children over eleven (so that was why they were compiled!); and I received a summons to report for job placement.

The whole of our former 4-A went to work. Zhorka Gorokhovsky landed at the Food Industry Machinery Trust where his father had once worked. There, dressed in oil-stained rags and blackened from head to foot with crude oil, he dragged all kinds of iron and bricks around—small, thin and a little frightening because of the crude oil ingrained in his face.

As for me, I was sent to join the kitchen garden crew at the Abandon Sorrows Sanatorium. It was not now a sanatorium, strictly speaking, but rather a big farm. There were about 30 of us, boys and girls. We were given mattocks and put to work, weeding.

I got up at dawn and packed a metal bowl, a spoon, a bottle of water and some bread in my bag. I started out at six because I had to walk almost two miles, and latecomers got no breakfast. We assembled at six-thirty and each received a ladle of hot broth with millet. Then we fell into line, and the old man we all called the "Gardener" led us to the vegetable patches.

Each of us had to weed a strip of potatoes or cabbage two yards wide. The plots stretched on endlessly, and the heat was frightful. I cheated—I covered weeds with dirt— although sometimes the Gardener followed in our tracks, kicked aside the dirt and boxed our ears. Still, I often finished my strip before the rest and could take a breather between the rows.

In the afternoon we had a ladle of soup each and a half hour for lunch. Then we worked until eight in the evening, thirteen hours in all. I got bone-tired and sometimes (because the sun was fierce) even collapsed.

But there were happy times, too, such as the time we were put to work picking tomatoes. They were still green, small and hard, but we fell on them like locusts. There were luxuriant orchards around us, too, but we were kept in line and not allowed to take one step to the side; we could only look at the apples. Fruit was for the Germans.

The German boss of the farm decided to build a rabbit hutch, and brought in ten prisoners of war from Darnitsa for the purpose. The grass on the sanatorium grounds was tall, thick and strewn with daisies. The prisoners sank to their knees in it and reached for the tastiest stalks, munching that grass and glorying in it.

We handed them cigarette butts, sat down in a circle and took smoking lessons. This appealed to me—taking up smoking like an honest-to-goodness worker—for who ever heard of a worker who didn't smoke?

I told Grandfather about the Gardener, and he exclaimed, "Why, I know him; he's a friend of mine, and I'll tell him not to hit you!" The next day when we were falling in, the Gardener asked, "Which one of you is Anatoly Kuznetsov?" I stepped forward. "Two more of you join him, you're being transferred to easier work."

We were sent to gather lime blossoms. Boys would rather climb trees than eat. The lime trees in the Abandon Sorrows park were huge, 200 years old, and perhaps they had even seen Empress Catherine II. According to local legend, the Empress had once come to this park with Potemkin, who was depressed about something, and said to him, "Look how lovely it is here! Abandon your sorrows!"

The richest clusters grew at the crowns and out at the very tips of the branches. Each of us had a quota. The Gardener weighed our harvest, and if it wasn't enough he gave us no soup, so we tried hard. I climbed to such heights that I was afraid to look down. One day I broke loose, together with a limb, and hurtled down from a height equal to that of a six-story building. Why am I alive today? Because on my way down I hit some thick branches, which caught me like a hammock; I would have gone all the way through them, but I managed to grab hold with both hands.

Thus began my official labor career. I was sent to work at the age of twelve and a half so that I would not grow up too clever, and so that I would not make trouble for those who thought everything out for me and had strictly determined my place in life for all time.

THE POTATOES
BLOSSOM

The No. 12 streetcar to Pushcha-Voditsa had formerly taken about an hour one way, most of it through the woods. It went fast, like an express train, flashing through the endless green tunnel of pine boughs, with twigs brushing against its windows.

The same trip on foot, walking along the ties, took Grandfather and me almost a whole day. The tracks were rusty now; grass was growing between the ties, and daisies and cornflowers nodded here and there. Occasionally we met disgruntled people walking the other way who told us:

"Don't go any farther. They are confiscating everything at the children's sanatorium."

And they were right. Three *Polizei* were sitting under a pine tree at the children's tuberculosis sanatorium, with a heap of bundles, milk cans and sacks beside them. They had set up one of their posts here. All roads into Kiev were covered, and plunder was the law.

Grandfather had worked at the grist mill at Pushcha-

Voditsa long, long ago; he had spent his youth here, and had lived here with Grandmother the first year they were married. So he knew the area well.

"Damn them!" he muttered worriedly. "But I know the paths. We'll avoid them by going through the woods."

Our feet were throbbing badly when we reached the Nine-Mile Line in the evening. There we found a pond and a dam. Protruding from the water next to the dam were the blackened pilings on which the mill had once stood. Grandfather stopped and stared at them pensively.

The sacks slung over our shoulders were full of Grandmother's clothing—skirts, blouses, high boots with laces—which we had brought along to barter.

On the other side of the pond was the village of Gorenka, where we spent the night in the empty shed of an old woodsman who still remembered Grandfather. At dawn, we set out across the dewy grass. For another whole day, we dragged ourselves over hidden forest paths. We were collapsing from fatigue and hunger when we caught sight of the Irpen River and the village of the same name.

Grandfather had meant to go even farther, but we were too tired and so we started trading right there. We went from cottage to cottage, knocking on doors and arousing the dogs.

We walked around the village a full day and part of another until we had gathered two bags of flour, corn and beans. And the trip back is something I shall never forget as long as I live.

We walked slowly and painfully, pausing to rest every quarter mile or so; the bags seemed to be filled with bricks. Grandfather moaned, sighed and sometimes even wept. After all, he was 72 years old. We had to cross a creek by way of a footbridge. It was nothing more than some planks laid across high over the water, and so it swayed. I ran across bravely, but Grandfather stopped cold—it was no go. I carried the sacks across, and then Grandfather, very slowly, clinging for dear life to me and the poles, crawled across on all fours. Anyone who watched us would have died laughing.

We spent the night in a haystack. In the morning our backs, arms and legs ached and burned fiercely. We trudged off again, went a short way and then sat down. We didn't have the strength to get up again. I told myself to stand, but my body would not obey.

We were surrounded by woods and more woods, broken by occasional clearings with farmhouses and lavishly blossoming potatoes; but I saw it all through a haze.

Grandfather, remembering the *Polizei* at the children's sanatorium, decided to skirt around to the west of Pushcha-Voditsa, and we emerged on a fairly wide, firm road. Suddenly we heard a motor behind us; we were engulfed in a cloud of dust as a truck with two Germans in the cab went by. It came to an abrupt halt and the driver leaned out to watch us as we approached. My heart sank.

"Bitte!" the German said, pointing to the back of the truck. "Ride, ride!"

It didn't look as though he intended to rob us. Well, whatever his intentions, we climbed aboard, and the truck dashed on. I set my face to the wind, luxuriated and relaxed. We rode on and on, farther than we would have reached on foot by nightfall. The city came into view, and we realized we would bypass it to the west, ending up somewhere on the Brest-Litovsk highway.

Grandfather rapped on the back window of the cab.

The truck stopped in the midst of some fields. We climbed down, and Grandfather held out a bundle of flour to pay for the ride.

But the driver looked at us and shook his head.

"No, no. Old people, little ones. No."

We just stood there, incredulous. The driver smiled and started up.

"*Danke!* Thanks!" I yelled.

He waved, and Grandfather bowed toward the truck from the waist. We slung the sacks over our shoulders and headed across the field toward the roofs of Kurenevka. We wound our way through lanes and back alleys for a long time, finally going straight down Beletskaya Street to our bridge, only three minutes from home. Our shoulders and legs were numb, but we dragged on, like marathon runners approaching the finish line.

That was where we were stopped by two *Polizei*.

"Been carrying these things very far?" one of them asked sarcastically.

We stood there without a word; this was incredible— it couldn't happen.

"Drop those things!" the other said, and started in a businesslike way to help Grandfather set down his sack.

"Dear sirs!" Grandfather whispered, dumbfounded, "dear sirs . . ."

"Move on, move," the first *Polizei* said.

"Dear sirs, kind sirs!" Grandfather was ready to fall on his knees.

The *Polizei,* paying no attention, carried our sacks to a post where several other bags lay. It turned out that they had set up a new checkpoint here at the approach to the bazaar. I pulled Grandfather by the sleeve; he was out of his mind. I dragged him home with difficulty and fell into bed to rest and sleep, because I had to go to work in the morning. Out of friendship for Grandfather, the Gardener had secretly excused me for a day so we could barter our things. Well, that was my day off.

Bribery is very simple. One loads the shopping bag with bits of potatoes and carrots; a half loaf of bread and a piece of bacon are laid on the top, and the whole thing is covered with a newspaper. Then Mother takes you by the hand and leads you to the city council. It is rather unnerving to enter here, for this is the place where everything is decided: human life, food, work and death. From here people are sent to Germany or even marked for Babi Yar.

There are no Germans. The desks are manned by *Volksdeutschen*—descendants of Germans who settled in Russia and the Ukraine in the eighteenth century—or "trustworthy" old Ukrainians wearing embroidered shirts and mustaches. These people cannot be fooled like the Germans; they know their own countrymen too well. They are all writing summonses and compiling lists. Strutting among them is a stout, energetic woman with a masculine air, dressed in a severe gray jacket with a skirt to match, her eyes cold, her voice peremptory:

"If you refuse to work, we can turn you over to the Gestapo." "In case of failure to comply, the Gestapo will deal with you."

Your mother takes you to the desk of some woman who holds your fate in her hands. Mother leans the shopping bag against a leg of the desk in such a way that the bread and an edge of the bacon peep out. It is a tiny bit of bacon, no bigger than a matchbox, but no one can tell its size under that newspaper.

Bowing abjectly, your mother explains that you are susceptible to tuberculosis, you find work in the vegetable garden too hard and other such nonsense. But meanwhile you aren't standing still either; you slouch and affect a wretched appearance with all your might.

The auntie at the desk looks you over, snorts irritably, rummages in the files, finds your name, crosses it out, enters it on another list and says:

"Be at the entrance to the cannery by seven tomorrow."

You pretend to be happy while your mother offers thanks, bows and hustles you out, conveniently forgetting her shopping bag under the desk.

The cannery had a sharp, sour smell that burrowed into your nostrils and stuck. But only a hopeless fool would go hungry here.

Long trucks filled with pumpkins drove into the wide yard, and our boys brigade unloaded them. Some of the pumpkins arrived broken open; if not, we broke them ourselves, dug into them, scooped out the slippery white seeds and stuffed our mouths with them. From then on I no longer ate at home, but fed myself pumpkin seeds all day. Once an accident occurred: When I wasn't looking, the tailgate of a truck fell open on me, and an avalanche of pumpkins poured out. They raised some bumps on my head and broke one of my teeth, but after lying down a while in the shade I was able to walk away.

I hated it worst of all when we were ordered to load the jam, which had been sealed in eighteen-pound cans. There I would be, carrying the jam right in my arms, but unable to eat any. It was all for the Germans.

The workshops were tightly guarded. But one day, after loading a truck, we saw that the watchman had vanished. I and another boy flew at once to the shop. It was half dark and very hot inside, and the vats were bubbling and gurgling. We rushed at the first person we saw—a woman in a spattered smock:

"Auntie! Jam!"

"*Oi*, poor dears, this way, quick!" She shoved us behind a forest of steel stanchions, disappeared and returned with a crumpled cardboard box half full of hot pumpkin jam. God, what luck!

Our working day lasted twelve hours. Then we were lined up, marched to the gate, searched meticulously and released one by one. Everything went well, and all in all I considered that I was pretty lucky. Back home I boasted to Grandfather about the riches at the cannery, and how I had been gorging myself. But he was ravenously hungry and therefore held a different opinion. It infuriated him that I never brought anything home.

"There's a sharp fellow in town who makes sausage on the sly without a license," he said one day, "and he's looking for an assistant. It has to be somebody reliable who can hold his tongue. If you'll let me, I'll get you the job; he promises to feed you and pay you in bones."

"We can use the bones," I said, "but how do I get dismissed from work? I'm on their lists."

"Take them a shopping bag," Grandfather said. "Nothing works without a little grease."

I worked at the cannery a while longer, then decided to try to make the change. I took a shopping bag to the city council, and I applied grease. It worked.

THE DYNAMO TEAM: LEGEND AND FACT

This almost incredible story occurred in the summer of 1942, and it was so popular that at one time people referred to the ravine as, "the self-same Babi Yar where they shot the soccer players." In those days it made the rounds in the form of a legend, one so fine and so satisfying that I want to set it down in full. Here it is:

Kiev's Dynamo soccer team had been one of the best in the country before the war. Its fans knew all about the players, especially the famous goalie Trusevich.

Because of the encirclement, the team had been unable to get away from Kiev. At first they sat tight, found work wherever they could and kept in touch. Then, longing for soccer, they began to hold practice in a vacant lot. The boys in the neighborhood discovered this right away, then the adults, and finally the German authorities.

They called in the players and said, "Why use a vacant lot? Look, here is an excellent stadium going begging, so by all means practice there. We have nothing against sports, in fact, the opposite."

The Dynamo men agreed and moved into the stadium. Sometime later the Germans summoned them again and said, "Kiev is returning to normal; the movie theaters and the opera are open, and it's about time we opened the stadium too. Let everyone see that peaceful restoration is in full swing. We offer you a match against the all-stars of the armed forces of Germany."

The Dynamo men asked for time to think it over. Some were against it on the grounds that playing soccer with the fascists would be disgraceful treason. Others felt differently: "On the contrary, we'll whip them, humiliate them in front of all the people and raise the morale of the Kievans." This side won. The team began to train in earnest under its new name, "Start."

Bright posters appeared on the streets of Kiev:

SOCCER
GERMANY'S ARMED FORCES ALL-STARS
vs.
CITY OF KIEV ALL-STARS

The stadium was filled; half of the stands were occupied by the Germans and all their important leaders, including the commandant himself. They were in fine spirits and expected a happy outcome. The poorer seats were occupied by the hungry, ragged populace of Kiev.

The game began. The Dynamo men were emaciated and weak. The well-fed German team played a rough game, openly tripping their opponents; but the referee noticed nothing. The Germans in the stands roared with glee when the first goal was scored against the Kiev team. The other half of the stadium kept gloomily silent: now they were spitting on us in soccer.

Then suddenly the Dynamo men seemed to rally. They were seized with fury. They drew strength from unknown sources. They outplayed the Germans and, with a desperate surge, drove home the tying goal. Now the German rooting section subsided into a disappointed silence, and the rest of the crowd screamed and embraced.

The Dynamo team recovered its prewar finesse and, with some brilliant teamwork, scored its second goal. The ragged crowds shouted, "Hurrah!" and "They're licking the Germans!"

This "licking the Germans" remark overstepped the bounds of sportsmanship. Germans swept through the stands shouting, "Stop that!" and firing in the air. The first half ended and the teams left the field for a rest.

An officer from the commandant's box visited the Dynamo locker room during the intermission and very politely told them, "Well done, you've played good soccer and we appreciate it. You have upheld your athletic honor sufficiently. But now in the second half, take it easy; because as you yourselves must realize, you have to lose. You must. The German army team has never lost before, especially not on occupied territory. This is an order. If you don't lose, you'll be shot."

The Dynamo men listened in silence and then went out to the field. The referee blew his whistle and the second half began. The Kiev team played well and scored a third goal. Half of the stadium was roaring, and many wept for joy; the German half was grumbling with indignation. Dynamo kicked in another goal. The Germans in the stands leaped to their feet and fingered their pistols. Guards ran out along the sidelines and cordoned off the field.

It was a game to the death, but the people in our section did not know it and so they kept up their joyful shouting. The German players were utterly crushed and dispirited. The Dynamos scored again. The commandant and all the officers left the stands.

The referee cut the game short with his whistle. The guards, not even waiting for the teams to reach the lockers, grabbed the Dynamo players right there on the field, loaded them into a closed truck and took them off to Babi Yar.

Nothing of this kind had ever happened in the history of soccer. In this game, however, athletics was purely political from start to finish. Because the Dynamo players had no other weapons, they turned soccer itself into a weapon and accomplished a truly deathless exploit. They had known victory meant death, but they had won anyway, in order to remind the people of their dignity.

In actuality, the story was not quite so tidy. The ending was the same, but like all things in life, the events were more complicated. Not one game, but several, took place, and the fury of the Germans mounted from match to match.

The Dynamo players wound up in occupied territory not because they had been unable to get away but because they had been in the Red Army and were captured. Because a large part of the team went to work as loaders at Bakery No. 1, in time they were enlisted on the bakery team.

There was a German stadium in Kiev, but Kievans were not admitted. But posters really did go up on July 12, 1942:

OPENING OF UKRAINIAN STADIUM
The Ukrainian Stadium will open at 4 p.m. today
(Bolshaya Vasilkovskaya, 51, entrance
on Prozorovskaya).
Opening program: gymnastics, boxing, track and
field events and, most interesting, a soccer match
(at 5:30 p.m.) [1]

The team of some German army unit really was defeated in that game, and the Germans didn't like it; but no arrests occurred. The Germans, annoyed, simply signed up the stronger PSG army team to play the next game, on July 17. Start routed, literally routed, this team, 6–0.

The newspaper report of that game was priceless:

> ... But this victory can hardly be called an achievement on the part of the Start men. The German team was made up of fairly strong individual players, but was not a team in the full sense. This is not surprising, for the team consisted of players who were in the unit for which they were playing by chance. Another factor was the Germans' lack of practice, without which even the strongest team could accomplish nothing. The Start team, as everyone well knows, consists mainly of former players for the select Dynamo team, so one would expect them to make a far better showing than they actually made in this match. [2]

The ill-concealed irritation and the note of apology that permeated every line of this commentary were only the beginning of the tragedy.

On Sunday, July 19, Start played against a Hungarian team, MSG Wal, and won 5-1. This is from the report on that match:

> Despite the final score, the two teams can be considered almost equally strong. [3]

The Hungarians proposed a return match, which was held on July 26. The final score: 3–2, in favor of Start. Now it looked as though the team was ready to be beaten, and the Germans would have their gratification.

A new match was announced for August 6 between Start and the "most powerful," "mightiest," "undefeated" German Flakelf team. The newspaper went simply wild in its advance coverage of the Flakelf team, citing its fabulous record of goals scored and prevented and other such statistics. This was the match described in the legend, that culminated in that German defeat. The newspaper carried no report of it. However, the soccer players were not arrested yet. On August 9, a small notice appeared in *Novoye Ukrainskoye slovo*:

> A friendly match between the best football teams of the city, Flakelef and Start (from Bakery No. 1), will be held at Zenith Stadium at five o'clock this evening.

Start was getting another chance. But it defeated the Germans in this game, too; and on August 16 it beat the Ukrainian nationalist Rukh team by a score of 8–0. After this game the Dynamo soccer players were finally sent to Babi Yar.

This was at the time when there was heavy fighting on the Don and the Germans had reached the approaches to Stalingrad.

The Author Speaking

A REMINDER. *Here you are, reading these accounts. Perhaps there are pages you skim through casually; perhaps there are others (my fault) where you yawn, "Well, that's the way fiction is, after all." I must insist on reminding you one more time that none of this is fiction. It all really happened. Nothing is invented, nothing is exaggerated. On the contrary, I am even leaving out certain things, some details of the murders, for instance. Everything I am telling here actually happened to real-life people, and there is not the slightest literary invention in this book.*

There is a bias, yes. I am writing tendentiously, needless to say, because no matter how we strive to be objective, we cannot avoid being biased.

My bias is a hatred—for fascism in all its manifestations. But regardless of this, I accept full responsibility, as an eyewitness, for the authenticity *of everything recounted.*

Now to you who were born in the 1940's and later, I admit, without fear of seeming sentimental, that I sometimes look in wonder at this world and think:

"What joy, imagine—now you can walk the streets whenever you like, at one in the morning, even at four. You

can listen to the radio to your heart's content, or raise pigeons. It's irritating when the noise of a car wakes you up in the middle of the night, so you growl sleepily, 'Oh, it's my neighbor coming home drunk in a taxi again.' Then you roll over and go back to sleep."

I don't like the drone of planes at night; it's enough to turn my soul inside out, but immediately I tell myself, "Calm down, those are our own—not theirs." And in the morning the newspapers arrive, with their reports of wars in remote southern and eastern countries. They say we never notice our health as long as it's good, and we cry only when it's gone.

I look in wonder at this tenuously secure world.

BABI YAR: THE SYSTEM

Davydov was arrested very simply and casually.

He was walking along the street and met a comrade, Zhora Puzenko, with whom he had gone to school, played on the same team and taken girls dancing. They stopped to talk, and Zhora smiled.

"What are you doing out on the streets, Volodya? You'll have to come along now."

"Where?"

"Come on, come on!"

"What's the matter with you?"

Zhora was still smiling.

"Coming with me or not? I can show you my credentials."

He produced the credentials of a *Polizei* investigator and shifted his pistol from one pocket to another, revealing it while appearing to want to conceal it.

It was a fine, sunny day, and the street was crowded with Germans. They started off, and Davydov asked quietly, "Aren't you ashamed?"

"No," Puzenko shrugged. "I get paid for this."

In this amiable, calm temper, they reached the Gestapo

at No. 33 Vladimirskaya Street. This building stands near Bogdan Khmelnitsky Square, almost opposite St. Sophia Cathedral. It is quite conspicuous—a massive, dark-gray building that almost seems black in comparison with the houses around it. With its columns and portico it rises like a giant chest of drawers over Vladimirskaya, which has breathed the dust of the ages. It had been begun before the Revolution for the Zemstvo Council, but was not finished. Under Soviet rule it became a Palace of Labor—a clubhouse. Then it housed one of the People's Commissariats of the Ukrainian Soviet Socialist Republic, right up until the retreat in 1941. Now it belonged to the Gestapo. Behind the magnificent facade were splendidly equipped interrogation rooms; and in the courtyard, hidden from prying eyes, was a stone prison, connected with the main building by passages.

Davydov, a private in the 37th Army, had been captured at the village of Borshch. He had been in the Darnitsa camp and several others and had escaped outside of Zhitomir. A doctor he knew in Kiev was in contact with the partisans of Ivankovo District, whom he supplied with medicines. Davydov was about to take some medicines to Ivankovo when this ridiculous arrest took place.

Just what Puzenko knew, or how, was never learned; but Davydov was lodged in the most ghastly cell, the so-called "Jew cell," where people awaiting shipment to Babi Yar were packed in like herring. Davydov realized that his situation was almost hopeless.

He was called in for interrogation and ordered to tell what he knew about the partisans, and also whether or not it was true that he was a Jew.

Davydov shouted that he was no Jew, and no partisan

either, but that Puzenko was merely settling a personal score with him. He was taken to a conference room, where German doctors examined him for Jewish traits, but their diagnosis was negative. Nevertheless, he was put back into that horrible cell because it was not customary to release anyone from there. It was like a conveyer belt—once on it, there was no way back.

People were taken out of the cell and never returned, but Davydov stayed on and on. Finally, when only ten prisoners were left, they were taken out to the courtyard. There stood a truck that they recognized at once.

It was one of the asphyxiation trucks, known all over Kiev; a *Gasenwagen,* as the Germans called it. It looked something like a refrigerator truck of today. The body was windowless, sheathed in boxcar panels and painted a dark color, with a hermetic double door in the rear. The inside was lined with steel, with the intake grating in the floor. There was plenty of room for the ten men, and a girl was also added—a very beautiful Jewish girl from Poland.

They all stood on the grating, steadying themselves against the walls. The doors were slammed behind them, and in this manner—in complete darkness—they rode off.

Davydov realized that soon they would reach Babi Yar, but would never see it, because gas was going to be released through a vent next to the cab.

There was no conversation among the doomed. They waited to say their farewells.

But the truck went jouncing on, with intermittent pauses, and finally appeared to come to a full stop. The hinges of the door creaked; there was a splash of light—then a voice, "Get out!"

They climbed out hurriedly, taking deep breaths, and out of habit formed into ranks. They were surrounded by barbed wire barriers, watchtowers and other structures, SS men and *Polizei.*

A healthy, sturdy Russian wearing a tall sheepskin hat, riding breeches and shiny boots came over (they later learned that he was Brigadier Vladimir Bystrov). He had a stick in his hands, and with a flourish he struck each of them on the head.

"That's your initiation! Obey orders. Drill practice, march! Double time! . . . Halt! . . . Form a circle! . . . Down! . . . Up! . . . Duck walk, march! . . . Fish step, march! . . ."

The *Polizei* fell on the prisoners and showered them with blows, kicks, shouts and curses. The "duck walk," it turned out, meant waddling in a squatting position with arms stretched forward. The "fish step" meant inching along on the belly by rocking from side to side, with hands clasped behind the back. (They learned later that these drills were calculated to bewilder newcomers; then the beatings could be administered with abandon, switches breaking on the backs of the prisoners, whereupon the guards would cut themselves new ones.)

The prisoners dragged themselves into a fenced-off area within the camp and lined up to hear the following lecture from a Cossack lieutenant by the name of Kuribko:

"Well, you'd better know where you've ended up. This is Babi Yar. Do you understand the difference between a resort and a camp? Find yourselves places in the huts. You're going to work. Whoever works badly, breaks the rules or attempts to escape will be sorry."

The girl was separated from the rest and led off to the women's side of the camp, and the men were herded to the mud huts.

These huts extended in two rows. They included ordinary

huts, a brigadier's, a Jews' hut, and a hospital hut. The one Davydov was assigned to was an ordinary hut: windowless, with one door, rows of double-decker bunks and a dirt floor. There was a stove at the back end. A dim lamp hung from the ceiling, and the air was as foul as in a bear cave. A place was assigned to each man, and camp life began.

Davydov later wondered why the Germans had not turned on the gas or shot them right away instead of granting them a reprieve by installing them in this weird camp. Why did it exist at all? There is only one likely explanation. The Germans had not struck upon their system of Auschwitzes, Buchenwalds and Dachaus all at once; they were experimenting. They had started out by simply shooting their victims, but being economical and thorough people, they were casting about for some form of "death factory" where use could be made of people before killing them.

The daily executions at the ravine continued as usual. Persons who would only have caused trouble if placed in the camp were killed. They were brought in, herded down a path into the ravine, laid out on the ground under a cliff and riddled with submachine-gun bullets. Almost all of them shouted something, but no one could hear what it was from that distance. Then the slope was blasted to cover the corpses, and the whole operation moved farther along the ravine. No cartridges were wasted on the wounded; they were simply finished off with shovels.

But a few, especially the ones who looked healthiest and whose guilt was in doubt—like Davydov—were put in the camp (built in the spring of 1942) above the ravine. Here, because of executions and the rigors of camp life itself, a kind of natural selection developed. The Germans were in no hurry to shoot the survivors: They knew no one would ever get away.

At five-thirty every morning, a gong was sounded. The prisoners dressed quickly, in roughly a minute and a half, and spilled out from all the huts to the shouts of the brigadiers. Grizzled, bony, looking like animals, they quickly fell in to be counted, and then followed the command: "Forward march! Sing!"

That's right. No one took a step in the camp without singing. The *Polizei* made them sing folksongs—"Unhitch the Horses, Boys," and *"Oi,* Galya, Young Galya!"—or "Sadly Sings the Nightingale Nestling"; and they were especially fond of "Dunya-ya, Dunya-ya, Dunya, My Little Cherry." The brigadier himself barked the obscene verses, and the entire column took up the refrain. There were times when the column could not contain its fury and struck up the Soviet Army song "Katyusha," and that precipitated merciless beatings.

Still singing, they would arrive on the central square, line up for breakfast and receive a slice of ersatz bread and a cup of coffee, which was more like lukewarm muddy water.

I asked Davydov, "What did they put the coffee in? Surely they needed some kind of container, didn't they?" He told me that some had bowls from army mess kits, others used empty cans from the trash heap; and many were dying, so the dishware passed along by inheritance.

After breakfast, the prisoners were separated into 20-man brigades and marched off to work, singing as before. What sort of work was it?

Listen to this, and try to picture it.

1. The inmates of the Jews' hut were sent to dig dirt, which they piled on litters and carried to another spot. Guards armed with clubs lined their path on both sides, and

the men had to carry their litters at a run through this passage.

The litters had to be loaded so heavily that they could hardly be lifted, and the Germans hammered away with their clubs, swearing and screaming, *"Schnell! Schnell! Faster!"*—it was not work, but a kind of sheer terror. People fell in their tracks, exhausted, and were at once hustled down to the ravine and shot; or else their skulls were simply smashed with a crowbar. Therefore they ran as long as they had any strength, falling only when they lost consciousness. The crews of Germans tired and were relieved, but the dirt hauling went right on into the night. Thus everybody was kept busy, and the work was strenuous.

2. Certain mysterious structures were being built on a remote stretch of bare ground, and some of the prisoners were sent there. This construction was top secret, so men who went there to work never came back. (Only later was the secret revealed: An experimental soap factory was being organized at Babi Yar to turn the dead into soap, but the Germans never had time to finish it.)

3. Soviet Army units stationed here before the war had left some run-down barracks, and these were being dismantled. The camp administration had decided that they were spoiling the view—blocking off the field of vision. This detail included the "nail-puller" brigade, composed of the feeblest prisoners from the Russian huts; before giving up the ghost, they pulled and straightened rusty nails.

4. Again for the sake of an unobstructed view, all trees were cut down and their stumps uprooted both inside the camp and around it; the Germans felt better when the ground was bare all around.

5. A small group of skilled workmen—carpenters, shoemakers, tailors and mechanics—worked in repair shops,

serving the guards and doing odd jobs around the camp. These were the "soft" jobs, and to land one of them was considered a great stroke of luck.

6. The "outside" brigades were transported under heavy guard to No. 5 Institute Street, where the Gestapo headquarters were being built; sometimes they were sent to clear away rubble.

7. Women were used in lieu of horses. Groups of them were harnessed to carts, and they pulled heavy loads or hauled filth to the dump.

The camp was run by *Sturmbannfuehrer* Paul von Radomski, a German of about 55, who had a hoarse voice and shaven head. He was well nourished but had an elongated, humorless face. He wore horn-rimmed glasses. He usually rode in a small black car, himself at the wheel. On the seat beside him sat his gray-and-black German shepherd Rex, well known to the entire camp because he was trained to rip human flesh. The back seat was occupied by the interpreter Rhein, a *Volksdeutscher*.

Radomski had two deputies: Rieder, known as the "Redhead," and Willy, a sophisticated sadist, very tall and lanky—a specialist in mass shootings.

Below these men were administrative personnel drawn from among the prisoners themselves: the lieutenants and the brigadiers. Especially distinguished was a Czech named Anton, Radomski's favorite and his right-hand man. Everybody knew that whatever Anton suggested to the chief would be done; in fact, Anton was more feared than the chief himself. The brigadier of the women was Lisa Loginova, aged 25, an actress from the Russian Drama Theater and Anton's mistress; she was fully his match in sadism, and would beat the women savagely.

Davydov spoke in detail about that savage existence, or rather, quasi-existence, for at any moment one could die without preliminaries. Most deaths occurred in the evening.

After work, all prisoners were assembled on the square in a horseshoe formation. Then the main event began— consideration of the day's accumulated transgressions. If there had been an escape, it meant a whole brigade would be shot then and there. If Radomski so ordered, they would shoot every tenth or every fifth man in ranks.

Everyone looked at the gate: If they brought in machine guns, it meant there would be a "concert" that day, or an "amateur show," as the *Polizei* ironically called it. Radomski and his aides would come out into the middle of the horseshoe and announce that every fifth man would be shot today.

A savage, silent struggle would break out among the first ten men from the end: Here each prisoner could see which number he would be. Rieder then began counting, and every man froze where he stood, cringing; if he turned out to be a "five," Rieder pulled him out by the arm, and all pleas or entreaties were utterly futile. If a man hung back and shouted, "Sir, sir, have mercy, sir!" Rieder simply shot him where he stood and went on counting.

In no event was it wise to look him in the eye: He might take notice of a man and haul him out irrespective of the count simply because he didn't like him.

The selected prisoners were prodded into the center of the square and ordered, "On your knees!" SS men or *Polizei* then circulated among them, neatly laying out each one with a shot through the base of the skull.

The remaining prisoners were forced to strike up a song as they marched one turn around the square before being sent off to their huts.

242

One time a contingent of prisoners arrived from Poltava. The gong was sounded in the middle of the day; everyone was assembled on the square, and the announcement was made that Ukrainian partisans were about to be shot. Some 60 men kneeled in the middle of the square, their hands behind their backs, with the *Polizei* standing in rows behind them.

Suddenly a young *Polizei* cried out, "I'm not going to shoot!" It turned out that one of the prisoners was his brother. The Germans had arranged this spectacle intentionally so that brother would shoot brother.

A German ran up to the *Polizei* and drew his pistol. Then the young *Polizei* fired, but he was sick at once; then they led him away. He was about nineteen, his murdered brother about 25. All the rest were shot with dumdum bullets for some reason, and their brains flew straight into the faces of the men in line.

Minor offenses drew floggings. A table made in the carpentry shop, with a recess to fit a human body, was brought out. The victim was placed in the recess and pressed in with a plank that covered his head and shoulders, while two hale and hearty numbskulls from among the camp hangers-on diligently flailed away with sticks, which they jokingly called "automatics." To receive 200 "automatics" was sure death.

One of the brigades was found to be one man short during evening roll call. A dog quickly detected him in a latrine, clinging to the underside of a toilet hole. He had meant to wait until night to escape. The lieutenants flogged him on the hollowed table until his flesh came loose in strips, kept on after he was dead and beat him into a paste.

A seventeen-year-old boy went to the garbage heap in

search of something to eat. He was noticed by Radomski himself, who cautiously tiptoed up behind him, drew his revolver, shot him down point-blank, holstered the revolver and walked away, pleased with himself as if he had just killed a stray dog.

Men were shot for standing in the food line a second time; failure to remove one's hat meant a beating with the "automatics"; when there were too many patients in the hospital hut, they were rousted out, laid on the ground and peppered with submachine-gun fire. As for the "drills," these were not even considered punishment, and they went on all the time: "Up! . . . Down! . . . Fish step, march! . . ."

Davydov saw all this with his own eyes. He took the beatings, sang the songs and stood in line with the rest to be counted by Rieder; but the fatal number never came around to him.

Radomski invented his own unique method of punishment. Prisoners were ordered to climb a tree and tie a rope to the crown. Other prisoners were ordered to saw through the tree. Then the rope was pulled, the tree crashed down and the climbers were killed. Radomski always came out to witness the procedure personally, and people say that it sent him into gales of laughter. Those not killed in the fall were dispatched by Anton with a shovel.

The quickest to die were the Jews and half-Jews from the Jews' hut, whom the Germans, with their characteristic "humor," called the *Himmel-Kommando* (heavenly crew). But the other prisoners clung to life with all their might, fighting for food and clothing.

No clothes were issued. Anything in decent condition—boots, coats, jackets—was stripped from new arrivals, and the *Polizei* bartered it all for homemade vodka in the city.

For this reason, every prisoner tried to peel the clothes off corpses.

Food was a more complicated matter. Besides the morning coffee—discolored water—and bread, some watery soup was issued during the day. One could not live long on this, of course, while doing such back-breaking labor. But sometimes there were food parcels from the outside. Women lurked around the edge of the camp, spotted their relatives and threw them bread across the barbed wire. Also, if they gave the *Polizei* at the gate a quart or two of homemade vodka, he would sometimes pass a little bag of cereal or potatoes along to a prisoner.

In the morning a special detail was picked to go out under guard along the 2,200-volt electrified fence and, using long poles, remove the dogs, cats and crows electrocuted during the night; occasionally there was even a hare.

All this was brought into the camp, and lively barter would begin: a hunk of cat for a pinch of cereal, and so forth. Potato peelings could be filched from the garbage heap. Prisoners pooled their scraps and cooked up a community soup on the stove, and it was thanks to this that Davydov and others like him managed to pull through.

No one, including him, could guess how long the end would be put off. The craving for life persists within us as long as we breathe. New prisoners came, others died—by themselves, on the camp square or in the ravine. The machine went on grinding.

GRANDFATHER, THE ANTIFASCIST

We lived, as it were, in the kingdom of the dead. Rumors provided our only news of what happened in the world, and there was no telling which ones were true. The German newspapers could not be believed at all; they were only good for reading between the lines. Someone, somewhere, was listening to the radio; someone knew everything, but not we. After a time, however, we didn't need a radio; we had Grandfather.

He would come running home from the bazaar or from some acquaintance's place, all excited, and report which town had been taken from the Germans on what day, and how many planes had been shot down.

"No, they'll never hold out!" he would shout. "Our boys will smash them. Mark my words! Lord have mercy—that I might live to see the day!"

After the fiasco on our last bartering excursion, Grandfather had been scared out of his wits. Now he hated the fascists with the most furious hatred he could muster.

The dining room for the aged had closed down long ago,

and it was pointless for Grandfather to try to find work as a watchman somewhere else; the pay was not enough to buy anything. One day he took a notion that Mother and I were a millstone around his neck. He promptly divided up all the junk in the house, taking most for himself, and declared:

"You will live by yourselves on your side of the wall, and I'm going to barter these things and find a rich wife."

Mother only shook her head. Now and then she would knock on his door and hand him two or three pancakes made of peelings, which he grabbed and ate greedily. It was obvious that he was dreadfully hungry, that nobody wanted the rags he was taking to the bazaar, that he wanted so much to go on living and was clinging to whatever he could. He envied my business and decided to sell cigarettes himself. He dug up all the patches of ground around the house, even our little yard, and sowed tobacco everywhere; he plucked the leaves, dried them, strung them on a cord and cut them up with a knife; he pounded the stems to crumbs in a mortar and sold them by the glass as shag. And this saved him.

The old Gardener would come to see him now and then. Grandfather would treat him to linden tea without sugar and tell him how fine it had been in the old days, under Soviet rule; what a big shot he had been then, owning a cow and fattening pigs—if only they hadn't died of distemper—and what sausages Grandmother used to prepare for Easter!

"I've worked all my life," Grandfather complained. "I could have lived on my pension alone, if it hadn't been for these cutthroats, thieves, idiots! But our boys will come back, mark my words!"

His hatred mounted in proportion to his hunger. Lyalya Engstrem's grandfather died of old age. My grandfather ran home in joyful excitement:

"There you are! Aha! He was a *Volksdeutscher,* but he died anyway!"

An apartment in the house next door, where Yelena Pavlovna lived, was left empty by evacuees. Some aristocratic-looking *Volksdeutschen* moved in and Grandfather was the first to see them.

"Oh, you vipers, you bourgeois pigs; the Soviet regime didn't whip you hard enough, but wait; you're fattening too soon, your time will run out!"

TO KILL A FISH

The more I think of it, the more it appears that the intelligent, the just and the really good people who come after us will find it hard to understand how this could have happened; to comprehend how the very idea of murder—mass murder—could begin in the dark recesses and convolutions of the brain of an ordinary human being: one born of a mother, fed at the breast, educated in a school. An ordinary human being like millions of others, with hands and feet, with fingernails that grow and (since a man) with hair growing on his cheeks; one who sorrows, rejoices, smiles, looks at himself in the mirror, tenderly loves a woman, burns his fingers with a match—in short, ordinary in all things, except for a pathological lack of imagination.

A normal human being, at the sight of another's suffering, even at the thought of it, will, in his imagination, see it all happening to himself, or will, at least, feel spiritual pain.

Fish was sold at the bazaar sometimes. We couldn't afford it, of course. But in my constant, frantic preoccupation with how to get something to eat, I thought, "Why not go fishing myself?"

251

I had gone fishing with the boys before. This is a great pleasure, as you know. True, I felt sorry for the fish. But I usually put them in a bag or kept them in a pail, where they skipped about until they went to sleep; and I didn't think about them too closely. And how good they were later in the soup—a dream!

My fishing rod was a rudimentary affair with a rusty hook, but I decided it would do for a start; I dug worms in the evening and was off to the Dnieper at the crack of dawn.

There was a wide, lush meadow between Kurenevka and the Dnieper, beginning directly beyond the embankment. In the spring it was often flooded, which turned it into a sea stretching to the horizon. I walked through the grass a long time and got my feet soaking wet, but hunger and the hope of catching a lot of fish inspired me.

The banks of the Dnieper are sandy, with magnificent beaches and cliffs, and the water is a brownish color. There was absolutely nothing here to remind one of the war or the fascists. And it occurred to me that the Dnieper was probably just as it had been in the days when its channel was plied by the ships of Prince Oleg, or by the caravans of merchant vessels sailing the vast route "from the Varangians to the Greeks." These and similar thoughts keep recurring many times in one's life and finally become stale. But I was only thirteen then.

I cast the line, put the little box of worms in my pocket and started following the float downstream. The Dnieper's current is swift. I could take two courses of action: either stay in one spot and keep casting over again every minute, or walk downstream after the float.

I must have walked more than a half a mile before reaching an impassable stretch of rushes and rose willows, but I had caught nothing. I ran back and covered the whole stretch again—with the same result. In this manner I ran back and forth like a fool, growing peevish and jumpy, but it was evident that I was doing something wrong; either the sinker was poorly hitched, or the place was wrong, or the bait. The sun was high and it was growing warm, but I hadn't had one bite; it was as if all the fish in the Dnieper had died.

Upset, hungry, almost crying, I knew that the best time for a bite was hopelessly gone. I decided to try my luck in a small pool amid the rushes, though I was afraid my hook would catch in the roots, and it was the only one I had.

This little pool was isolated and only indirectly affected by the current. Its water moved, barely perceptibly, in a circle. I did not know how deep it was, but took a guess, put my sinker as high as I could and cast my line. The float began to quiver almost immediately.

The instant it dipped below the surface I yanked and pulled the hook out of the water—empty. Something had eaten my worm. This was good—the hunt was on. I baited the hook, threw the line again and the game in the depths began anew.

But whatever I did, no matter how I baited the hook, it invariably came up empty. The fish was slyer than I. I was hot now and wanted so badly to catch something—if only a minnow no bigger than my little finger!

Suddenly, as I tugged, I felt something heavy. I was horrified by the thought that the hook had finally snagged, but in the same instant I realized that it was a fish. Impatient, never considering that it could still break away, I pulled so hard that it flew up high over my head. Triumphantly, I plunged into the grass where it was thrashing about. "Aha, smart alec, foxy! You've played your last game! I got you this time!" What a happy moment! Anyone who has ever caught a fish will know what I mean.

It was a perch, and at first it looked bigger to me than it was. It was a lovely one, with green stripes and bright red fins, resilient, shiny as glass and fit for a picture!

But luck was against me: The perch had swallowed the worm too greedily and deeply. The line hung out of its mouth, and the hook was caught somewhere in the stomach. I clutched the springy, wriggling fish firmly with one hand and, maneuvering with the other, tried to free the hook from its stomach, but it seemed to have caught on a bone. I kept yanking—tugging harder and harder, and the fish kept thrashing its tail, opening its mouth and staring at me with bulging eyes. Losing patience, I pulled with all my might; the line broke, and the hook remained in the fish. At that moment I was imagining that someone was pulling a hook out of me, and I broke into a cold sweat.

I know perfectly well that this was a child's "soft-headedness." I would readily submit to ridicule from any fisherman. But I was alone there at the river's edge; it was a fine day, the sun was warm, the water sparkled and the dragonflies settled on the rushes; and I had nothing to fish with.

I threw the perch as far out on the grass as I could and sat down to wait for it to go to sleep. From time to time I heard a rustling and slapping in the grass: It was still jumping. Then it was quiet. I walked over and touched it with my toe, and it began to twitch in the dust, crushed with dirt and bereft of its beauty.

I walked away, lost in thought, and waited a long time. Finally I lost my patience completely and went back, but it was still jumping; this was beginning to torment me in earnest. I grabbed the perch by the tail and started beating its head on the ground, but it opened its mouth, stared and wouldn't die: The ground was too soft.

In a rage I swung it over my head and hurled it to the ground as hard as I could, so that it bounced like a ball, but it continued to wriggle and leap. I went to look for a stick, found a crooked twig and jabbed it at the perch's head, but it continued to stare at me with its dirt-covered, mindless, fishy eyes. I jabbed harder, pierced its head with the twig, which went all the way through, and finally the fish lay still.

Only then did I remember that I had a pocket knife. I ripped the perch open, not without some trembling, and poked around in it for a long time, turning my nose from the strong smell. Somewhere in the slippery entrails I found my rusty hook with the worm intact. By now the perch looked so battered and disgusting that I might have pulled it out of a garbage can. I wondered: To what had life clung so tenaciously? And why, when the fish was so elastic, so ingeniously designed with green stripes and red fins, did it have to be destroyed so clumsily? I held in my hands the pitiful, stinking shreds of fish, and I knew that I'd never be able to eat them after all this, no matter how hungry I was.

I was just beginning to get acquainted with life then. Later I killed many animals, both large and small; it was especially unpleasant to kill horses, but I killed and ate them nonetheless. But that came later.

It was a sunny day, and while I was fussing with the perch there were machines that were grinding on at Babi Yar and all over the continent. What I am telling about has very little to do with killing animals. I am talking about imagination. If you have any, you'll find it far from easy even to kill a fish.

A CHAPTER OF DOCUMENTS

NOTICE

It is most strictly forbidden to help Russian prisoners of war to escape in any way whatever—by giving them either shelter or food.

Violation of this rule will be punishable by imprisonment or death.

STADTKOMMISSAR ROGAUSCH [1]
Kiev, May 8, 1942

All able-bodied inhabitants of Kiev between the ages of 14 and 55 are obliged to work at the jobs specified in their notices from the Labor Exchange. **ABLE-BODIED PERSONS MAY DEPART FROM KIEV ONLY WITH THE PERMISSION OF THE DISTRICT COUNCILS.**
In the event of unauthorized departure from Kiev or failure to appear in response to a summons from the Labor Exchange, the guilty will be tried FOR SABOTAGE within seven days of their willful defection, **AND THEIR PROPERTY WILL BE CONFISCATED.** [2]

May, 1942.

NOW PLAYING
AT THE MOVIE THEATERS:

GLORIA—*That's What Men Are Like, Thrice Married.*

METROPOL—*First Love, A Wedding Night for Three.*

ECHO—*Yes, I Love You, Marriage with Obstacles.*

LUX—*Woman with Intentions, Somersault.*

ORION—*Dance Around the World, Only Love.*

RECRUITS WANTED FOR UKRAINIAN POLIZEI

Requirements: Ages 18 to 45, height no less than 5 ft. 4 in., irreproachable moral and political past. [3]

OPERA, 1942 SEASON
(For Germans only)

OPERAS: *Madame Butterfly, Traviata, The Bells of Corneville, Pique Dame, Faust.*

BALLETS: *Coppelia, Swan Lake.*

RENAMING OF STREETS:

Kreshchatik Avenue to von Eihornstrasse.
Shevchenko Boulevard to Rovnowehrstrasse.
Kirov Street to Doctor Todt Street.

NEW STREETS:

Hitler Street, Goering Street and Mussolini Street.

"LIBERATED UKRAINE WELCOMES REICHSMINISTER ROSENBERG."

Under this headline the newspaper presented a

lengthy and ecstatic report on how the *Reichsmin-ister* of the occupied eastern regions attended a din-ner with the General-Kommissar, inspected the sights of Kiev, attended the ballet *Coppelia* and visited a farm in the vicinity of the city, "where he talked with the peasants and learned at first hand that they were ready to cope with their tasks." [4]

NOTICE

Anyone who directly or indirectly assists or harbors bandits, saboteurs, vagrants or fugitive prisoners, or who gives them food or other aid, will be pun-ished with death.

All their property will be confiscated.

The penalty is the same for those who know the whereabouts of bandits, saboteurs or fugitive pris-oners and do not immediately inform the village elders, the nearest *Polizei* inspector, the army com-mand or the German agricultural director.

Those whose information helps in the capture or destruction of members of any criminal band, vag-rants, saboteurs or fugitive prisoners will be re-warded with 1,000 rubles, or with priority in the issuance of food or with the right to receive a plot of land or to enlarge his holdings.

MILITARY COMMANDANT OF THE UKRAINE

REICHSKOMMISSAR OF THE UKRAINE[5]

Rovno, June 1942.

Headlines of
Reports from the Fuehrer's Headquarters:
"STARVATION AND TERROR IN
LENINGRAD."

*"OFFENSIVE PROCEEDS ACCORDING TO
PLAN. LARGE ENEMY FORCES DE-
STROYED ON THE DON."*

*"SOVIETS CONTINUE TO SUSTAIN HEAVY
LOSSES."*

*"YESTERDAY THE SOVIETS AGAIN FRUIT-
LESSLY ATTACKED THE CENTRAL AND
SOUTHERN SECTORS OF THE EASTERN
FRONT."*[6]

Market prices in the autumn of 1942: one pound of
bread—100 rubles; one glass of salt—200 rubles; one
pound of butter—1,450 rubles; one pound of lard—
1,700 rubles.

The wages of workers and office employees: 300
to 500 rubles a month.

AT THE MOVIE THEATERS TODAY
ESHNAPUR TIGER

A big, excellent adventure film.
On the screen for the first time, REAL LAND-
SCAPES OF INDIA.

Starring LA-YANA, a favorite dancer of exceptional beauty. SENSATION! MUCH-AWAITED
EVENT! ADVENTURE. DRAMA.

At the Gloria and Lux Theaters, starting Friday.
INDIAN TOMB
Starring LA-YANA.

Even more powerful, dramatic and gripping, this
second part of ESHNAPUR TIGER is a complete
film in itself.

See it at the Gloria and Lux Theaters. [7]

CHAPTER XXXIV

IN THE MIDST OF
TRAPS

I went to see *Indian Tomb* and landed in a raid.

Trucks zoomed into our square at top speed, and Germans, dogs and *Polizei* poured out of them. A cordon was set up. The women in the marketplace screamed and scattered in all directions; baskets fell off counters, and potatoes rolled all over. Some managed to elude the cordon, others did not; and the crowd surged in waves from one exit to another, where *Arbeitskarten* were already being checked.

What did this mean to me? I was under fourteen; that is, eligible for work but not for Germany. I sat down on the threshold of a booth, hunched down to look smaller than I was (just in case), and observed the scene.

They were taking mostly women, the various village girls who had come to the bazaar. These girls were quickly loaded into covered trucks, where they wailed, shook the canvas and shoved their hands through the openings: "Oh, Mama, help! Save me!" One disheveled woman shouted, "I've got an infant at home. Look, I've got milk!" The *Polizei* formed a line and moved across the bazaar, flush-

261

ing out the strays. But they did not touch the women who were obviously old and feeble, nor did they say anything when they saw me. The raid was over as suddenly as it had begun. The trucks departed with a full load. The ground was littered with crushed potatoes and broken bottles, and splashed with milk.

I had my wages in my pocket in new Ukrainian money, and I was more excited about going to the movie theater than about any raids.

Soviet money had gone out of circulation in one day: it was simply announced that Soviet money was no longer valid. Ukrainian money, printed in Rovno, appeared in its place. True, there were announcements that the Soviet money would be redeemed in due time, but such notices did not make it so. This, in my opinion, was one of the most uncomplicated monetary reforms in the world—just throw your old money into the garbage, and that's it. The new money was printed on very bad paper, almost like notebook paper, and was decorated with swastikas. On one side all the words were written in German; on the other side they were in German too, but at the very bottom stood the Ukrainian words: "Odin karbovanets" (one ruble), or "Desyat karbovantsiv" (ten rubles). And this was called Ukrainian money.

At the Gloria (formerly the October) Theater I bought a ticket and entered. Suddenly I heard a happy cry, "Tolik!"

I turned, and it was Shurka Matsa. He threw himself at me, hugging and squeezing me, and I too was very glad that he was still alive—that nothing had happened to him. He waved his hands, charged out to the lobby and brought back a bottle of soda and two paper cups, and we poured and drank it right there in our seats, feeling like real men— dear old comrades to whom friendship is sacred.

·"Nobody knows me in Podol," Shurka related. "They all think I'm a Ukrainian."

"What are you doing with yourself?"

"Same as before. Selling silver rubles left from Tsarist times."

"Did you know that Bolik came back?" I exclaimed. "He ran for it, right under the eyes of the guards, and he said a machine-gunner very nearly got him! The minute he reached home, they nabbed him and he was off to Germany. This time he skipped straight out of the transfer camp and came home again."

"He just can't be killed!" Shurka shook with laughter. "No matter where they take him, he comes back! But they'll get him."

"Not if he stays in his cellar, catching mice."

"Wha-at?"

"He sets up mousetraps."

The lights went out and people began shushing us. The newsreel started. It was called *Come to Lovely Germany!*

Brisk and cheerful lads and girls, their chests out, seeming to gaze enthusiastically into the future, vigorously climbed aboard a freight car. They gazed reflectively through the open doors as forests, fields and glades drifted by. They sang Ukrainian songs to the rhythm of the wheels. And here was lovely Germany—amazing cleanliness everywhere, little white cottages, excellent roads. Laughing with joy, the newcomers donned the new clothing issued to them and pulled on their shiny boots. And here the fellows were valiantly driving teams of sleek horses, and the girls were hugging fat pedigreed cows. It was evening. The sun was setting. Now for some recreation! They arranged themselves along the edge of an enchanting pond and sang delightfully the Ukrainian folksong, "The Moon Is Shining, Shining

263

Brightly." And the good-natured German boss, moderately respectable and moderately genial, quietly appeared, sat down, smiled affectionately and listened to their wistful song in a fatherly way.

I hadn't been to a movie since Kreshchatik was Kreshchatik. Therefore, every scene is lodged firmly in my memory, especially *The Indian Tomb*.

I watched it trustfully at first, then gradually grew wary. Thoughts came to mind which the film was never intended to stir—tangential, unexpected thoughts. Suddenly I was choking with hatred.

Behind the rajahs, the likable German engineers and the dazzling European beauties that flashed on the screen, I spotted an endless string of slaves building that thrice-cursed, absolutely meaningless tomb. They were subordinate to the main story, merely part of the background, but I saw enough to set me shaking with anger. I saw right through that film.

Already they were reaching for India, photographing its actual landscape. They—all the exploiters of the world, the slave-drivers, rajahs, kings and rulers—led their own special lives; and way off in the background, of minor importance, were the slaves, toiling away in crews.

Shurka and I came out of the theater as sullen as hyenas. German soldiers were strolling along the sidewalks of Podol, their arms around the waists of local girls. The girls were done up in the latest fashion, their wavy hair falling carelessly to their shoulders, their loose, beltless coats open, their hands invariably in their pockets. Two couples parted company just as we approached, and we heard the following exchange between the girls.

"What did he give you?"

"Two marks, a tangerine and one candy!"

"Yeah? Well, mine gave me three tangerines!"

Shurka shrugged contemptuously:

"They're only amateurs. The real ones are in the Young Pioneer Palace—the *Deutsche Haus,* a full-fledged whorehouse; and there's another at 72 Saksagansky Street. Listen, do you happen to have 3,000 marks? There's a pimp I know who's selling a sack of Soviet money. He thinks it'll never be any good and wants 3,000 for the lot. Shall we take it?"

"I've only got 200, my whole pay."

"Too bad. Oh, let him take his money and stuff it. Will we ever live to see our army come back?"

The showcases carried caricatures of Red Army men and Stalin. In one picture he was shown as a falling clay giant, with Roosevelt and Churchill trying in vain to prop him up.

We looked and yawned.

"They hanged some fellows in May Day Park," said Shurka. "They shouted, 'Long live Stalin!' They had 'Partisan' labels pinned to them, but the next morning these labels had been replaced with others saying, 'Victims of fascist terror.' The Germans were as furious as tigers, and they posted *Polizei* to stand guard. The morning after that the corpses were gone, and the *Polizei* were hanging in their places. Think I'll go now. Tell Bolik I'll be around."

"Where do you live?" I called after him, wondering why he was walking away so fast.

"Over there!" he waved. "Run for it, there's a raid on! Regards to Bolik!"

It was only then that I noticed the covered trucks roaring down the street and the people scurrying through backyards and darting into entranceways. But I leaned against a wall, not very troubled—I was still under fourteen.

HOW HORSES ARE TURNED INTO SAUSAGE

Degtyarev was a heavy-set man in his fifties, slightly bent and dumpy, but still agile and vigorous, with graying hair, a big, meaty nose and knotty hands.

His clothes were abominable: greasy jacket, dirty, patched pants, a cap as flat as a pancake and shabby boots adorned with manure.

His most frequent expressions were "a pound of smoke," meaning "nonsense"; "perturbation," meaning "a change of regimes"; and "devaluation" or "burned by devaluation," which meant "losing your shirt in the currency reform."

I reached work at six in the morning, and the first thing Degtyarev did (quite properly, I might add) was feed me up to the ears.

His home was clean and cozy, full of white napkins, coverlets and snowy linen on the bed. Amid all that cleanliness, he looked like a grizzly *muzhik* who had strayed into an expensive hotel.

I gulped down the fatty borsch with mutton, the milk kasha and the doughnuts which an old woman there kept shoving at me. Degtyarev, with curiosity and some pity, watched me stuff myself while he briefed me on his business.

He had owned a small sausage factory long, long ago,

but the Revolution had taken that away. Then came NEP (Lenin's New Economic Policy in the 1920's), and once again he came into possession of what was almost a factory, though smaller. But it was later taken away. Now he had only a workshop—an underground one, since a license cost an arm and a leg. So at any moment this, too, could be taken away.

"Revolutions, insurgencies, perturbations, and we're supposed to live somehow! As I see it, if you're lucky, you dance; if you're not, it's a pound of smoke anyway! The neighbors know all about me, and I buy them off with bones. But others musn't know. If anybody asks what you do, just say, 'I help around the house.' Like a day laborer in the old days. You'll drive the horses, because if I do everyone points at me and says, 'There goes Degtyarev with another nag for sausage.' "

I put my cap on and we headed for the school on the square. This was a boarding stop for the two-horse hay-wagons that now did the work of streetcars, buses and taxis. Women with baskets, *muzhiks* from the villages and a few men wearing felt hats climbed on, quarreling, handing up their sacks and bags, sitting down and hanging their legs over the sides of the big wagon.

We squeezed in among some baskets of radishes. The driver cracked his whip, and we were off along Podol. We were going faster than the wind—and the bushes fairly flew past. I was shaking, but proudly aware that I was a paying passenger (usually I either stowed away or else walked, but this time Degtyarev had paid my fare, making me a law-abiding citizen). With feelings of superiority, I watched downcast figures dragging along the sidewalk in torn sweaters and rotting trench coats, some in galoshes, and others barefoot.

Zhitny market was a human sea, the womb of Podol (I had already read Emile Zola, having found his works in the garbage somewhere). The marketwomen were screeching, the beggars whining and the children chanting, "Who wants water, co-old water?" At the gate stood a skinny, or rather a skeletal (a *shkiletik,* as our people say) little girl, about ten years' old, who was selling pastry off a plate: "Fresh pastries, very tasty, buy them, please!" My God, what a scene!

A colossal flea market stretched along the Nizhny Val —endless rows of traders: "What's this?"—"A coat!"— "You call this a coat?"—"It's a fine coat! Warm as a coffin!"

Degtyarev pushed his way purposefully through the crowds. I clung to the hem of his jacket to avoid being left behind, and almost knocked down an old woman who was selling one spoon. She was standing there and holding out her single steel (if only it were silver!) spoon. My God, what a scene!

The big plaza was full of carts. Manure and trampled hay lay underfoot, cows mooed and pigs squealed. "What'll you take for it?"—"Seventy thousand!"—"You can choke on it!"—"Give me sixty!" Degtyarev was only pricing the pigs for old times' sake. What he got hold of finally was an old, lame, mangy gelding. The gelding's lips hung loosely, dripping spittle; its mane was full of burrs. It stood there with its head down, its walleyes half closed, ignoring the flies that swarmed around its muzzle. "I'll take it for five!" —"What are you saying? It's a stallion!"—"It has a head and four ears, what about six?"—"You can have it for seven, mister, and it'll pull anything you like—a fiery stallion! You can take it over the jumps at the hippodrome!"

Degtyarev bargained furiously and doggedly, waving his

money, pressing for a deal, spitting at the price, walking away and coming back. But his adversary proved to be not so dumb as he looked. They came within ten rubles or so of agreement. Then at last the reins were passed to me, and with some difficulty we made our way out of that seething caldron. At the wagon stop, Degtyarev gave me my instructions:

"You can mount him, if he doesn't fall down. But for God's sake don't ride him past the *Polizei*. I'll be waiting for you."

I led the gelding to the curb, climbed on his back and dug my heels into his sides. His spine was like a saw. He dragged along slowly, limping and trying to stop, while I hit him with a switch and did everything I could to keep him going. Finally I took pity on him, got off and led him by the reins.

For a long time we wound through quiet side streets, half overgrown with grass. I called him Gray, and I found myself liking him because he never tried to kick or bite. I began to let him graze beside the fences, even letting go of the reins, and I told him, "Eat over here, Gray; the grass is better!"

He raised his head, looked at me and walked over: an understanding, sedate, intelligent, kindly old fellow. We were friends by now.

Degtyarev was waiting for me in Koshitsev Alley. We were there for a long time, poking our noses out, waiting for the street to be absolutely empty. Then we ran for it, chasing Gray into the yard and right into the shed.

"Give him some hay so he won't whinny!" Degtyarev ordered.

Gray showed some animation at the sight of the hay

and began munching and snorting; evidently he hadn't expected such a windfall.

Degtyarev was in good spirits and full of energy. He used a whetstone to sharpen two knives made of steel strips, bound with friction tape at one end for handles. From the hallway he took an ax, a tub and a pail, and we went to the shed, followed by two cats that yowled and darted in front of us so excitedly you would have thought we were bringing them meat.

Gray was munching the hay, suspecting nothing. Degtyarev turned him around, set his head toward the light and told me to take the reins and hold on tight. Panting a little, he bent down and tied the horse's legs. Evidently Gray was used to everything in this life, for he stood there indifferently, not resisting.

Degtyarev then stood up in front of the horse's face, moved it a little, like a barber, so it would be straight, took a fast swing and struck the horse in the forehead with the ax.

Gray didn't move a muscle, and Degtyarev struck again and a third time, so that the skull caved in. After this the horse sank down to its knees and rolled over on its side, and its legs shot out straight and started to tremble. Degtyarev tossed the ax aside, lunged at the horse like a hawk, sat on it and barked, "The tub!"

I dragged the tub over. Degtyarev gathered up the horse's quivering head with both hands. I shoved the tub under the neck, and Degtyarev slashed the throat with a knife. Blood gushed out of the throat in a rapid stream; it flowed like water from a faucet, in spurts, and the red foam rose in the tub. Degtyarev clung to the horse's trembling

271

body with all his might to prevent the blood from missing the tub. His hands were blood-soaked by now, and there were drops of blood on his meaty face. The way he crawled on top of that horse, rising and falling with its body while clinging tightly, he looked somewhat like a spider who had caught a fly.

I hiccoughed for some unknown reason. Degtyarev raised his bespattered face.

"What are you scared of? You'll get used to it, you just haven't seen much yet. A horse—that's a pound of smoke! Roll that log over here."

All the blood had flowed out; it stopped as suddenly as if someone had shut off the faucet. Degtyarev turned the horse onto its back and propped a log on either side; the four legs, slightly splayed, pointed at the ceiling. Degtyarev made cuts around them at the pasterns and straight cuts from these to the belly; then we began to pull off the skin. It slipped off, as if coming unglued; we only had to help it along with a knife now and then. Once the skin was gone the carcass ceased to be a living creature and turned into meat—the kind that hangs from hooks in the butcher shop.

Now the cats crept in and latched onto the meat, each one grabbing what it could, gnawing off shreds and yowling viciously. Degtyarev paid no attention to them—he was in such a hurry he didn't even wipe the sweat off his face. And so the four of us started pulling old Gray to pieces.

Degtyarev piled the hoofs, the head and the hide in a corner, opened the belly with one sweep and dug out the entrails. Before I knew it the liver was flying into one pail and the lungs into another. The legs and breast came off at the first touch, as if there were no bones in them. Degtyarev was a master at dividing a carcass. Wet and sticky, his hair clinging to his red forehead like gray icicles, he nodded toward the shapeless pile of meat, "Carry it into the house!"

It was an ingenious house indeed. In front were the porch and rooms, as one would expect; but behind these was another room, a separate one, entered only through a narrow opening in a partition that was concealed by a pile of junk so that no one would ever guess there was a door.

On big metal-sheathed tables, we separated the meat from the bones and sprinkled it with salt. The knives were like razors—I cut myself a hundred times—and the salt stung fiercely. So after that I went around with rags on my fingers all the time. Degtyarev consoled me:

"That's the way I started, as a laborer. I'm feeding you, but nobody gave me a damned thing to eat; I worked for the training alone. You've got a head on your shoulders, so learn, and I'll make a man of you. You'll learn the vocation of sausage-maker, and that's not to be sneezed at; you'll never be down and out, you'll survive all perturbations! Don't ever try to be a minister of state, they get shot; be a humble sausage-maker!"

And learn I did.

There was a meat grinder screwed to the floor in the middle of the room. It was about the height of a man, with two handles and a funnel as big as an end table. Degtyarev knocked on the wall and the old woman came in. She was flabby and phlegmatic and had a pale peasant face. Wheezing, she climbed on a stool and began pushing the meat into the funnel with a rolling pin. We reached for the cranks and the machine began to stutter and scrape, its old gears rattling. I was not very strong after half-starving for so long, and my boss did most of the grinding. He labored like an ox, breathing heavily, turning the crank mightily. It was hard work. I was gasping for breath, and at times I was not pushing the crank—the crank was pulling me.

273

The ground meat plopped into a pail. When the meat was all ground, Degtyarev tumbled it into a trough and sprinkled it with salt, pepper, crushed garlic and pinches of some white crystals.

"That's saltpeter," he explained, "for the color."

"Isn't it harmful?"

"Damned if I know. Anyway, people eat it and no one's died yet. I don't eat sausage myself and advise you not to. Now we pour the water in; two pails of meat will absorb one pail of water, and there's your weight and your profit!"

I was amazed. After putting on aprons, we kneaded the ground meat in water, just as housewives scrub laundry on a washboard. And the more we rubbed, the more water was absorbed. My eyes went bleary again.

I struck on something in the ground meat and cut myself: a piece of tin.

"The funnel is cracking up inside the meat grinder," Degtyarev said worriedly. "Go and bandage your finger so it won't bleed."

"Are people going to eat that?"

"Quiet. They can do as they like. They don't have to."

The injector, which looked like a red fire bucket laid on its side, also had a crank, gears, and a long pipe at one end. After packing the injector with ground meat, Degtyarev turned the handle and pushed, while I slipped a casing onto the pipe and tied up the end when it was full.

We worked for several hours, like a crew on a conveyer belt, and ended up hemmed in by gray rings of sausage. But the blood sausage turned out to be the most unpleasant: The mash oozed out of the injector, which had leftover blood from the last time. It was so rancid and malodorous you could hardly breathe; and the end of the job was nowhere in sight. My hands were covered with slop and blood. When it was finally over, I tottered into the yard and stood there breathing fresh air for a long time.

Degtyarev labored on like a demon. There was a stove with a walled-in boiler in the corner. It was full of green, stinking brine left from previous cookings. He tumbled the sausages into the boiler so that they would turn red by cooking. Then we strung them on sticks and hauled them out to a smokehouse—disguised as a privy—in the kitchen garden.

Late at night we hauled the last sausages—hot and fragrant—out of the smokehouse. We packed them in baskets, covering them with sheets of *Novoye Ukrainskoye slovo.* I can't even remember how Degtyarev got me to my makeshift cot. I slept like a log all night, but he shook me awake when it was barely light outside.

"To the bazaar, the bazaar! The early bird catches the worm!"

We carried our baskets to the wagon stop on yokes balanced on our shoulders, then took them to Podol, where we sold them to marketwomen in a dark, dirty yard. Degtyarev came away with bulging pockets. We went again to the flea market, where he exchanged whispers with various characters, then walked away for a while, leaving me at a signpost. He came back with his pockets reduced and asked me slyly, "Ever see gold money?"

I never had. He took me behind a locker and brought out a handkerchief tied into a little bundle. Inside were four ten-ruble pieces of Tsarist mintage. He let me hold one of them.

"For one horse," he said cheerfully. "Everything we earned."

Dumbfounded, I clutched the tiny coin that represented all that was left of old Gray. I appreciated Degtyarev's confidence because there had been decrees ordering the surrender of gold a long time before. For possession of gold, or failure to report such possession, one could be shot.

"Through all revolutions, wars and perturbations, it's only with this that you'll never be lost. All the rest is a pound of smoke!" Degtyarev said. "You'll understand when you grow up. Take my advice—stick to this business, and you'll live to remember old Degtyarev more than once! Now let's go bargaining for a new racehorse."

I worked hard and furiously at Degtyarev's. Now I had to do the whole job of delivering the baskets to the market-women, for Degtyarev had already attracted too much attention with his baskets. He gave me carfare, but I saved the money by riding free or hanging onto a streetcar. The teamsters chased me off their wagons, lashing me with their whips. The baskets made maneuvering difficult. Once I fell off a truck and a crowd gathered. I became very ragged and was always fidgety and touchy, like a stray kitten.

One day, while cleaning up the shop, I mustered up the courage to steal a ring of sausage which I hid in the snow under the window. Degtyarev always counted each sausage, and so I shook all evening, even though I had filched it before the count. When I was leaving for home I dug under the snow and—no sausage. My heart sank into my boots. Degtyarev would surely throw me out. Then I took another look and noticed cats' footprints in the snow. Oh, those damned wretches—I robbed Degtyarev, and they robbed me. So I never tasted the sausage. Degtyarev gave me four of old Gray's bones the first day, and after that he gave me a bone or two from each horse. But you couldn't get much soup out of them. Horsemeat, in general, is tough and tasteless.

I'VE BEEN VERY LUCKY

Yes, I considered myself very lucky. I worked hard but had enough to eat and came home with bones besides. It was worse for Mother. At the factory she only got a plate of soup once a day. Grandfather made the smartest move—he began paying court to a woman.

He had wooed the collective-farm women at the bazaar long and gallantly, plugging his status as householder and master. But the old single women had cottages of their own in the countryside and did not want to move to the starving city, even for such a dashing bridegroom as he.

Grandfather soon realized this and understood that if the mountain would not come to Mohammed, Mohammed would have to go to the mountain. He hurriedly fell in love, therefore, with a single collective-farm woman named Granny Natalka from the village of Litvinovka. He locked his room and went off to the village to woo her.

Grandfather diplomatically reckoned that Granny Natalka would make borsch and doughnuts, serve him his meals and throw in a little homemade vodka on Saturdays, but he forgot that a contract worked two ways. Granny Natalka, just as crafty as he, was counting on him to do the plowing, the sowing, the harvesting and the threshing. Grandfather Semerik's visit to Litvinovka, therefore, ended up in a complete misunderstanding—it was one continuous dogfight.

This went on for several months because Grandfather still clung desperately to his hope of eating borsch and kasha every day, but at the age of 72, he could not plow; and Granny Natalka, deeply hurt, threw him out with a crash. He found solace in the fact that he had managed to get acquainted with everyone in Litvinovka. More and more often now, the collective farmers would come to spend the night at his place, some paying him with potatoes and some with a glass of peas. These payments became his livelihood. Then he became envious of me once more and wanted Degtyarev to take him on as a second worker, but nothing came of it—after all, what kind of a worker would he have made?

Then suddenly Degtyarev vanished.

I showed up early in the morning, as always; but the old lady, looking worried, told me to go home. She said that Degtyarev had gone out on business and would be back tomorrow. But he did not come back the next day, nor the day after. Finally, carrying a big basket, he came for me himself and said excitedly, "Hurry up, let's get to work!"

In the basket there were fresh fish he had contracted to smoke. He scribbled a few notes which he gave me to take to the marketwomen in Podol. When I returned the fish were ready, heaped on the table in his workshop. They were a shiny bronze color and had a dizzying aroma. Degtyarev was sitting in front of them thoughtfully, pinched and tired —his once busy hands resting impotently on the table for the first time. I didn't understand, but my heart ached for him.

The marketwomen had sent him the money tied up in rags, but he did not bother to count it (also for the first time); he merely shoved the parcels indifferently into his pocket.

"Those fish look pretty good," I said.

"Pretty good! But I really did a bad job on them," Degtyarev said. "I haven't smoked any for a long time, and so they didn't turn out too well. I'm ashamed to deliver them myself."

He began to pack the fish carefully in a basket lined with newspapers. I couldn't see that he had done a bad job.

"I'll tell you what. You'll deliver them," he said. "Say that Degtyarev doesn't feel well and can't come himself. God help you if you snatch one of them, because they're counted. Go along Syretskaya Street to the cannery. The road will turn left and go uphill beyond the brickyards. Keep following that road until you reach an army camp with watchtowers. At the gates, say, 'This is for Herr Offizier Radomski.' Explain that I couldn't come. Leave the fish there in the basket. You don't have to bring that basket back."

"It's a new basket."

"Never mind. And don't mention that I've spoiled the fish. They won't know the difference. As soon as you've given them the basket, home you go! Understand?"

What was there to understand? I swung the heavy basket to my shoulder (which was always hurting since it had been rubbed raw by the sausage-basket yoke) and trudged off. My strength was gone by the time I reached Syretskaya Street. But I knew that when you seem to have no more strength left, you must keep dragging on and on, somehow finding more strength.

I sat down for a rest on the windward side of the basket to keep from smelling the damned fragrance of that smoked fish. I passed the cannery and then the brickyards and saw the road go uphill to the left.

How happy I was when I saw the army camp on the left side of the road at last. But it was a gigantic place, and I walked and walked without seeing an entrance. Signs read: *"FORBIDDEN ZONE. APPROACH NO CLOSER THAN 50 FEET! FIRE WILL BE OPENED WITHOUT WARNING."*

Therefore I clung instinctively to the right side of the road and squinted at the sentries in the towers. There were three rows of wire, and the middle one, studded with little cups, was obviously charged with electricity. This meant that the camp was very important, perhaps even a secret one.

Finally I tottered to the corner where the gate was. I decided that the 50-foot zone was not in effect here, and approached the bored sentry leaning against a gatepost.

"For Herr Offizier Radomski," I said, pointing to the basket.

He nodded toward a long, low building beside the gate and said something. I only caught the word *Wachtstube*, which means "guardhouse." I climbed the stairs to the porch, entered and found myself in a long corridor. There was no one around, but I could hear the tapping of typewriters and headed in that direction.

The door to the room was ajar and several girls sat chatting inside—local girls—secretaries, you might call them. The place looked like an office of some sort. There were ink-stained desks, abacuses and scribbled notices with columns of figures. The girls were Kurenevka beauties: rosy-cheeked, plump and curly-haired. They were all staring at me.

"For Herr Offizier Radomski," I said.

"Ah! Put it over here." One of the girls helped me set

the basket on a desk, peeked under the newspaper and snatched out a morsel of fish. "Oh, its good . . . m-m . . . Delicious!"

They surrounded the basket, shredding the fish with their plump little ink-stained fingers and popping it into their mouths. They were simple, mischievous Kurenevka girls. I became a little worried; but if they were digging into the fish so boldly they must have had the right to do so—or so I thought, at any rate—and I was overjoyed that they liked it. Have fun, girls—eat up!

"It's from Degtyarev. He couldn't come," I explained, completing my mission.

"Oh? . . . M-m . . . We'll give it to him. Thanks!"

I set off a little worried. I had not given the basket to the "Herr Offizier" himself, and the girls might devour half of it. Then I was sorry, too, that I hadn't eaten at least a small fish: Nobody had even thought of counting them, and I surely could have eaten one, perhaps even two.

Degtyarev was extraordinarily glad when I returned and told him in detail whom I had given the fish to. He was not pleased that I hadn't given them to the "Herr Offizier" himself, but he jumped up and paced the room when I told him how the secretaries had eaten and praised the fish.

"That's good, perhaps even better! Those silly girls wouldn't know the difference. They even licked their fingers, did they? This perturbation might blow over, thank God. I'll never try it again. To hell with it! Thank God. Whew! Run home now, there's no more work."

I went away, wondering why all this had made him so apprehensive. What if he had spoiled the fish—that was no tragedy. I understood, of course, that being a master of his trade he'd be ashamed to face his German customers.

But something suddenly occurred to me. Wait a minute! Where had I been?

I leaned against a fence, unable to take another step.

I had been in the camp at Syrets, at Babi Yar: the place that people told all those horrible stories about. I had been too tired and stupefied by the basket to realize that I was approaching the camp from the rear. People were taken there from the center of the city, through Lukyanovka, and I had reached the place from the opposite side.

Did this mean that Degtyarev had been there—and got away? How? For what? For gold, or the basket of fish? And it was pure luck for me that the "Herr Offizier" had not been there. If he had lost his temper because Degtyarev hadn't come, he might have kept me there! Oh, Degtyarev, you're a . . . you're a rotten snake, sending me there in your place! It was like sending me into a mine field.

I started thinking about that electrified wire. I remembered that I had seen some miserable prisoners of war in the yard, but I hadn't looked at them closely because they were everywhere nowadays. And I'd heard some firing beyond the barracks and hadn't listened because there was also shooting everywhere nowadays, I had flown in and out of the cage like a sparrow. I had been lucky.

In fact, generally speaking, I had been awfully lucky till then. I don't know whom I should thank for this. There was no God, and Providence was a pound of smoke! I had simply been lucky. Quite accidentally, I had not turned out to be a Jew or Gypsy in this life, and I was not old enough to go to Germany. The bombs and bullets had missed me, and the patrols had not caught me. Good God, what luck! Evidently, only those who are very lucky keep on living. If I hadn't been lucky, I might have been sitting behind the barbed wire of Babi Yar that very moment, quite accidentally, by the sheerest chance—if the "Herr Offizier" had been out of sorts, or had suddenly scratched his palate with a fish bone.

I walked along for a while, stunned. Dusk was falling and the heavy clouds were a lilac color. Again I suddenly slumped against the fence. I felt very sick. And melancholy enough to howl!

It was oppressively muggy; the world was very still, and there were red stripes across the sky. I felt like an ant, walled in, trapped in a foundation. The whole world was made of bricks and stone. There were no openings anywhere. Wherever you put your head there was stone, there were walls and prisons. I was in a sea of despair—in real anguish. I imagined that the earth was a prison, with prohibitions posted all over; everything was rationed out from first to last, and everything was fenced in and fenced over. Walk only thus, and live only thus! How did all this come about? Why? And who wanted me to be born, live and crawl about this world as if in a prison? Humans, like ants, have erected a maze of barriers in their anthills and locked themselves in.

Good God! What are they doing to man?

CHAPTER XXXVII

FLIGHT FROM SILENCE

A thousand years ago Vyshgorod was a great and splendid city, the rival of the "mother of Russian cities"—Kiev herself. Now it is only an ordinary village on the high bank of the Dnieper.

Degtyarev had arranged to buy a foal from a Vyshgorod peasant, and it was my job to hand over the money and bring back the foal. I had done this more than once before. Since I had 10,000 rubles in cash with me, I decided to avoid populous places; the most populous were now the most dangerous. I did not take the highway, but went straight across the meadow, along the Pochaina River and through the Dubki forest groves. Nor was I sorry, for I didn't meet a soul along the way.

Halfway through the village I saw some German soldiers from afar. I had a foreboding and could have turned back and hidden; but strangely enough, I kept going straight toward them, while my mind cast about frantically for a way out and came up with nothing.

They stopped me in an accustomed, businesslike way. One of them took me by the shoulders paternally, turned me around and marched me back along the same path, while the other continued on his rounds from cottage to cottage.

I understood immediately what it was all about, sub-

285

mitted at once and tramped obediently into a yard behind one of the cottages. About fifteen peasants were there, old men and boys, some sitting on the mound around the cottage and others just on the ground. Their faces were passive, indifferent, empty of expression. Just to make sure, I asked a boy of my age, "Are they taking us to Germany?"

"Uh-huh," he sniffled. "They're taking everybody."

Leaning against the wall, I thought absently, "Now Degtyarev will think I've run off with his money. True, when Mother turns up later and raises an alarm he'll know misfortune overtook me; but by then I'll be on my way to Europe. So it's happened to me at last!"

The raid was a quiet one. The soldiers went from cottage to cottage, hauling people out; the men came submissively, silently, just as I had come. No documents were examined now, for your age didn't matter anymore. It was all very simple and straightforward: If you were caught, you were caught—and that was that.

Everybody was driven into the street and grouped into something like a prisoners-of-war column. And off we went —a gray mass, raising a cloud of dust. The guards walked beside us, their rifles under their arms. Moving along with my eyes fixed on the ground, I could not help feeling that I was being herded. When my neighbors jostled me, I didn't feel like a human being, but more like an animal in a herd.

We were driven into a collective farm yard surrounded by barns and sheds and were halted amid the rusty remnants of drag-harrows and seeders. Our few guards were evidently so used to obedience from people that they didn't come into the yard with us. Two of them stayed at the entrance to watch, and the others went off.

The peasants seated themselves in a long row along the wall of a cottage, which formerly might have been the Vil-

lage Soviet Building. Looking for a place to sit, I walked to
the corner of the building, spotted a brick and sat down on
it. It was in the sun, but the shady places were all taken.
Wretched as I was, I was dressed a trifle better than these
people from the village. They were all gray and ragged, and
they sat in silence, in a dull stupor. The feeling that I was a
part of a herd never left me, but I rebelled against it in-
wardly.

When something in the street caught the attention of
the guards, I got up from my brick, went around the corner
of the building and urinated. The nettles here were littered
with bricks and scraps of metal. I stumbled over them in-
cautiously, making them rattle, reached the wattle fence
and scrambled over it with a crash. I was sure the guards
would come now to shoot or bring me back.

An alley descended on the left. On the right it opened
into the main street along which I had come; at that juncture
it was quite wide, almost like a village square. In the middle
was a solitary unfenced cottage. I walked into the main
street like an idiot, passing the cottage on the left only because I had come that way before and knew that side of the
road. I hardly knew what I was doing and trusted to luck
alone.

All went well. The guards never noticed me, though
they could have. But up ahead I saw the soldiers who had
gone off before. I picked up a twig and pulled my cap down,
making myself look as small as I could. Sniffing blithely, I
walked right past those chatting soldiers. I had gone about
20 yards past them when apparently they changed their
minds and called out to me, "Hey, boy!"

I kept going as though I hadn't heard.

"Hey!" came the cry behind.

I began to run. Their rifle bolts clicked, but the street

was crooked, so I flew to the first bend with popping eyes, snorting like a motorcycle. I heard a shot, *my shot,* and two more of *my shots* right behind it; but evidently they couldn't see me anymore, and were only shooting in my general direction.

With all my body, especially the back of my head, I felt my vulnerability to a bullet, so I zigzagged down an alley which dipped sharply to a little bridge. I was thinking of curling up under the bridge, but my legs carried me across it even while I was thinking, and I found myself in some vegetable gardens. Behind them I recognized the meadow through which I had come to the village.

And again—just because I had come exactly this way— I ran across the flat meadow, where I could have been shot down like a hare. But I ran on because my thoughts could not keep up with my legs. I dashed on in blind terror, without looking back, regretting only that I couldn't run any faster.

They didn't pursue me! I don't know why. I ran until my eyes were dim—all the way to Dubki, where I fell on the grass, rolling about and gulping for air. "I'm not Grandmother's little boy anymore," I thought. "I'm not Grandfather's little Tolya."

Vyshgorod lay far behind, in a blue haze. I drank my fill from the swamp, wet my head and gradually regained self-possession. I was alive! "You vermin, so you thought you had caught me! You have rifles, but I have legs and my wonderful life. How many times have I saved myself by my legs alone! Glorious legs that have saved my life! I need my life. Now I know why I've been living, hanging around the markets and gnawing bare bones. I've been growing up to hate and to fight you—you scum who are turning the world into a prison and a rock pile. D'you hear me, you plague?"

THE EARTH ON FIRE

Mother woke me up one night.

"Get up, quick! Look out the window!"

The windows were blood red. Sparks rose over the railroad embankment, and tongues of pale flame flickered above its crest. Immediately I thought, "What could be burning there? Rails, stones, earth?" Our cartridges were buried there. It was incredible, an unbelievable nightmare, but the ground was burning.

"It's the plant," said Mother.

And then everything fell into place. The Sport Plant lay directly behind the embankment, out of sight.

We did not sleep all night. Mother paced back and forth, wringing her hands and worrying about what would happen now. Her job was to heat the furnace and stoves at the plant.

It was an ordinary manufacturing plant. Before the war it had mainly specialized in producing beds and sports goods. There were only a few workers now, and those few worked on the principle, "We're all in this together." They would gather in the corners and talk, while one of them banged a hammer on metal to make the manager think they were working.

The plant now produced all sorts of junk. Some workers repaired things, others took things apart. Each man worked for himself, taking away cigarette lighters, shovels and pails for barter.They would tell the manager that one of the lathes had broken down and ought to be thrown out; he would believe them, and then they would haul it out. The engineer would give them absurd blueprints. They kept building, riveting and welding until they discovered that what they were working on should have been done the other way around, and then they would have to start all over again. All this went on because the manager couldn't have cared less about the plant. He had arranged a splendid apartment for himself in the office and he used to lock himself in with Lyubka, the assistant manager's daughter. In return, the assistant manager could steal anything he liked.

Mother cleaned the office, delivered notices and papers to the shops and heated the stoves. Since she had to come to work earlier than anyone else, she worked fifteen hours a day.

In the winter we rose at three in the morning, took a sled and went to the plant, where I hid in a corner, waiting for Mother to bring out a bundle of wood fuel. Then I dragged it home, terrified of being caught by the patrols. But what could we do? We would have died from the cold if it hadn't been for those bundles of wood.

The investigation and interrogation began the morning after the fire. The day before, about 100 army sleighs had been brought in to have new runners put on. They had been hauled into one of the shops. The sleighs caught fire during the night. All the main shops burned down, and so the plant, in effect, was gone. The manager was hysterical, and everybody was questioned and questioned again for days on end.

No one had been at the plant that night, it seemed, except the watchman; and by the time he discovered the fire there was nothing he could do.

The event was ordinary enough. In Kiev, which was seething with hatred, the Germans sat astride a volcano. Every night something burned down or blew up, and several fascists were assassinated. People said that when the Mixed Feed Plant behind the streetcar depot burned down, there had been an inscription in chalk on the wall the next morning: "This is for Babi Yar. [Signed] The Partisans."

The Dnieper bridge to Darnitsa was dynamited, and locomotives at the railroad yards were blown up. There was talk everywhere, now of a collision, now of a train blown up by mines. The huge SS garage in Pechersk burned down. Bombs were placed in the Musical Comedy Theater building before an officers' meeting which Erich Koch, the *Reichskommissar* for the Ukraine, was to attend; the Germans discovered them quite by chance, fifteen minutes before they were to go off. Leaflets kept appearing here and there in the city, and there was constant talk of the partisans.

Right across the way from our cottage, we heard a locomotive hoot frantically on the embankment as a freight train came to a halt, its cars burning. One of them, a platform car loaded with hay, was where the fire had begun. *Polizei* swarmed up the embankment and fire engines dashed to the scene with clanging bells, but the cars burned down. Later, the burned hulks were hauled away.

The partisans freed entire districts, establishing Soviet power beyond Irpen and Dymer (they could accomplish this because of General Kovpak's raids).[1] Rural *Polizei* and village elders came pouring in from beyond Dymer, reporting that hordes and hordes of the partisans were advancing and there was no stopping them. Panic spread. Kiev *Polizei* were paraded forth to be sent to Ivankovo. Before setting out, they got drunk, danced and wept that they would never come back alive.

The Germans and the *Polizei* now went about only in groups, and always with rifles.

Trenches were dug in the yard of the Kurenevka police station. A big blockhouse was built in front, with embrasures facing the street.

Now the German communiqués spoke of "defensive battles," "counteroffensives," "repelling counterattacks successfully," "shortening the front" and "the enemy made minor advances." When the Germans retreated from a city, they did not say so, but simply declared: "Fighting is going on west of Orel"; everything was obvious, and we envied Orel.

Time and again I noticed that no matter how the newspapers twisted and dodged, no matter what persuasive lie they handed out, the people always, invariably, knew the truth. The dodging was only wasted effort and self-consolation for those who engaged in it. The Soviet people had learned to read between the lines and to hear between words. They had their own grapevine. Not a word, for instance, was published about the rout at Stalingrad, but the people knew absolutely everything about it. They knew about the battles of Moscow and Kursk, as well.

When the whole lot of the witnesses of the Babi Yar massacres were shot on September 29, 1941, Kurenevka knew all the details within an hour after the first shot.

Those elusive partisans were everywhere, but how could I reach them? What was I to do? Everything inside me was bursting at the mere thought that our side was advancing, that our men would come and this darkness would end forever. The day after the train burned on the embankment, I was alone in the cottage. I hunted around for a notebook, opened the ink bottle and wrote the following on one page:

COMRADES!

The Red Army is advancing and beating the fashists. Wait for their coming. Help the partisans and strike at the Germans! Soon they will be *kaputt*. They know it and they are frightened. The *Polizei* and their dogs are quaking, too. We'll settle with them. Wait! We are coming!

Long live the glorious partisans!
Death to the German ocupiers!
Hurrah!

—THE PARTISANS.

In the remaining space I drew a five-pointed star and filled it in thickly with ink. The sheet looked quite heroic to me that way, especially the courageous "Hurrah!"—my only original contribution, since I had copied all the rest from the many real partisan leaflets I had seen. I ripped a second page from the notebook, preparing to make 100 copies, but I just couldn't wait. I felt I had to run out and paste it up immediately at the bridge where everybody passed and would surely read it.

Hastily finishing the second copy, I put it near the stove for the inky star to dry. Then I mixed some paste in a vodka glass and smeared it on the back of the first copy. I folded the page in two, thrust it under my shirt, holding it in place with two fingers, and was off.

As if to spite me, there was one passerby after another; by the time a safe moment came the page had dried and the two halves were sticking together. In a panic I started pulling the page apart, licking it to help the procedure. Then I pasted it crookedly on the cement wall of the bridge and walked off rapidly, my heart racing. That's all there was to it. Very simple.

I opened the door and stopped. Mother and Lena Gimpel stood in the room, attentively reading the second copy of my opus which I had left by the stove to dry. I strode to the coat rack in an independent sort of way and took off my coat.

"It's not bad, on the whole," said Lena. "But if you've decided to write leaflets, don't leave them where anybody can find them. You'll manage to get yourself killed yet. And the word 'fascist' is written with a 'c,' and 'occupiers' with two 'c's. Didn't they teach you how to spell at school? The star and the 'hurrah' are silly. They show at once that it was written by a young boy."

"Tolik," said Mother, very pale. "Do you want to be sent to Babi Yar?"

Their scolding was brief but thorough. They said that fools like myself who did things on their own only got themselves killed uselessly. That my future lay before me. That I had to grow up and learn.

And learn I did.

In the spring, at last, the air raids began—those glorious, wonderful, red-letter days.

The Soviet bombers came at night. First the antiaircraft guns roared, the sparks of their exploding shells flashing in the sky. Then red tracer bullets flew up like strings of peas. The black sky continued to quiver to the drone of invisible planes.

Grandfather's windows faced north, so he hurried to our side of the house. We opened our windows, climbed out on the sills and waited for the raid, which was never long in coming.

The flares, dropped by parachute, burned brightly. They hung in the sky and a gray mist seemed to drip from them. Their transparent light spread over the whole city—the towers, the chimneys, the roofs, the cupolas of St. Sophia and the Lavra. The planes droned and circled for a long time, selecting their targets and aiming. Then the bombs thundered, sometimes quite near. One of them landed squarely on the Kobets Tannery.

We were not afraid of them. No Soviet bombs ever fell on homes, only on factories, bridges, barracks and railroad yards. Everybody knew that the partisans reported the targets first and signaled to the planes with flashlights when they came in. This meant standing by the target and signaling for the bombs to drop on oneself.

That's what was said in Kurenevka, and it seemed to be so.

A gala performance was to be held at the Opera House on May 2, 1943. The entrance was thronged with Germans in a festive mood. Automobiles drew up with generals and their ladies. The plain soldiery walked to the balcony.

The raid began after dark. A bomb struck the Opera House, cleaving the ceiling and burying itself in the pit. Those theaters were always a jinx. The bomb didn't go off. It was the only Soviet bomb that hit Kiev and didn't explode, damn it! It killed just seven Germans, who were in the pit. Pieces of their bodies even flew onstage. There was a terrible panic. The lights went out and everybody made for the exits, clambering over one another. The maddened crowd poured out and fled in all directions. The performers ran along the streets in their makeup and costumes.

The raids went on all summer. The very air seemed charged with tension, alarm and expectation. Explosions and fires kept spreading.

An event of no small importance to me occurred on August 18, 1943; I turned fourteen and came of age—that is, became eligible to be driven off to Germany, and all the rest of it.

The Author Speaking

So much time has passed that I am writing all this not about myself, but about someone else—a young person. I keep looking at this boy from the outside, studying him and trying to understand him; and if I write in the first person, it is only because by some queer chance I happened to have been that boy. Nowadays I look back at parts of my life with the interest of a person watching a movie, and I am just as much of an onlooker as you, the reader.

I have not tried to present a full history of Kiev's occupation and its struggle against the German invaders. That struggle alone could fill several books twice the length of this one. And besides the mass of known facts, much is still unrevealed. Astonishing material lies preserved in the files of the Kiev Historical Museum, awaiting discovery; nor are these files the only such source.

I am not writing a history book, but a study of character —a wholly contemporary study. It is contemporary because it is natural for a human being to want to be a human being, *to grow, to mature and to fight for his right to live and think.*

I keep thinking how amazing human life really is! It is stifled, bent, usurped, squeezed into straitjackets conceived by idiot minds and devalued completely; but it is still there,

297

vital, struggling, resisting evil and fascism. I am writing not about a unique and outstanding hero, but about a most ordinary boy. And still, when Lena Gimpel said, "You'll manage to get yourself killed yet," I was aware that this was entirely possible; I was ready for it and I knew why.

I should like to look deeper into my hero in this respect, for he seems quite characteristic of his time and generation.

After all, it is his generation that is taking control now, after having come through that, *through a war that shook it to the core; the experience must affect everything this generation does. I believe that what I am relating is not simply an engaging story, nor will it merely help people remember themselves as they once were; it will help them to understand themselves now.*

It is imperative that we understand ourselves, that we know where we came from, where we are and what we are— if only to keep us from repeating these tragic events.

Outwardly, all lives are different. While my hero was saving himself from roundups and composing his first naïve leaflet, some were already fighting splendidly at the front, in partisan units or underground; others were making cartridges; and still others were peacefully going to school. But we all lived in the same twentieth century; the smoke of the Babi Yars was spreading over the world, and the war was battering the best time of our lives—our youth. This we shared, and it left an imprint on our lives forever.

BABI YAR, FINALE

All the inmates of the Babi Yar concentration camp were marched out onto the central square on August 13, 1943. Army trucks rolled in, discharging helmeted SS men and dogs.

Everybody realized that this was the beginning of the end.

Soviet planes had bombed the camp a few days before, and the bombs had landed neatly around its fringes, obviously to destroy the barriers. The barbed wire was only damaged in one place and was quickly repaired, but the fascists apparently realized that it was time to liquidate the camp.

A table was brought out with registers and files. Everybody was lined up and sent past the table. Rieder looked at his lists, sending some prisoners to the left and some to the right. Exactly 100 of the most dangerous politicals were selected first. The SS men bawled, *"Schnell, schnell—* quick!"* With blows showering upon them and the dogs barking, the 100 went through the gates.

"We've left our things in our huts!" they cried.

"You won't need anything!" answered the Germans.

Outside the gates they were told to remove their shoes. They left their shoes and went on barefoot. Davydov, who found himself in one of the front rows of the 100, kept thinking, "Well this is it, the end at last."

Landslides along the edge of Babi Yar ravine had produced terraces overgrown with thick grass. The 100 descended to the first terrace along a narrow path and found a new, freshly completed hut.

The ravine was noisy and crowded, seething with Germans: SS men wearing badges and officers wearing ribbons. Some trucks had even been driven down. All sorts of tools were heaped everywhere.

The 100 were brought to a standstill and asked, "Are there any fitters or smiths among you?"

The few who responded were separated from the rest and led off behind a low earthen wall. The remaining men were then divided into groups of five and also led off behind the wall. There was no shooting.

Davydov began to hope that they were not to be shot yet. He looked hard at everything but could make nothing of what was going on.

Finally he, too, was taken behind the wall. Here there were anvils, with piles of chains between them. Everybody was being shackled. A fat, phlegmatic German sat at an anvil, like the prisoners who were smiths, and, like them, he was busy riveting. Davydov landed in front of him. The chain was like the kind used in wells. The German put it around his leg, fitted a metal cuff to his ankle and riveted it in place.

Davydov shuffled off, taking very short steps. The chain hurt him. Later it bruised his legs abominably. Some men put rags around the chain, and others tied it to their waists to keep it from dragging on the ground.

When all were fettered, dinner was announced, and each got a very full meal. The soup was the real thing, rich and filling.

All were given shovels. Their chains ringing, the prisoners were marched to a narrow gully leading off from the ravine and told to dig.

They dug for a long time, until evening. The pit they dug was long and uneven. No one knew exactly what it was for, but the Germans appeared to be looking for something. They were watching constantly to see if something had been dug up. However, nothing was unearthed.

The 100 were driven back into the hovel for the night. It was pitch dark inside. The only sound from the outside was the voices of the many guards. The fascists had built a watchtower in front of the hut and had trained a swivel machine gun on the hut entrance.

In the morning the men were marched down the ravine again. It was just as crowded, just as full of noise and cursing as the day before.

A tall, handsome, elegant officer with a riding crop was shouting hysterically. He was about 35 and he was called Topaide. From snatches of talk Davydov realized with surprise that it was Topaide who had supervised the first shootings in 1941.

Topaide had not been present the previous day. He had sent a map of the quarries where the dead lay, but the local Germans had not been able to decipher it and had blundered. He shrieked that they were all boobies, unable to understand simple plans, and that they had begun to excavate in the wrong place. He ran around and stamped his foot:

"Here! Here!"

The digging began again on the spot he indicated. In half an hour the first corpses turned up.

The Germans addressed Topaide respectfully, but among themselves they called him, ironically (or perhaps seriously), "the executions engineer." Now he had turned into an exhumation engineer. He chased about the ravine all day, giving instructions, commands and explanations. From time to time his face twitched strongly with an unpleasant grimace—obviously some kind of nervous tic. He was a bundle of nerves, constantly on the edge of hysteria. He could not be a minute without roaring, rushing about or striking someone. His "engineering" had apparently exacted a toll, even from him.

The work was in full swing. The Germans hurriedly ringed the ravine with fences for concealment and camouflaged these with twigs. At other places they were planting trees and shrubbery. It was clear that everything happening here was the deepest secret.

The road to Babi Yar from town was blocked off. When trucks approached with supplies, the German drivers dismounted far from the ravine, and guards took their places at the wheel and drove on into Babi Yar. The trucks brought rails, stone slabs, lumber and oil drums.

Thus began the final phase of Babi Yar—the attempt to efface it from history. At first there were hitches in the work.

Topaide rushed about, raging, and all the Germans were nervous; they beat the prisoners desperately and shot several.

Additional groups of prisoners were brought from the camp as reinforcements; within a few days there were 300 here, later even more. They were split into brigades, and the unflagging, productive toil exacted of them was a model of methodical German efficiency.

Davydov served in various brigades. At first he nearly

fainted from the stench and the frequent handling of the corpses, but in time he got used to it.

THE DIGGERS dug out the pits, exposing the layers of blue-gray and decomposing corpses; they had been tightly stamped down and were intertwined. Extricating them was torture. The stench made the Germans hold their noses, and some were sick. The guards sat on the slopes of the ravine, each with a bottle of vodka in the sand between his boots. They reached for these bottles frequently; and all the Germans in the ravine were perpetually drunk.

The diggers got no vodka. It was hard for them, but, as I said, they got used to it gradually and labored away with their chains clanging.

THE HOOKERS ripped the corpses apart and dragged them to the furnaces. Each of them had a specially forged metal rod with a handle at one end and a hook at the other. These tools were made from a design that Topaide had prepared. After many experiments Topaide himself evolved a system for pulling out a corpse so it wouldn't fall apart. One had to grasp the body under the chin with the hook and haul it by the lower jaw. It then came away in one piece, and could be dragged to its destination. Some of the bodies had stuck together so firmly that the hook dragged two or three of them at a time. Axes often had to be used, and several times the lower layers had to be dynamited apart.

THE GOLD-SEEKERS were armed with tongs for tearing out gold teeth. They examined each corpse on its way to the furnace, removed rings and earrings and searched the pockets of those corpses still dressed, for coins and other valuables. This brigade gathered a pail or two of gold each day. A sentry stood over each seeker to see that the gold wasn't stolen or tossed into the sand.

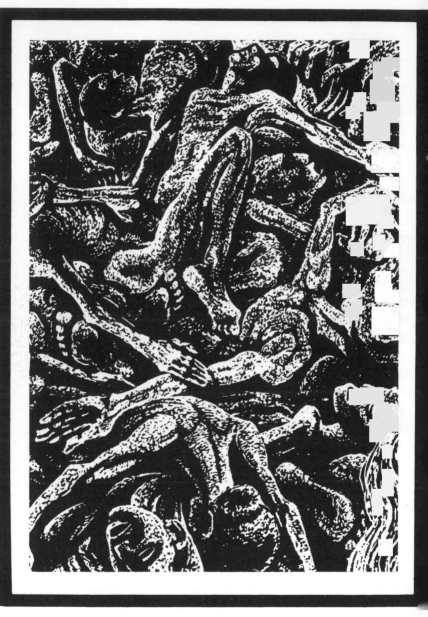

THE BUILDERS were engaged in constructing the furnaces. Under heavy guard they crossed the whole ravine to the Jewish cemetery on the opposite side, where the Germans told them which of the granite monuments to dismantle.

The prisoners took the tombstones down and carried them into the ravine. The granite slabs were then laid down in rows. Atop them, once more following Topaide's instructions, was erected a technically superb and carefully designed furnace. Almost five feet high, it had a draught chimney, complicated passages and gratings. When it was loaded with wood, the corpses were laid on the gratings with their heads outward. The second row was laid crosswise over the first, for binding; then came a layer of wood; and so on until there was a pyre nine feet high and eighteen feet wide.

Each pyre contained about 2,000 bodies. Scaffolding was required to get them into place, and the dead were carried up like building materials on a construction job. The completed structure was drenched with oil, pumped from the drums and through a hose by a special compressor.

THE STOKERS started the fire below and also applied torches to the protruding heads. The oil-soaked hair burst into flames at once—this was why the corpses were laid with their heads outward. The pyre turned into a great, solid bonfire. The heat it gave off was unbearable. All over the ravine and far beyond one could smell the pungent odor of scorched hair and burning flesh. The stokers kept stirring the fire with long pokers like those used by foundrymen. They scraped out embers and ashes, cleaned the furnace when it had cooled enough, overhauled it, replaced the burned-out gratings and prepared it for a fresh load.

THE CRUSHERS dealt with the ashes. They had to crush

half-burned bones into smaller particles on some of the slabs brought from the cemetery. This was done with ordinary rammers such as roadbuilders use to tamp down the road surface. The ashes were then put through a sieve, again in search of gold.

THE GARDENERS got their name because, after shoveling the ashes onto litters, they carried them to nearby areas and spread them on vegetable gardens—all under heavy guard. They had a better time than the others, for they could dig up potatoes in the gardens, bring them back to the ravine and bake them in empty cans on the embers left from the cremations.

Meanwhile, routine executions went right on in Babi Yar as before. But the dead were no longer buried; they were tossed into the furnaces at once. Prisoners on their last legs, those who couldn't work anymore, were also dumped in—alive.

The Germans were in a great hurry, and all one heard was "Faster, faster! *Schnell!*" But there was no end to the corpses. Davydov had to help empty a pit containing 400 hostages shot on Eberhard's orders. He dug up other pits containing 100 and 300 hostages. They were all there to the last man, as Topaide knew they would be. He pointed out the sites, and seemed to remember absolutely everything.[1]

Gaswagen often came from town with living passengers. They drove right up to the furnaces before the gas was turned on. From inside came muffled cries, followed by wild banging on the doors. Then all was quiet. The Germans opened the doors, and prisoners unloaded the bodies. These were warm, moist with sweat and perhaps still half alive. They were laid on the pyre. Davydov remembers the contortions of some of them in the fire. They thrashed about as though alive.

An asphyxiation truck filled with women arrived one day. After the usual procedure, when the screaming and banging had subsided, the door was opened. A light smoke wafted away, and it turned out that the truck was stuffed with naked young girls. There were more than 100 of them compressed into that space, sitting on one another's knees. Each had tied her hair up in a kerchief, as women do when going to the bath house. Perhaps when they were squeezed into the truck they had been told that they were going to the bath house. The drunken Germans laughed and explained that these girls had been the waitresses in the Kiev cabarets. Perhaps they knew too much. When Davydov carried them up the pyre and laid them in place, some of them emitted faint snores and he thought that they were still alive.

Some high-ranking officers drove up in luxurious cars. They shouted at the Germans working in the ravine, complaining that the work was going too slowly. There were not enough men to do the job, and so the prisoners in the *Gasenwagen* were let out on several occasions to be put to work.

Prisoner gangs were now led beyond the ravine, to a nearby antitank pit about 200 yards long. This was filled to the top with the corpses of Red Army officers—the prisoners deduced this from the uniforms, dispatch pouches and binoculars. There were probably 25,000 to 30,000 bodies here. Other prisoners were sent to dig up the pits at Kirillov Hospital.

Distant artillery fire could be heard at Babi Yar from across the Dnieper. The prisoners knew that the last pyre would be their own. The Germans did not seriously regard them as humans, and during the morning roll call would report, "Three hundred and twenty-five corpses in formation." They considered this funny.

The prisoners were unshaven. They were given no water, and many could hardly stand; they were covered with sores, soot and the slime of the corpses. Through the long nights they thought of only one thing: how to escape.

One such prisoner was Fyodor Yershov, a Party member. It was he who began serious preparation for an uprising; he simply talked to those who worked beside him. Groups of conspirators formed, and got together whenever they could to discuss ways of escaping.

Some suggested hurling themselves on the guards in the middle of the day, seizing their submachine guns, shooting their way out and scattering. Fyodor Yershov was against this plan, for the prisoners were all in chains and too weak to cope with the burly Germans.

There were some former truckdrivers among the prisoners. One of them, Vladimir Kuklya, suggested seizing a couple of the trucks bringing wood to the ravine, or even a *Gaswagen,* and smashing through the guards. This was a somewhat fantastic plan: They would have had to drive all along the ravine and through the city among Germans and *Polizei.* It would have been simply heroic suicide.

The group being driven to Kirillov Hospital asked for permission to escape on their own, since their guard was relatively light. They might have succeeded, but Yershov objected, "You may get away, but it would kill the others' chances. No, we all have to rise at the same time."

In a far corner of the hut, however, some young fellows hatched a plan of their own. Consulting no one, they began desperately to dig a hole, hoping to escape at night. They could not finish the passage in one night, and in the morning the guards discovered it and immediately shot all who had occupied that corner of the hut: seventeen young men.

There was one man who made an exceptionally daring singlehanded escape in broad daylight. No one knew his name. Working apart from the others, he suddenly jumped into a gully, raced off, and hid in one of the defiles leading to the cemetery. The Germans began shooting. There was an alert, and the work stopped at once. Scores of Germans ran after the man, but did not find him. Evidently he had managed to remove his chains and was therefore able to run fast. In their rage the Germans killed twelve prisoners that day and shot their own officer who had been in command of the guards responsible for the fugitive. Machine guns were set up to cover these defiles of the ravine.

Escape plans were discarded one by one. Finally, Fyodor Yershov's proposal was adopted: to burst out of the mud hut and hurl themselves on the guards at night. This, too, was very risky, but the dark offered hope that at least some would get away.

The hut was a deep dugout with a steeply descending, narrow entranceway. A machine gun on the watchtower was trained directly on this entrance. At night the hut was surrounded by as many as 60 guards. There were no windows, and the solitary door was a grating so that the men inside would not suffocate. From time to time the sentries flashed their torches through the grating to see if everything was quiet. It was locked with a huge warehouse padlock.

The drunken guards would grow bored with their night vigil, and sometimes would rouse the prisoners suddenly and bring them up into the searchlight beams for a mock execution. This was a gruesome joke, for the prisoners took it seriously. Then the guards laughed and chased everybody back. The nights were dark, damp and cloudy.

One of the prisoners insisted they should wait for the next "joke," tear off their chains and hurl themselves on the guards. But the chains could not be removed easily; they had to be prepared for such an emergency and left barely hanging. And who could tell whether the "joke" would be repeated on just the right night?

Incredible as it may seem, there was a traitor among these doomed men. He was a former *Polizei* from Fastov and had landed in Babi Yar through some extraordinary circumstance. He was always toadying to the Germans and listening attentively to the conversation around him. It was not improbable that the death of the seventeen young men had been his doing. If he had known of the planned escape, he would have betrayed it at once. There might have been others who were not to be trusted; Fyodor Yershov, therefore, was very cautious.

This is why only 50 men were informed of the plan beforehand. This fact alone was enough to prevent a concerted uprising during the next "joke."

"We have to get that lock open at any cost," said Yershov. "Then we'll tell everyone, make the preparations, get our chains off, and at last break out. We'll save our lives, friends! What if only half of us get away, a quarter of us, even just five men? Someone has to get away, to reach our side and tell them what's been going on here."

The work in the ravine already resembled a huge construction job. The Germans had brought in construction machinery—excavators and bulldozers. These machines clattered on, day after day, excavating the pits and leveling them when they were empty.[2]

One important circumstance should be noted. The prisoners found all sorts of unexpected objects, especially among the bodies of those who had been executed in 1941, for these people had expected to be shipped out somewhere. Craftsmen had carried their tools with them to the very edge of the pits. The women had taken scissors, hairpins and so on. The prisoners found pocket knives, nailfiles and chisels. One even found a bottle of Red Moscow toilet water. He wanted to drink it, but was persuaded to sprinkle it in the hut.

The pockets of many of the dead contained keys: keys to apartments, sheds, storage houses, even bunches of keys.

Yershov divided the conspirators into groups of ten, and each group prepared its part of the uprising. The group assigned to open the lock collected keys. They rejected scores and scores of them. Finally a prisoner called Yakov Kaper found a key that must have belonged to a warehouse padlock. A 1941 victim had brought it to Babi Yar in his pocket, never dreaming that thanks to him other condemned men would be able to save themselves in 1943. The key fitted the lock, but did not open it.

The prisoners were herded into the hut during the day for dinner, but the door was left open. While someone stood in front of the lock, Vladimir Kuklya swiftly tried the key. It was done so quickly that it passed unnoticed, even by the other prisoners.

There were no former thieves among the prisoners—no one to whom opening such a lock would have been an easy matter. They were all honest men; and though a file was found, Vladimir Kuklya struggled with it for a long time, regretting that he had never done anything of the sort before.

Finally, he succeeded in filing the key to open the door. Only a few of the men knew this.

Meanwhile, other groups of ten collected anything that might help to remove their chains or serve as weapons, brought it all to the hut and hid it in the earthen walls.

One of the prisoners was Yakov Steyuk, a well-educated young man from the Transcarpathian region. He knew several languages and had even studied in Berlin.

"We'll succeed even better than we expect!" he said. "Courage! You can't imagine how cowardly and superstitious the Germans are. We must break out of here with yells, howls and whistles. When we charge them with a 'hurrah!' they'll be terrified, stunned. You'll see."

The key was ready, as were the weapons. Night after night passed, but the prisoners awaited a convenient moment. As luck would have it, the guard was increased. The guards kept coming to the mud hut at night, flashing their torches at the prisoners and checking repeatedly.

"Today?" Yershov would suggest impatiently.

But the majority would put it off to tomorrow. "Today" meant facing almost certain death. No one wanted to die today, and what if a better chance came the next day?

The escape was touched off almost by accident; it was just a coincidence that it came on September 29, exactly two years to the day from the first executions at Babi Yar. Some of the prisoners superstitiously hoped that the day would bring good luck.

When the brigade sent to the Kirillov Hospital was returning, one of the guards, an elderly German of whom no one knew anything, except that he came from Lorraine, whispered to one of the prisoners, *"Morgen kaputt."*

Why that warning? Nobody knew. Simply out of kindness? But the prisoners could see for themselves that the camouflaged fencing around the ravine was being taken down and the tools were being stowed away.

Two vats of boiled potatoes were brought to the hut that

night. This, too, was unusual. Had the Germans decided to feed the potatoes to the prisoners because otherwise they would go waste?

"That's that," said Kuklya. "I'm opening the door to-night."

Fyodor Yershov sent word down the line among the initiated, "Today! Keep cool!"

They waited until late at night. At about two o'clock Kuklya reached through the bars, put the key in the lock and began to turn it. He turned it once, and the lock gave a loud click. Kuklya managed to pull his hand in and fell back in a cold sweat.

The guards heard the click, ran down to the door and flashed their torches in. All the prisoners were lying on their bunks. The Germans withdrew. They could be heard up above, talking and striking matches.

Two turns were needed to open the lock. In a whisper, Kuklya confessed that his hands were shaking. The others encouraged him.

"Go ahead, Volodya, try again!"

But he mumbled, "Look, fellows, let's wait until the guard is changed, because if it clicks again . . ."

The guards were about to be relieved, true enough, so the prisoners waited until this happened. Then Kuklya put his hand through again. He took a long time turning the key, but he kept the lock from clicking. At last he literally fell back into the arms of his comrades.

"Awake everybody, shed your shackles and arm!" ordered Yershov.

There was a great stir in the hut. Everyone's nerves were on edge as he began to hurry; there was a loud rustling, clanging of chains, scraping and talk. As if crazed, the prisoners hastened to split or pry apart the shackles with chisels, knives, scissors, anything. All this seemed thunderously loud after the silence. The guards rushed to the door.

"What's going on here?"

Yakov Steyuk answered in German for the others, "There's a fight over the potatoes!"

The hut grew still. The Germans began to laugh. Naturally, they found this funny: These prisoners were going to be shot in the morning, yet here they were, fighting to fill their bellies with potatoes.

Fifteen minutes passed. The door was softly opened.

"Come on, fellows!" shouted Yershov.

And into the narrow passage and up the ten stairs rushed the mob, bellowing, howling, whistling.

Steyuk was right. Not a shot was fired in the first few seconds. The Germans were paralyzed. Dozens of prisoners broke into the open before the machine gun opened fire. Only the dogs attacked at once.

It was dark and foggy out, and it was impossible to see what was happening where: who was strangling a dog, who was hitting a German over the head with a hammer, who was rolling over and over grappling with another German.

The guards found it difficult to shoot: They could not distinguish their own men from the others. However, the prisoners did not succeed in seizing the machine gun.

Flares shot up into the sky. There was shooting all over Babi Yar. The prisoners scattered. The firing was as heavy as at the front. Motorcycles hurtled over all the paths and trails.

Davydov rounded the hut, ran into one German, then another, plunged into the dark—and ran blindly toward the heart of the camp. He turned away sharply, met another prisoner in the vegetable gardens, and the two ran on together toward some cottages. Dawn was approaching; the shooting continued, trucks and motorcycles were dashing about and the air was filled with shouts and curses.

Davydov and his companion saw a woman beside a cottage.

"Hide us, Sister!"

She saw them and grew faint.

"Lord! You're from the ravine! I have children! They'll shoot me!"

Her sister came out.

"Go to the hen house. Hide in the straw!"

"You won't betray us, will you?" they asked, scrambling under the straw.

"No, comrades, we'll do you no harm."

Then the sister went off, cooked some borsch and brought them a whole pot of it—real, fragrant Ukrainian borsch. [3]

CHAPTER XL

NO SUCH CITY
WILL REMAIN

A constant roar of artillery fire came from across the Dnieper. Darnitsa, Svaromye, Vigurovshchina and Trukhanov Island were in flames.

The railroad station was jammed with fleeing Germans and *Volksdeutschen*. Refugees from Rostov, Kharkov and Poltava said that the retreating Germans were leaving a scorched earth behind them.

The bridges across the Dnieper were blown up, killing the people fleeing from their homes on the opposite bank. It was said that their bodies fell into the river along with the girders. Several Soviet scouts reached the beach on Trukhanov Island after dark and shouted, "We'll liberate you! It won't be long now!"

Arrests continued at a fierce rate. One of the victims shot was Grabarev, who, it turned out, had not stayed in Zverinets by accident.

Everything that could be removed from the factories was taken: door knobs from the offices, window latches, even toilet bowls. The fascists were doing a thorough job of packing their bags.

Before going out into the street now I looked about carefully. Once I started out and ran back immediately. A great crowd of old men and youngsters, some of the boys even smaller than I, were being driven down the street.

One day, Grandfather went to the bazaar with some old clothing, torn felt boots and galoshes. He hoped to exchange this rubbish for a couple of potatoes or a bit of cereal. A soldier stopped him and took the bag away. Grandfather, angry and offended, followed the soldier for a while. A group of Germans had started a bonfire, and the soldier emptied all the junk into the flames and went off with the empty sack. He did not want the galoshes, only the sack.

"Scoundrels, scoundrels!" Grandfather came home sobbing. "May you perish, may you be struck down by the fire and thunder of the Lord!"

Thunder, though not the Lord's, thundered. People paused in the streets or climbed the roofs to look eastward over the Dnieper. They listened to the artillery fire, shaken but elated.

Waves of dark, greasy smoke drifted from the ravine; and sometimes, when the wind blew our way, we could hardly breathe because of the smell of burned hair and flesh.

SUCCESSFUL GERMAN ATTACKS ON NORTHERN AND SOUTHERN SECTORS OF THE FRONT

THE FUEHRER'S HEADQUARTERS, SEPTEMBER 25.

... At many points in the middle reaches of the Don the enemy vainly attacked bridgehead defenses east of the river. German tanks north of Cherkass routed some small enemy vessels.

Stubborn defensive fighting is still continuing in

the central sector, east of the Unech railroad junction and south of Smolensk. The cities of Roslavl and Smolensk were abandoned *without any enemy resistance* after the complete ruin and destruction of all important military structures. [1] [*My italics.*]

TO THE POPULATION OF
THE CITY OF KIEV

German troops will defend the western bank of the Dnieper and the city of Kiev by every means. The sections of Kiev near the Dnieper will turn into a battle zone.

German troops are now taking up their positions there. To avoid unnecessary casualties among the population and to guarantee unhampered combat operations, the battle zone in the city must be cleared. . . . I hope the populace will in its own interests obey this order without resistance.

Anybody found in the forbidden zone without a pass after the date indicated will be severely punished. . . .[2]

The Soviet troops forded the Dnieper and emerged on the right bank; the artillery fire now came from the north, beyond Puscha-Voditsa and Vyshgorod.

The order to withdraw from the battle zone applied to half of the city. Our cottage lay within the forbidden zone. Grandfather and Mother argued about whether or not to leave.

Finally Grandfather took all our remaining possessions down to the cellar. Then we carried pails of earth into the shed, spread it over the cellar hatch, stamped it down firmly and covered it with straw and sawdust.

After this we took old boards and nailed them crosswise over the windows. Then Grandfather took his bundle and went off to his friend, the Gardener, while Mother and I burrowed into the hay in a corner of the loft and arranged a hiding place. We laid in a supply of rusks, a pail of boiled potatoes and a can of water, and settled down to await further events.

Earth has a pleasant smell and I've always been fond of digging. It's also pleasant to sit in a trench, breathing in the fragrance and looking at the wet walls scarred by shovels. In the spring especially, when you come out to the rested earth with a rake, shovel or plow and begin to dig, you grow dizzy with delight from that fragrance. I dare say that those who have never burned last year's weeds, who have never dug until they sweated in the smoke of campfires, those to whom the fragrance of earth bears no message, or who have forgotten that message in their daily cares, are deprived of much that is delightful.

Therefore, when Degtyarev asked me to dig a hole in which to hide some of his things before he left, I dug one so deep that I had to be pulled out by the handle of my shovel. I helped to camouflage the hole with black soil and twigs, but only time could hide it well.

The cart in the yard was piled high with all sorts of articles, and harnessed to it was the mare Mashka, which Degtyarev hadn't had time to turn into sausage. The old lady wept, and he chided her cheerfully. He had decided to leave Kiev and go west.

People abandoning the battle zone were wearily trudging through the streets with sacks, two-wheeled carts and baby carriages. Mashka despondently pulled her load uphill past Priory Church into the open stretches where I had once cut down pine saplings. Degtyarev would not risk driving through the center of town. Instead he made his way through back alleys and paths known only to him, and emerged on the highway far outside the city.

"Why so down in the mouth?" he asked. "All this is strange to you, but I've watched these perturbations all my life. Anything can happen. Soon you'll see the Reds."

"Where are you going?"

"The world is big, and a sausage-maker will never be lost."

"Maybe you ought to wait."

"What for? The stuff they write in the newspaper is a pound of smoke. The Reds are near Vyshgorod already. It's all the same to me, of course, and I could stay and get work in some warehouse or other. But it's better to be your own boss."

The suburbs ended and the cart creaked through fields. The telegraph poles with their rusty, swinging wires reached to the horizon.

"It's time to say good-bye," said Degtyarev. "We'll probably never see one another again. Be well, and hold on!"

"And you? Where are you going?"

"Don't worry about me! Look here!"

He unbuttoned his shabby, shapeless jacket. His broad shirt beneath it was studded with bumps, as if covered with warts. I could not make anything of this at first, but Degtyarev shook one of the bumps and I heard the jingle of coins. The bumps reached across his chest and midriff in uneven rows, went under his arms and up along his back. That shirt was worth millions—perhaps even billions in the old currency.

Degtyarev broke into a strained smile, watching the impression he had made, "Feel them!"

I felt the bundles, hard as rocks. He wanted someone to appreciate his wealth, his labor, his importance! Those bundles represented his sweat, my sweat, the old lady's sweat and all the slaughtered horses. At last he was able to show someone all his gold; for I was staying behind and did not know where he was going, so I could not report him. We were destined never to meet again, and so he could show off before me. Then Degtyarev lashed Mashka and strode off briskly beside the cart, following the telegraph poles toward the horizon.

Plodding homeward, lost in thought, I suddenly saw I was in trouble. It was too late to do anything. The street had been cordoned off by German soldiers, and they were herding boys and old men out of the yards.

Immediately I went into my customary act: I hunched over, assumed a bored look, pulled down my cap and made straight for the soldiers. It must have been funny this time, for they received me with glee, as if they had been waiting for me; they even laughed. I was shoved toward a group of men standing beside a fence, and immediately I started thinking of a way to escape.

Advancing down the street, the soldiers chased us in front of them. Three with rifles stood by to guard us, while the others combed the street from house to house. We were silent, and so passed five or six houses quietly and meekly; but in the next house there was a crash, as though furniture had fallen, and a shot rang out. Our guards grew uneasy, peering anxiously into the yard.

That's when I took off, as though out to break the world's record. Flying for the corner, I pricked up my ears for the shot meant for me, turned swiftly—and saw that everyone had taken off in all directions.

The shooting began after I had already turned the corner, and I don't know how it ended, because I kept running for at least a mile until I reached the Gorokhovsky house, where I wedged myself behind a wardrobe.

There was no one home but Kolka. After listening to my story with a knowing air, he told me that his mother and grandmother had carried their possessions to the church; it seemed that all the old women had gathered at Priory Church, intending to stay there and pray until our soldiers came. The grandmother had hidden Zhorka in the cellar of the clergyman's house, and he was forbidden to go into the street lest he be seized. As for Kolka, because he was under fourteen he was still running about. And he had just managed to get some hand grenades.

"Where?"

"I stole them from the Germans. Careful, they're loaded! These are lemon grenades."

I clutched a grenade. The German "lemon" was very much like a lemon, only bigger and with a blue cap at one end. If you unscrewed the cap, it hung by a string. All you had to do was to pull the string and throw.

"Give me a couple!" I begged.

"Take them. But let's steal some more."

I thought it over. The terror of my last escape was still with me, but I had to have those weapons. And whatever happened, my legs were well oiled!

"Stand here, next to me," I said.

Kolka got up. He was exactly my size, only a little thinner.

"Could anyone tell I'm fourteen?"

"Of course not!" Kolka assured me.

We brazenly climbed the fence of the former Antiaircraft and Civilian Defense School, which was once more stuffed with soldiers, and walked through the yard as if we belonged there.

The soldiers stood looking out of the windows. They were bored. Some of them were playing wheezy mouth organs, others were cleaning their weapons; and nobody paid any attention to us. Meeting Germans out on a roundup was one thing; encountering them off duty was quite another.

A rifle stood against the wall in a back entranceway, and we had a look at it.

A stout, red-faced cook stood over a steaming field kitchen, chewing his cigar as he went through his ritual over the vat. The cigar was nearly finished and its smoke rose poisonously into his nostrils, but this didn't bother him. We stood watching for a while, but he paid as little attention to us as he would have to a pair of mongrels licking their chops.

We circled the building again and saw the rifle still there, leaning against the wall. We came a little closer, then grabbed it and tumbled into the cellar. This had once been the boiler room; but it was now demolished, and littered with bricks, straw and paper. While one of us kept watch, the other quickly wrapped the gun in hay and paper, turning it into a queer, unrecognizable parcel. Finally we took it by the ends, threw over the fence and climbed after it.

Kolka took some cartridges from his collection and we crossed the road to an empty lot where some buildings had been under construction before the war. There was nothing here but the excavations and remnants of the foundations, from which most of the bricks had been pilfered. We unwrapped the gun and conferred together, trying to figure out how its different parts worked. When we decided we knew enough about it, we set up a brick as a target and started blazing away.

Shots could be heard in all directions anyway, so we didn't even bother to be cautious. The kickback from the rifle was as heavy as a blow from a good-sized fist. It almost made me angry.

We fired about 50 shells, until our shoulders were swollen and we could hardly raise our arms. But we were happy, for now we were real armed fighters. We hid the gun in one of the foundations, and agreed that it would be taken from its hiding place by whoever really needed it.

Even before reaching the house, I realized that something was wrong. Wailing women, burdened with bundles and children, were running. Soldiers stood at our gates, with dogs dodging around them on the leash, their tongues lolling out. Mother stood in the yard, disheveled, pleading in a wailing voice.

"Here he is!" She pounced on me. "We'll go right away, now!"

Accepting her promise, the soldiers moved on to drive other people from their homes, while we dashed to the loft and hid in the hay. Mother quietly scolded me in the dark. I didn't tell her how I had nearly been caught in a roundup, nor about the rifle. And of course, I said nothing about the grenades in my pockets. Why aggravate her? She was distraught enough as it was. She had aged, become bent and so thin that her nose protruded; and her former pupils did not even recognize her in her sweater and black shawl when they met her in the street. When they did, they were amazed: "Maria Fyodorovna! What's happened to you?"

I pried a few splinters from the wall, making a peephole through which I could see the vegetable gardens of the collective farm. It was growing dark. Suddenly a shot rang out nearby and there was a desperate howl or cry, not at all human. Mother shook all over.

A German ran across the garden, took aim and fired, finding his mark again. I heard a hoarse snarling and barking, and I realized he was shooting a dog.

Stillness descended as night came. We drank some water now and then, but ate nothing. I fell asleep, but woke up and saw a cold, feeble light. I reached out my hand and gathered a bit of rotten bark that was shining mysteriously and beautifully. I played with the piece of rotten wood through half the night, but it began to fade from the pressure of my fingers and at last ceased to shine.

Then I heard a light rustling. Somebody was creeping into the loft. I froze with fear, but it occurred to me that it might be Grandfather, back from seeing his friend the Gardener. Then came a tentative, wistful meow. It was Titus. I threw myself on him, hugged him and felt better.

Cats are amazing creatures. They live among us, depend upon us, but hold their independence dear. They have their own complicated lives that barely touch our own. They have their own calendars, their own special paths, passages and gathering points that rarely coincide with ours. I had always respected Titus' private life, but was boundlessly happy that it touched on mine this night.

Thus we spent an entire day in the loft, not going out at all. Then I awoke in the morning and found neither Mother nor Titus. I tossed the hay apart feverishly. Somebody was walking down the street with a sack. At the Babarik cottage across the way, Vovka's mother was closing the shutters. I felt relieved. Mother saw me and called determinedly from the yard:

"Bring the things, we're leaving! There's an empty room

beyond the streetcar line. They're going to spread barbed wire around this place."

I looked for Titus for a long time, calling and whistling for him everywhere, but he seemed to have vanished from the face of the earth. We went without him. On the square we saw a fascist darting from post to post, aiming at something. We flattened ourselves against a fence at first, but then saw that he was shooting at a cat. Dead dogs and cats lay everywhere. In my mind's eye I said good-bye to Titus; now he, too, had fallen into disfavor with Hitler's occupation troops.

Prisoners were digging holes all along the streetcar line, planting posts and unrolling barbed wire. A sign had been put up at the newspaper stand that read:

FORBIDDEN ZONE.
TRESPASSERS WILL BE SHOT.

Directly opposite the sign stood a long low hovel with tiny rag-covered windows. The whole house was fit to be torn down. It had five doors facing the yard, each leading into a small entry. All the rooms were occupied by refugees, but around the corner of the building was another door to an empty cubbyhole. There was a stove and a bench inside. We made our bed in the corner, promoted a stool to the rank of a table; and I went off to look for wood to heat the stove.

The last announcement published by the occupiers of the city of Kiev read:

UKRAINIANS! MEN AND WOMEN!
After two years of restoration in these parts, the war is approaching once more. The German command wants to conserve its forces and is not afraid to with-

draw from certain districts for that reason.

The Soviet command, on the contrary, recklessly counting on its allegedly inexhaustable manpower reserves, spares neither its soldiers nor officers.

Therefore the Germans, with their reserves, will hold out longer, which is decisive for final victory.

You realize that now the German command is compelled to adopt measures which sometimes entail grave inconvenience to individuals in their personal lives.

But this is war!

Work diligently and willingly, therefore, when summoned to do so by the German authorities.

THE GERMAN COMMANDER [3]

Monday, November 1.

In reality it worked this way.

The troops began the roundup on the outskirts of town, driving everyone out into the streets—those who could walk and those who couldn't—prodding them with rifle butts, with blows or by firing in the air. People were given only a few minutes to prepare. They were told that Kiev was to be evacuated to Germany; there would be no such city anymore. [4]

It was dismayingly reminiscent of the procession of Jews in 1941. Masses of people were on the move, including wailing children, the aged and the sick. They carried bundles bound with ropes, crude plywood satchels, bags and tool boxes. An old woman wore a string of onions around her neck. Infants were wheeled in baby carriages, several to a carriage. The sick were carried on the backs of friends and relatives. There was no means of transportation except handcarts and baby carriages. The crowds had already jammed to a standstill on Kirillovskaya Street. The people with their sacks and bundles, the carts and the baby carriages all waited, moved a few steps and waited again; the din mounted and the crowds looked like a weird demonstration of paupers. No one was here to see anyone off—everyone was leaving.

Mother and I watched the procession through our little window. Streetcars appeared out of nowhere; never had I seen such a sad string of streetcars. The Germans had set them going to hasten the exodus. Streetcars circled Petropavlovskaya Square—the extra large ones that used to run along steep Kirov Street before the war.

The refugees were driven aboard, screaming and crying. They pressed through the doors, had their belongings handed to them through the windows, found seats for the children. All this went on directly before our window. A *Polizei* ironically remarked, "You wanted to welcome the Bolsheviks, did you? All aboard, quick!"

We did not wait for dogs to rout us out, but gathered our bundles and went out into the street. We were just in time, for the last crowds were being driven forth. A cordon of soldiers in gray-green stood shoulder to shoulder across the street about 100 yards from the school. The section of the street behind them was empty, utterly deserted. We turned toward the streetcars.

"Let's take the next one," said Mother. "There's more room."

We came up to it but hesitated.

"The next one!" Mother said.

The procession of streetcars moved a bit and stopped again. We ran from one car to the next, unable to make up our minds. The Germans were neither yelling nor shooting now, just waiting patiently.

Mother caught my hand and pulled me back to the hut. We ran into the yard. All the doors were open, but there was not a soul around. We dashed to our little room, shut the door and turned the key. Mother slid to the floor, staring at me with terror in her eyes, her pupils large and dark. We sat very still, not stirring an inch until the last of the extra big streetcars had pulled out.

The window darkened. Now and then we heard the click of boots. Petropavlovskaya Square was completely empty, littered with paper and rags. A German sentry stood on the sidewalk with a submachine gun, some five paces from our window. I could get a view of him only out of the corner of my eye as I pressed against the wall. Whenever he turned around I froze like a little animal and held my breath.

The next day more groups of people, newly ferreted out, were driven past our room. The Germans combed the houses, and the sentries kept relieving each other beside our window. It was this that saved us. Ducks sometimes survive this way, by living safely beneath the very nest of a hawk.

We had no idea what would happen next. What had become of Grandfather? Was he alive? Still, I had a plan. If we were discovered, it was unlikely that they would shoot us in the room; they'd probably take us into the yard first. Once out there we would leap apart and run in opposite directions, not toward the street, however, but deeper into the yard, across the vegetable plots and to the embankment. The latter was long and overgrown with shrubs. It would be hard to find us there without dogs. But since the Germans would be sure to have dogs, we would have to run farther, zigzagging across the meadow. We'd have to plunge into the swamp and get down in the water amid the reeds. If necessary, we could put our heads under the water and breathe through a reed. I had read about this in a book on ancient Rus. People had sometimes saved themselves that way from the Tatars. This would give us complete security, splendid safety.

I whispered all this to Mother and offered her a hand grenade. She waved the grenade aside, but reflected on the possibilities of the swamp. We neither talked nor moved. The silence was complete all around.[5]

"THE WAR OF THE WORLDS"

When our water was gone and there was nothing more to eat, when the sentries had been removed and the city stood utterly empty and dead, we crept out of our cubbyhole. We parted the barbed wire directly under the sign "Trespassers will be shot!" and started for home across the square. This zone was less likely to be searched, we thought.

There had once been flower beds, playgrounds and swings on the square. Who would have thought that one day we would have to steal across the place at the risk of our lives? We ran across in short spurts, bending low, looking around sharply and ready to fall flat at any moment. But the square was empty and there was not a sound anywhere.

Mother wrung her hands when she saw our cottage. The gates hung open, the doors had been smashed and torn from their hinges, the windows were broken, the floors littered with books, broken dishes and my photography equipment. Evidently the Germans had been quartered in our house for a while. The rooms were full of hay, magazines and tin cans. The doors of the wardrobe had been torn off and the zinc washtub had been riddled with bullets.

An icon lay beside the wall of the shed, though I well remembered that Grandfather had hidden this one in the cellar. We hurried to the shed. The Germans had not found the hatch, but had simply scraped the ground apart and pounded a hole through to the cellar with crowbars. Scraps of cloth lay about below. We also saw an old bare fox-fur neckpiece with its tail worn off. Mother clutched her hands again and wept.

I descended through the hole, rummaged about and found an empty satchel and the crowbar that had been used to break into the cellar. Icons lay about on the ground inside the shed as well as out.

Suddenly, from behind some rubbish, we heard the frantic cry of a cat. Titus had evidently hidden when we approached, and had recognized us only now. He came into the open and rubbed against us as hard as he could, complaining in a pitiful basso about the hard time he had had, how lonely he had been and how, terrified, he had hidden. He sprang onto my chest, clinging with his claws, trying to shove his nose into my mouth and pounding my chin with his brow: in short, pouring out his joy in every way he could.

I was delighted he had been smart enough to keep away from the Germans. We cheered up and set to work cleaning the place.

The barrel beneath the drainpipe was full, so at least we wouldn't die of thirst. I dug about in the vegetable garden and found a few forgotten potatoes. Rabbits gone wild hopped about the garden, as quick as hares. It was impossible to catch them. Mother was afraid to heat the stove. Someone might see the smoke from the chimney. Instead, she put two bricks on the ground and lit a fire between them.

The neighboring houses had been gutted too: the windows were smashed, the doors stood open; in the street lay stools, books, a pail, trash. I decided to explore the neighborhood and went to the Engstrem home.

Entering, I stumbled over tin cans and pans loose on the floor. I carefully searched the shelves of a buffet, rummaged through a little closet and then looked under a bed. I was not mistaken—there on the floor was a forgotten crust of dry bread.

Encouraged, I climbed over the fence and went on. The next house had been no less thoroughly ransacked. Someone had even moved his bowels on the floor. I searched the cellar. Having no matches, I had to feel my way about in the dark. My fingers touched damp boards, but at last I found what I wanted: a heap of rotten potatoes and a few carrots. This was great!

Homeward bound with my booty, I paused at the cottage of our neighbor Mishura, recalling that she had had a cellar. Unfortunately her cellar too had been cleaned out, though I did find some old crushed pickles at the bottom of a barrel. I fished one out of the fennel and slime, wiped it on my pants and sank my teeth into it. Sitting there munching pickles in a dank, dark corner of the cellar, I thought of *The War of the Worlds,* by H. G. Wells, in which the Martians had come to earth and then started dying off themselves. Everything lay deserted and in ruins. There were no people.

CHAPTER XLII

I READ PUSHKIN

We lived in complete solitude and silence. German troops passed down Kirillovskaya Street once or twice; and some tanks lumbered by, but not past our house. At times we could hear the thudding of cannon from the direction of Vyshgorod, but on the whole all was quiet, as if the front were nowhere near.

I explored all the houses in the neighborhood. For convenience I made holes in the fences so I wouldn't have to show myself in the street. My routes were much like Titus', stretching across the roofs of the sheds, through trapdoors and windows. I was still looking for food.

Then suddenly our street was in an uproar, filled with the thunder of wheels. Terrified, we hid, for a German unit had arrived. Officers entered the yard swiftly, stamped across the porch, opened the door—and fell back in fright. The first of them snatched out his pistol and pointed it at Mother.

"Mother! Boy! Why? Evacuate! Evacuate!"

Mother started to explain, but the officer wasn't listening.

Instead he said, *"Piff-paff!"* which was the way the Germans imitated the sound of shots.

We stood there, terrified. But they quickly looked through the apartment and then gestured to us: "Out!"

Outside, soldiers were parting the gates for an elegant automobile evidently bearing a very high-ranking commander. No one paid any attention to us, and we withdrew to the shed as fast as we could.

Feverish activity ensued. Telephone equipment and a radio were brought into the house. Communications men came running up, unrolling great reels of cable. Orderlies quickly brought a nickel-plated bed, a couch and some flowerpots from neighboring houses. Mounted messengers halted at the gates.

This officer had a whole store of possessions: women's overcoats, felt boots, rolls of fabrics, even a baby carriage, all of which apparently he meant to ship to Germany. The radio was turned on full blast, while the cook twisted the necks of some geese and disemboweled them.

A soldier came and called Mother to clean vegetables and chop meat in the kitchen. She was busy until evening, when she came back for only a moment, bringing me some of the general's rich soup.

I decided it was best to remain unseen and not run about for a while. So I ensconced myself in the loft with all of Pushkin's collected works, and proceeded to read *Eugene Onegin*. I had begun it several times before, but didn't take to this novel in verse. Of Pushkin's works, *Belkin's Tales* and the story of Pugachev (the leader of the peasant rebellion in the reign of Catherine II) had appealed to me much more. But when I opened *Onegin* this time, I could not tear myself away. Forgetting all about the loft and the Germans, I drank in the music of the lines.

> *You came in dreams to me, so near*
> *I knew your features, always dear;*
> *I languished in your wondrous gaze;*
> *I heard your voice on many days*
> *Remembered   long.[1]*

I read until it grew so dark I could no longer make out the print. Then I lay still, thinking of the poetry and grieving for Titus, who had vanished in a flash the instant the Germans reappeared.

The Germans remained for three days and then took off as suddenly as they had come. They rewound their cable quickly and drove northward toward Pushcha-Voditsa.

HOW MANY TIMES SHOULD I HAVE BEEN SHOT?

By the time I had lived fourteen years on this earth I had committed so many crimes, according to the fascists, that I should have been shot at least 20 times.

1. I had failed to betray a Jew (my pal Shurka).
2. I had helped a prisoner (Vasily).
3. I had hidden a red flag.
4. I had violated the curfew.
5. I had not returned everything I had taken from a store.
6. I had not delivered our fuel to the authorities.
7. I had not handed over our surplus food.
8. I owned a pair of felt boots.
9. I had pasted up a leaflet.
10. I had stolen (beets, wood and so on).
11. I had worked for a sausage-maker illegally, without a license.
12. I had run away from Germany (at Vyshgorod).

13. I had run away again (at Priory Church).
14. I had stolen a rifle and used it.
15. I was in possession of ammunition.
16. I had failed to obey the decree on gold (not having reported Degtyarev).
17. I had harbored anti-German sentiments and encouraged such sentiments in others (there was a decree about this too).
18. I had failed to turn up for registration at the age of fourteen.
19. I had failed to report members of the underground.
20. I had stayed in a forbidden zone for 40 days, and for this alone should have been shot 40 times.

And all this without having been a member of the Communist Party, the Young Communist League or the underground. Nor was I a Jew, a Gypsy, or a hostage. I had not made any speeches or owned pigeons or a radio. I was just a most ordinary, average, nondescript little fellow in a cap. But by their rule—whatever you do, you'll be punished—already *I did not have the right to live.*

If I'm alive, it's only through a misunderstanding; only because, in all that haste and confusion, the Germans could not fully enforce their laws and rules.

If a fascist scoundrel turned up one day with an arbitrary rule of his own, another turned up the next day with a second, then a fifth, then a twentieth. And God knows how many more might be conceived in the murk of fascist brains.

But I wanted to live!

I want to live as long as I was meant to, and not as long as you degenerate bipeds decide I should. How dare you?

What right have you to decide *my* life, to decide:

> *HOW LONG I SHALL LIVE,*
> *HOW I SHALL LIVE,*
> *WHERE I SHALL LIVE,*
> *WHAT I SHALL THINK,*
> *WHAT I SHALL FEEL,*
> *AND WHEN I SHALL DIE?*

I want to live until the very trace of you is gone.

I hate you, fascists, enemies of life, I loathe you as the most nauseating thing ever born on earth. May you be damned! DAMNED! DAMNED!

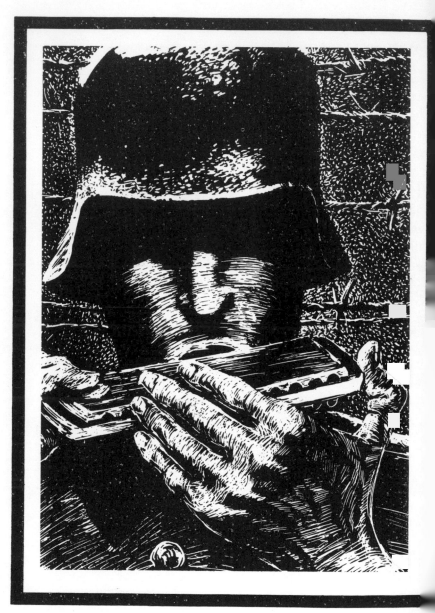

FIVE DAYS OF AGONY

Monday, November 1. I felt a mortal dread on the Sunday night before. There was no immediate reason. It was simply that the night was totally black and a dead city lay within it. I had a presentiment that my life would end that day.

Each of us at one time or another has felt the imminence of inevitable death. Some feel it sooner, some later, but it is sure to come: that sudden frozen awareness of the inevitable moment when one's "I" shall cease to be, when one shall cease to breathe, to think, to see. Each of us chokes on this thought. We fight this horrible feeling, we clutch at the straw, "Well, it won't happen today, nor for a long time to come."

I first had this feeling when Grandmother died; but that was nothing as compared with the dread that descended on me on Sunday night. The trouble was that I couldn't console myself with, "It won't happen today"—every day might be "today" for me. I could hardly breathe.

Dizzy with horror, I climbed down from the stove, groped for the wick lamp and a box of matches with icy hands and cautiously felt my way through the dark into the open. I felt as if my ears were stuffed—I heard nothing, not the bark of a dog, not a rustle anywhere.

I took a shovel and crawled under the house.

The gap leading to the crawl space beneath the house was narrow. I could hardly push through. Farther on there were some nine inches between the beams and the ground. Still I pressed on, pushing up dirt with my chin. I squirmed on, clutching the wick lamp in one hand and dragging the shovel with the other. My head kept hitting posts, broken bricks and dead rats as dry as parchment. I hurled one aside with irritation, and it rattled like an empty box.

When I had crept far enough, I lit the lamp and set it in the sand. Then I wiped the dust and cobwebs from my face and, lying on my side, began to dig.

It was awkward at first, for I had to turn my body with each shovelful. Finally I rolled into the hollow I had already dug. Now I could rise on my elbow and dig faster.

The sand was loose and dry, but full of brick fragments that my shovel scraped on. I was soon sweating, but could already rise to my knees. The hole was uneven, and sand kept seeping back. It was shaped like a long funnel. I kept digging up tiny animal skeletons, four-sided nails and scraps of newspaper. Everything here was just as it was in the time of the Tsar, when this house was built. The people who had printed and read those newspapers or who had tossed these broken bricks aside had probably died long ago.

I needed the hole to hide in. In fact, I felt calmer now. I would die in this hole only if one of three things happened: if they tracked me down with dogs; if the house were hit by a bomb; or if the house burned down.

I thought I was alone, and nearly fainted when a pair of green fires lit up beside me. It was Titus, staring with enormous eyes.

When I recovered I almost wept for gratitude at his joy

and warmth. I hauled him onto my knees, and he did not protest. On the contrary, he hit my chin with his brow and started purring. Thus we sat there while I read scraps from the press of a half century ago.

I pored over the advertisement of one Schmidt: he was honored to offer a large selection of the finest Swiss phonographs with superb "Amour" needles, to say nothing of a fine collection of records at low prices. For some reason he was also ready and willing to buy watches, pearls and antiques. It was maddening to think that there had been a time when people had lived serenely, buying watches, phonographs and pearls. It was hard to believe. A phonograph was just what Titus and I needed at that moment.

I fell asleep, curled up in the sand. When I awoke it was growing light in my hole under the house; another day had come. The cat had left while I was asleep, and I was shivering. The hole did not seem as cozy and safe as it had at night. Curtains of cobwebs hung from the floor beams, and those low beams seemed oppressive, crushing. Once again my nerves were on edge. I imagined that the house might collapse and kill me. Flattening against the ground, I wriggled madly toward the gap and into the open, as if rats were gnawing at my heels.

To calm myself, I leaned over the barrel of rainwater for a drink. Leaves floated on the surface, but I blew them apart and found the water fresh and sweet. It even occurred to me that if I ever lived to see a real sink again I would go on drinking rainwater anyhow. I really liked it.

Then I heard a noise. I was startled, raised my head and saw a German soldier with a rifle entering the yard. From the corner of my eye I spotted another in the street. Instinctively (and stupidly) I squatted behind the barrel, though I knew I would be seen at any moment.

When I thought they weren't looking my way, I doubled over and started toward the corner of the house without looking back, as if they couldn't see me so long as I didn't see them. "Hey!" I heard, "Hey!" I straightened up and stood still.

The soldier was eyeing me sternly. He was a swarthy, stocky man of about 30. His uniform was baggy, and his boots were dirty and worn. He had a plain face, an ordinary, everyday sort of face which was somehow familiar—he could have been a mechanic at the Sport Plant. His fatigue cap was crooked, exposing rakish black curls.

"Komm hier!" he said.

I took a few faltering steps along the wall.

He began to raise his rifle.

There was a cartridge in place all right, for he didn't bother to slap back the bolt. The other German came up, touched his elbow and said something in a calmly indifferent voice. I interpreted his words to mean: "Leave him alone! Why bother?" (So I thought, at any rate.)

The second soldier was older, almost elderly, with sunken cheeks. The swarthy one objected, turning toward him for an instant. That was the moment—I was sure of it!—when I should have dashed off and run wherever I could. And to think that my grenades lay hidden in the hallway right then! This was the very moment I had been saving them for.

There was no time even to plead. *"Pan, Pan! Wait!"* The swarthy soldier simply raised his rifle, but turned his head for a minute to say something to the older one. And that was to be the last minute of my life.

I knew all this before I had time to move. That's how you feel when you happen to hit a pitcher or a flowerpot with your elbow. You see it teeter and fall; you even have time to think that you ought to catch it before it breaks. But it shatters before you manage to move. You can only watch it go, with pain and regret—and it is smashed.

Right there, before my very eyes—not in a movie, a picture, a dream—I saw the black hole of the barrel. I was physically aware of the sooty **O**, of its acrid smell of powder and fire (the old fellow was still talking, but the dark one—alas, alas!—would not listen); and why was that spit of flame so long in coming?

The **O** descended from my face to my chest, and, so shaken I could have cried out, I realized instantly how I was to be killed—shot through the chest.

And the gun went down after all.

I couldn't believe it and waited for it to rise again. The elderly soldier glanced at me casually, patted the swarthy one's shoulder and left the yard.

"Weg!" snarled the swarthy one.

Now, more dead than alive, I broke into a cold sweat for the first time. As if in a dream, I wandered around the corner of the house on cold, wobbly, pipestem legs. I entered the hallway, pressed my face into a corner and stood there, swaying.

Much as I have thought about that incident, I cannot understand what it really meant. A joke? Had the older man merely said, "Stop this foolery. Why scare the boy?" Or had it been serious, with the older soldier saying, "Leave him alone! Why bother with him?" If it had been a joke, why hadn't the swarthy man smiled afterwards, at least a little? If he was serious, why hadn't he shot me?

Tuesday, November 2. I am one of those who are unreservedly fond of bright light. I never find that there are too many electric bulbs or too much sunshine. This trait is neither good nor bad; it's simply the way I am. I have never worn dark glasses, for the brighter everything is all around, the more dazzling the beaches or the snowy fields, the better my spirits and the better I feel. Far from hurting, my eyes delight in brightness.

But Mother complained that her eyes hurt. She kept drawing the curtains, and I kept parting them. When everybody was suffering from the heat of summer, I was just beginning to enjoy myself. During the annoying dreary autumn days, I sometimes thought that the sun was probably shining brightly and was even baking hot at that very moment in the Crimea, in Africa, or on Pacific islands, and this brought on such a fit of longing that I could have wept.

I hate the processions of clouds that keep turning off the sun for long intervals. I look and look at the cursed cloud, waiting for it to pass. When I recall events of many years back, I can always remember whether they occurred in good weather or bad.

I mention all this because I was so glad when the sun came out again after the dreary October days. I almost forgot that yesterday someone had wanted to shoot me. I grew carefree and confident, feeling that since I had been so lucky thus far, it was plainly my destiny and I would squirm out of future troubles too.

I kept a grenade in each side pocket now, for I had learned my lesson. Never parting with them, I checked them from time to time to see that the caps were still in place. I moved as warily as a cat, ready to vanish in an instant. Eager to be active, I dug a trench under the house and widened the hole so that Mother could sit in it too.

She climbed in once and looked around, but was not delighted. But she suggested that we hide our satchel there. This was quick work. I buried it deeply to save it from fire. I never doubted that our cottage would burn down, and I

350

kept looking at the house so I would remember what it had been like.

Once again we heard footsteps and voices in the street, and I darted to the gap under the house. Peering out, I recognized my godmother Lyaksandra and my godfather Mikolai moving slowly, ever so slowly, across the deserted square.

The old woman led her blind husband very carefully, guiding him around holes and bricks. She was telling him something. He wore his familiar spectacles. When they discovered us, both of them burst into tears. They had been looking for people.

Mother took them into the house at once and gave them a meal. They hadn't been able to find any food and hadn't eaten for two days.

"We've been sitting in the cellar," complained the old woman. "Well, it's time to die anyway, we're old; so we went looking for people."

Mother almost cried. It is hard to imagine what solitude can be like in a city that has died, a city without people. She invited the old couple to stay for the night, and they agreed we should join forces. We would save ourselves together or die together. They made and remade their beds and then lay down. But they suddenly decided that they had to see to their own apartment, and that they would be better off sleeping in the cellar in their own building. They were as willful about it as children. They wanted their cellar, and nothing else would do.

Mother gave them some potatoes, which they accepted with a bow before dragging themselves back across the square.

"Search the yards and cellars!" I advised them.

The old woman brought her hands together in dismay:

"Go into other people's cellars? To steal? God forgive you, my child!"

I stood watching them for a long time, afraid they would be shot down on the way. They were such an unusual pair, so very unworldly. There they went across the square, through this shattered world, arm in arm and chatting.

I was almost asleep when a motor roared and shafts of light slid over our windows. Something like a tank came clanking straight across the vegetable garden, its headlights pointed directly at our house. Without checking its speed, it smashed through the fence, the splinters flying. For a moment I thought it would crash through the house as well; but it stopped beside the wall, exactly alongside that wonderful gap to my hiding place. It was too late to escape. The doors of the machine outside slammed, and we heard Germans talking briskly.

As though by command, Mother hastened to light the wick lamp so the Germans would see that someone lived here and not be startled when they entered. She was right, for they even wiped their feet on the porch and knocked on the door. Mother answered and in they came, energetic, smartly uniformed and smiling.

"Guten Abend!" they said, and gestured to show what they wanted: *"Schlafen, schlafen!* Sleep."

"Bitte," said Mother.

They entered the room with their usual familiarity and made themselves at home, knowing at once where to hang their trench coats and drop their dispatch pouches. They brought some blankets and boxes from their vehicle. In the meantime we folded our bedding and withdrew to the other half of the house. I recovered my courage and went into the yard to see what kind of machine they had. It was an armored halftrack, with an artillery piece coupled behind.

The Germans were talking cheerfully as they carried things from the back of their vehicle. In ten minutes or so they rapped on the door to our part of the house.

"Mother! Boy! Come here!"

We entered the room. In addition to the wick lamp, which Mother had been afraid to take away, there was a dazzling carbide lamp. It kept going out, however, and one of the Germans was trying to adjust it. There was a mountain of food on the table and plenty to drink too. The wine was in clay bottles with various labels. In lieu of glasses there were small metal cups. The Germans gestured, inviting us to the table like genial hosts, *"Bitte, bitte! Eat!"*

One of them offered me a slice of bread covered with ham. Amazed, I began to devour it and at once grew dizzy.

There were three of them: Franz, a placid, elderly man with red hair; Herman, about seventeen, dark, handsome and well knit; and a third fellow, whose name we didn't learn. He was the driver, the man who kept adjusting the carbide lamp. After a few bites of food, he rolled over fast asleep, obviously exhausted.

Old Franz poured the drinks, shaking the clay bottle and boasting, "France! Paris!"

The wine was sweet and aromatic. Mother drank her cupful and told Franz that they were good Germans, but that there were others who wanted to *piff-paff* us.

Franz frowned.

"Those are no *Soldaten*. Those are bandits, a shame to the German nation. We're front-line *Soldaten*, artillerymen. War—*piff-paff!* Mama, *Kinder*—no *piff-paff*."

Herman drew a mouth organ from a side pocket and

353

began to play, while Franz poured himself another drink. Laboriously but stubbornly he struggled for words to tell us how brutally tired they were. The three of them had fought first in Norway, then in Africa with Rommel. Now they had been brought from the Western Front. And everywhere they had to fight:

"*Mein Gott,* Mama! War here, war there! War, war!"

Franz impressed me as a serious fighting man, a seasoned soldier steeped in battle, and I was afraid of him. But young Herman, only three years or so older than I, was a naïve and likable boy, much like Bolik; and he talked mostly to me.

"Franz is *von* Hamburg *und ich von* Berlin," he confided. "I a whole year fight!" he said proudly.

"Aren't you afraid?" I asked.

He smiled, "To tell truth—afraid. In France not very afraid, but in Russia very."

He brought out a snapshot of himself and his father. His father was an impressive-looking gentleman with a hat and cane, and beside him stood a shy, skinny boy in short trousers. In the background was a park of some sort.

Mother asked where the front lines were and whether the Germans would give up Kiev.

Franz's face darkened. "No, Kiev give up we shall not. The front is in the woods, but the Russians will not enter Kiev. There will be terrible battles. Now that troops are here from France, *ach,* what a battle there will be! A Stalingrad!" He reflected for a while and emphatically reiterated, "A Stalingrad!"

"November seventh is the biggest Soviet holiday," said Mother.

He understood what she meant at once.

"*Ja, ja!* Soviets want to take Kiev on holiday—October

Revolution holiday. But they will not, they will die. I understand, you waiting for Soviet, but Kiev they shall not take,
never! Drink, Mama!"

My heart sank. He wasn't lying. Why should he lie?
These Germans were practically the first who had talked to
us as if we were human beings; and this was a serious talk.

"But what if they do take the city? You're retreating,
aren't you?"

"*Ja, ja,* I understand," old Franz answered gravely.
"You're waiting for Soviet, but I tell you, I'm an old *Soldat.*
Go away, go away please; here—you will die."

He said again that we simply had to run away, to some
village or to the forest, where we could dig a hole and stay
in it until the front moved away. For on Hitler's orders,
Kiev would be razed and turned into a dead zone.

He pointed to his chest with his thumb, "It's I who am
saying this, the old *Soldat* Franz. I fought in Poland even. It
is all like that: advance, retreat. The Russian is tired."

The driver slept on the couch in his clothes. Herman
grew morose and put his mouth organ away. Franz was getting drunk. Mother and I retired to our part of the house,
but Franz and Herman did not sleep for a long time. We
heard them talking.

That night Mother's cries woke me up. She was calling frantically, "Tolya, Tolya, help!"

There was a commotion. A stool fell over. Sleepily I
cried, "Who's there? Who is it?"

I lit a match. At first the light blinded me, but then I saw
Mother struggling with red-haired Franz. He was very drunk,
mumbling persuasions in German, and grabbing at her.

I always kept some wood tapers on the stove, and I lit
one of them now and advanced resolutely. Red-haired Franz

turned to look drunkenly at the flame, then thoughtfully at me. He let Mother go.

"It's *Krieg*, Mother! War, *nichts gutes*," he said "Ah!" He staggered, bumped into the door and went out.

Trembling, Mother wedged a pole against the door.

"He's drunk! Quite drunk," she said. "Thank goodness you lit that taper! Go to sleep now. Everything is all right. And thank you, dear."

For the first time I felt like a man, like someone who could and should offer protection. I was enraged too. I woke up many times before morning, listening carefully and feeling for my grenades under the pillow. But all was quiet. When I got up I counted the days and hours until the October holiday. (The October Revolution is celebrated on November 7 by the new calendar.) Only 96 hours were left. But there was silence all around.

Wednesday, November 3. Wednesday began with a splendid morning. The sky was clear and blue. I came out on the porch and stood breathless, marveling at this freshness and cleanliness, and at the morning sun. Everybody knows the feeling one gets from a clear sky in the morning. You want to spend the day as well as you possibly can. If it happens to be a holiday, you are eager to prepare—to make a lot of sandwiches, wrap them up in a newspaper and go fishing or else simply roam the countryside.

This was the day of the decisive battle for Kiev; and when I relive its beginning I find again and again that I cannot, for the life of me, understand how such a delightful, joyous world—with such a sky and such a sun—with people, endowed with minds and the faculty of thought—not animals guided by instinct, but thinking, understanding people —could harbor such boundless idiocies as aggression, war and fascism.

356

Yes, yes, it's all very clear, of course; for it has been thoroughly explained, politically, economically and psychologically. It has all been analyzed time and again, diagnosed, elucidated and thoroughly expounded. But for all that, *I cannot understand*.

Herman and the driver were dipping water out of the barrel, laughing and splashing each other as they washed. Red-haired Franz was subdued. He must have had an awful hangover. As for the incident in the night, his manner showed that he wanted it forgotten.

Mother laid some twigs under the bricks and started preparing breakfast. The halftrack did not look so sinister by day. It had wheels in front and caterpillar treads in back, and the body was covered with canvas. It stood peacefully by the house, watching the world with attentive, quizzical headlights. It smelled of gasoline and looked very dusty.

Franz and Herman raised the canvas and started unloading sacks of potatoes. I stood watching and wondering why they needed all those potatoes.

But beneath the potatoes were cannon shells. Either the quartermaster had made them carry these sacks, or they had picked them up themselves somewhere. They were not out to sell them, at any rate. Emptying the truck, they asked for a broom and swept out the back of it. Herman untied one of the sacks, dumped about 50 pounds of potatoes on the ground and winked as though to say, "Take them away. They are for you!"

Suddenly the earth heaved.

This was so queer and wrong that I had no time to be frightened. The earth was in motion underfoot, as it probably is in an earthquake. The woodpile in the shed scattered, and all the doors slammed. The earth kept heaving for several seconds under the clear, sunny morning sky; and then there was thunder from the direction of Pushcha-Voditsa.

This was not thunder so much as a great roar—an avalanche, a sea of roars. Never in my life have I heard anything like it again. It was as if the whole world were exploding, turning inside out.

One of the shocks hurled me into the middle of the yard. I could not grasp what was happening. Was the world falling apart? Or was this like a giant tidal wave? The Germans too were staggering about, staring in the direction of the thunder; but the sky was clear out there, beyond the embankment.

The driver quickly climbed on top of the cab of the halftrack and craned his neck. But he could not see anything either. The three exchanged brief words and started loading their shells and potatoes aboard the halftrack as fast as they could. Herman ran to the house and returned with their submachine guns, while Franz brought out the helmets and gave one to each.

Mother, very pale, stood fidgeting over the bricks, wondering whether she would have time to go on cooking breakfast.

Black dots we knew were planes appeared far in the sky beyond the embankment, over Pushcha-Voditsa. We could not hear them in that uproar, but they kept drifting across the sky like gnats. The air around them was suddenly filled with bits of white fluff. They flew quickly over Pushcha-Voditsa and had hardly vanished when a second wave appeared from beyond the Dnieper. These came a little closer to us. Flying through the exploding antiaircraft barrage in a swift arc, they were followed by a third wave, even closer. Wave after wave they came, bombing Pushcha-

Voditsa, covering more and more territory, thoroughly and with precision.

Franz, Herman and the driver left the halftrack and stood by the shed, helmeted and carrying submachine guns. Wary and grim, they watched. Planes traced another arc over the edge of the forest, this time already near Abandon Sorrows. The next group came still closer; another two or three such arcs, and it would be our turn.

I went up to the three Germans and stood beside them, listening. The artillerymen were talking quietly, never taking their eyes from the gripping, crackling performance in the air.

"Ilyushin bombers."

"*Ja.*"

"There's a trench over there."

"Fix the gunsight."

Red-haired Franz took me by the shoulder and spoke earnestly, in a worried tone. He pointed to the vegetable garden, then to Mother, and gestured as though to say "Run for it, hide!"

"*Piff-paff!* Soviet! Ilyushin—*schwarzer Tod!*"

I nodded but didn't go—I don't know why. I was almost bursting from tension.

One of the planes exploded into flames at that instant. It came down slowly, down and down, tilting, and vanished behind the embankment. A parachute unfurled in the sky. The pilot had bailed out and the wind was carrying him over the forest. This tiny dot of a human hung wretchedly helpless beneath the little white disk amid the shellbursts and tracers. I doubt if he reached the ground alive, and if he did he must have fallen into the hands of the Germans. The artillerymen did not seem happy at this. They stood watching him vanish, as somberly as I.

The black, furious assault planes roared over the embankment in threes, almost hedgehopping. They were bombing and shooting, unleashing a squall of fire. Boards, earth and other debris flew into the air. The sky was packed with shellbursts. The next wave was sure to be ours.

And then it came.

Planes sprang crazily from behind gardens and houses, monstrously low, seeming almost within reach. Their roaring drowned all words. They dived in, three by three, each with a jet of fire at the nose. The last thing I noticed was red-headed Franz, flattened strangely against the wall of the shed, his blazing submachine gun shaking. It was like a silent movie: The gun shook in his hands, but there was no sound from it, for there was only one continuous roar. Then everything began to totter.

Hurled through the air and thrown to the ground, I let out the piercing cry, "Bombs!" but did not hear it myself. And the cry was wrong too, more like "Bo-a-u-i!" Everything turned black and then bright. The soil flew apart and then back into place, and I discovered that I was running on all fours and was just about to bang my head against the porch. The planes were gone.

Covered with sand from head to foot, Herman came out of the shed. His face was contorted. He snatched a fresh magazine for his submachine gun from the halftrack, but had no time to reload.

Another row of planes swooped from behind the gardens and houses, like black arrows. Herman dived between the caterpillars of the halftrack. I lunged into the house. I had barely managed to flatten my back against the stove, almost pressing myself into the stove wall, when both house and stove were set rocking; and through the window I saw a blinding jet of fire rise amid the lilac bushes by the gate.

Parts of the gate and the fence rose into the air, and the windowpane cracked. I was showered with plaster and dust, and my hair was all blown about. The planes vanished, and I could now hear the ring of glass disintegrating.

I began mechanically to clean up, shaking my head so the plaster would fall off. Then I saw the stove and was petrified. There was a perfectly round hole in it exactly a finger's breadth higher than the spot where the top of my head had been. I could not believe it and put my back to the stove again, feeling the hole above the back of my head. My finger went through it. I went round the stove and looked at it from the other side. There was no hole there. The shrapnel lay embedded inside.

This made me realize, at last, that I had to take cover in the trench. What had become of Mother? I did not know. I went into the open, looked around and thought, "Perhaps she's in the trench already." At that instant more planes swept in from behind the houses and gardens.

I must have been in a state of shock, for I sped across the flat, open vegetable garden to the trench like a hare, though I realized that I was a good target and would probably never get there.

Half-consciously I noticed that the planes were ahead of me already, that there was a huge crater in the vegetable garden beside the house, that there was fluffy sand all around and that I was plodding softly across it, leaving a string of tracks.

New planes were already above me. I glimpsed the heads of the fliers and the red stars on the wings. Dazed, I mechanically noted the sand spouting around me, and realized with anger that they took me for a German, fool that I was. I was greatly annoyed at myself and fate, for how could the fliers, moving at that speed, tell whether I was a German or not? They knew, besides, that the population was gone.

The sand flew all around me, but again I was uninjured. The planes seemed to have been gone for a long time, but I was still running to the shelter. I dived into it and sped to the darkest and farthermost corner, badly bruising Mother. What joy! She was here and alive! But the roaring began again.

Planes leaped from behind the gardens and houses, and the earth shook as from the blows of an infuriated giant. The props of our shelter started rocking and swaying, and sand seeped down. Mother hurled me to the ground and threw herself on top of me. When the thunder stopped she peered out, mumbling, almost praying, "Oh, lovely! Give it to them, give it to them!"

She embraced me, hardly knowing what she was doing, and rocked me in her arms, talking to the planes rather than to me, "Even if you kill us, hit them hard! Keep it up! Kill us, but get them too!"

I'm afraid you won't understand or believe this. Hysterical tears were pent up within me. I *loved* those planes. Those were *our* men up there. They knew there could be no one here but Germans and so they were hammering away with all their might. They had the fascists on the run!

"Keep at them, friends, pound away!"

That was how it began.

Man's adaptability is astonishing. By midday I could tell from the sounds where the planes were coming from, where they were going, how they were flying and whether the danger was great. I was getting used to this life, and even ran to the house in the intervals.

The house was a bizarre sight. The walls were pocked with shrapnel. Not a windowpane was left. As for the roof, it looked as though someone had half buried it with sand and charred bricks, although the chimney was intact. The bomb crater beside the cottage could easily have held two trucks. There were smaller craters all around.

The artillerymen sat huddled in a slit beyond the shed. Covered with dirt and no longer shooting, they obviously had only one thing on their minds—how to survive. Their submachine guns lay where they had flung them in the courtyard.

Franz gestured again, "Go away, boy, go away."

I shrugged to tell him I wouldn't go, and smiled grimly. Looking around I thought, "What a pity that bomb fell ten yards short; it was headed straight for the halftrack and cannon."

A worried soldier appeared through a gap in the fence and called to our artillerymen. They climbed into the open, but a plane came over just then, and they hopped back into the slit like rabbits. "Aha!" I thought, "So you're afraid of even a single plane now!"

When it passed, they climbed out again and ran after the soldier. I followed to see what was up. The Korzhenevsky house, the third from ours, was gone. The huge crater in its place was partly filled with boards and spattered with blood. So this was where the bricks on our roof had come from! A poplar stripped by shrapnel stood beside the crater. The door of the house hung in the top of the tree, lodged between branches.

The soldier and the artillerymen started pulling apart the boards in the crater.

I had often noticed that heavy shelling seemed to spoil the weather. Perhaps it was a coincidence; but in all that thunder from Pushcha-Voditsa, the sky, which had been so clear in the morning, clouded over by afternoon. Dark and low, the clouds made the day dismal and sinister. But they didn't stop the planes. The Ilyushins kept flying, almost sweeping the ground.

The artillerymen were washing at the water barrel when a messenger galloped up and shouted to them in a sharp, guttural voice. The three ran for their halftrack. The motor snarled, and the halftrack, belching smoke, trundled through the gate. It veered sharply and the cannon rocked behind it. Somewhere other halftracks roared. They were clanking over the cobblestone pavement, heading north to Puscha-Voditsa—into the maelstrom.

Thursday, November 4. We thought we would never see the artillerymen again, but they came back. The artillery barrage and the heaving of the earth stopped after dark. Suddenly our windows were lit up by a pair of headlights, and the halftrack was back in the yard. It stopped beside the lilac bush. "It's just as if they had gone off to work," I thought, "and now that it's evening they've come back for the night."

They did not enter the house at once, but gathered twigs in the dark and camouflaged their vehicle. When I came out they hardly noticed me. They uncoupled the cannon and dragged it into the street, its barrel trained on the embankment.

The canvas of the halftrack hung in tatters. When the men entered the room and lit the carbide lamp I could see how awful they looked. They were scorched and sooty, and their bandaged hands shook. Young Herman seemed the most shaken. He paced aimlessly and was almost crying. Franz, handing me the kettle, asked for water.

"Heavy fire?" I asked.

"*Ach!*" shuddered Franz, and then they were all talking, explaining and reporting. They had to talk about it, to unburden themselves. Gesticulating, they tried to tell me how awesome it had been: impossible to describe, a deluge of fire, a burning hell. Herman brought out a handbook and searched it for words. He repeated several times with eyes brimming with despair: "*Uzhas! Uzhas!* [Horror! Horror!] Understand? *U-zhas!*"

I gathered the general meaning from their flood of words. France and Africa had been a picnic compared with today. The Russians were firing Katyusha rocket throwers. The Katyushas accounted for the thunder and earthquake of the morning. The Russians had advanced from the village of Petrivtsa and had taken Pushcha-Voditsa. The German units were smashed, the forest was on fire and the ground was burning too. The three artillerymen didn't know how they had survived.

"Oh my boy, my boy!" moaned red-headed Franz. He clutched his head and rocked from side to side. Then he put his elbows on the table and buried his face in his hands. I hadn't expected this. These soldiers had arrived so boldly and heartily, and now they were behaving like terrified women. I didn't know what to say.

"Does Franz have any children?" I asked Herman quietly.

"*Ja,*" he answered. "Three children."

I went out and looked at the horizon. There was a red glow. Guns rumbled in the distance now and then.

From the school came the sound of motors, commands, shouts. A demon must have led me into the street. Dark against the darkness, I flattened myself against a fence. I stole off to the school to see what was happening. I wanted to steal a submachine gun.

I had reached the Engstrem house when I suddenly stopped in fright. Pressed against the wall, I spun my head about, trying to spot the danger. Then, by the feeble glow from the horizon, I saw a man directly opposite me behind a lattice fence.

He was carrying a bag or box, and stood motionless, looking straight at me. I was riveted to the spot. I tried to imagine that I couldn't be seen, while he probably hoped he was invisible himself. We stood facing one another for a minute. There were no Kurenevka men left here, I was sure of that. And this was no German. He moved too carefully. Besides, he was wearing civilian clothes.

I stepped slowly back and noiselessly made my way home. When I darted into the house I was trembling. Who was that man? It wasn't until the next evening that I realized who he was.

The glowing patches in the distance kept dimming and brightening all night. The artillerymen didn't drink or play the mouth organ. They slept, exhausted. But I woke up and stood on the porch, watching the red horizon.

In the morning Lyaksandra hurried to us. The school was occupied by Germans, she said. Halftracks and cannon were ranged about the yard. The whole first floor was full of wounded men, screaming and dying. The floors were slippery with blood. There were not enough doctors. Lyaksandra and Mikolai had had to give them all their sheets and towels for bandages.

She had heard that many people were hiding in a cave right here in Kurenevka, somewhere in the gully. If one could only reach them! A cave? I liked the idea. But where

366

was it? Mama gave Lyaksandra some more potatoes, and she hurried off to her husband.

We expected the barrage and the air attacks to begin at any moment. Mama carried our bedding into the shelter, preparing for a long stay. But time passed, and all was quiet.

The artillerymen started patching their halftrack. Somewhat uncertainly they kept saying the Russian breakthrough had been stopped. I doubt that they really believed it. Still, the day passed in tormenting silence from the front.

The glowing patches reappeared at twilight. A cannon rumbled at rare intervals. Suddenly shells came shrieking and hissing directly over our house. Explosions shook the earth close to us. A glaring flash burst from the school yard: The shells had landed in the thick of the halftracks. The machines burned fiercely, and the ammunition in them began to explode.

I climbed the fence with a racing heart and gleefully watched the Germans scurrying about in the glare. They scattered, falling flat and hiding in the holes and craters as their ammunition kept exploding, raising clouds of sparks. Shrapnel sprayed in all directions. The uproar was like the bombing. It was beautiful!

When the shells struck I had fallen flat in the grass, but then impetuously climbed the fence to watch and exult. I was ready to hug the man I had seen behind the fence last night. Now I realized that he was a reconnaissance man and that this shelling was his work. I am still amazed when I think of the precision with which the shells struck the yard and landed right among the halftracks. No more than two shells were expended, I think, and both struck home without preliminary adjustment fire.

The Germans began hauling their halftracks out of the yard with a cable. But the shells in the red-hot trucks continued to explode, some of them flying out like fiery bombs. Several of these set fire to a building across the way. It was the building where Lyaksandra and Mikolai lived.

I ran home and told Mother; she threw a kerchief over her head, and we set off at once to save the old couple. But we met them in the street.

Lyaksandra and Mikolai had been sitting in their cellar when they saw that their house was on fire. After leading Mikolai into the open, Lyaksandra hurried back into the house, but was able to grab only a pot, a kitchen knife and a spoon. And that was how we found her, leading Mikolai by one hand and carrying an aluminum pot in the other.

Their building burned all night like a torch; no other light was needed. Now we were four, since there was nothing the old couple could do but stay with us. As for Grand-father, we thought he was dead. But he was not; at that moment, he was sitting in a sewer.

Friday, November 5. Titus our tomcat had grown quite fat. While I slept in my hole under the house that night, he came and lay on my chest, giving me a string of nightmares. I shooed him away several times, but he persistently climbed back, as round and heavy as a suckling pig.

Rats and mice had multiplied in the deserted houses, and Titus pursued them through the sheds. He slept in his leisure time and seemed to be the only creature who had benefited from the war. He was entirely alone, for there were no other cats or dogs anywhere about.

I was awakened in the morning by the sound of firing. The barrage seemed near, and the assault planes were making their runs again. This was a repetition of November third, but with a difference.

The nerves of the Germans were giving way. They scattered at the first drone of a plane. The assault craft flew almost at ground level, operating with impunity in a routine manner, as if spraying the fields with insecticide. No one fired at them from the ground.

Once more a messenger roused the artillerymen, and again they trundled through the gate, heading for Pushcha-Voditsa. The halftracks still left at the school were also on the move. Tanks, trucks and motorcycles hurtled through the streets.

At noon, other artillerymen set up a cannon in the vegetable gardens and began firing across the embankment. They fired as often as they could, as if to fulfill a plan of some sort, but scurried off disgracefully at the first sound of a plane. I kept out of sight, watching through a small opening as they loaded their gun, swung back the lock and discarded the golden, clanging shell cases. "I'll collect them when you're gone," I thought. "They'll all be mine!"

The shooting of this gun, as of the others, troubled me as little as the noise of a passing streetcar. Things were worse when the assault craft flew in, but I dived smartly into some shelter or other; afterwards, I crawled out to explore the new craters and marvel that our cottage was still in place and whole.

Soviet shells, too, whistled past from time to time. They described a low arc directly overhead, and had a peculiar whining, scraping sound of their own. They exploded in various places: on the square, in the Park of Culture, at the agricultural station. Sometimes I could see where they landed by the stones and twigs flying into the air.

I found Titus in the shed, completely ignoring the war. I picked him up just as he was, curled up and sleeping, and brought him to our shelter, where I put him to bed on a sack He slept peacefully on, without so much as twitching his ear at the explosions.

Mother didn't nag or plead with me not to go out, or not to show myself. She gave up completely, for how could anyone tell where the next bomb would fall? And there were hits all around. I'd be tearing for the shelter and meet her halfway, dashing for the house. This was both funny and terrible. Luck was our only hope. This fatalism gained such a hold on her that later when I was engaged in the risky business of roaming the mine fields or defusing and blowing up bombs, she no longer scolded me and even gave up objecting. It was as if something had snapped in her. She had been so solicitous before, always worrying about me—and there had been endless reason to worry—that now she went to the opposite extreme. No ordinary human could have borne it otherwise.

Old Lyaksandra and Mikolai flatly refused to join us in the shelter. They stayed in the house, and I served as a liaison between Mother and them. They took the spring mattress from the bed, leaned it against a corner of the stove and covered it with padded quilts, the result being a sort of lean-to in the room. They would crawl into this and sit there, huddled together. I would come in, turn back a fold of the quilt and ask, "Are you alive, in there?"

"Alive, thank God!" Lyaksandra would answer. "And Mama? Is she alive?"

"Everything is fine. We're going to have dinner soon."

Blind Mikolai, who had extremely sensitive hearing, said, "There's a humming. I hear it! Two planes are coming."

I heard nothing, but Lyaksandra caught me by the hand.

"Come in here, hide!"

I crawled into their lean-to, and sure enough, two planes came roaring over, scattering a lot of little bombs.

"They're taking the cannon away," announced Mikolai.

I dashed for the yard and found that the Germans really had rolled their gun away. Feeling glad, I set out to collect the shell cases, but could only stamp my foot in disappointment: They had taken the shell cases with them. Here they were, dying, but they carried their shell cases off with them!

Suddenly I saw Lyaksandra and Mikolai shuffling frantically through the vegetable garden toward the shelter. She kept pulling the old man along by the hand, telling him to hurry, but he could hardly keep up.

"There are Germans there! Germans!" cried Lyaksandra.

Several limousines rolled into our yard. The communications men were running about already, unwinding their reels of red wire.

Tiny figures of German soldiers could be seen running about on the embankment. They were setting up machine guns. Rifle and machine-gun fire could be heard from the direction of Pushcha-Voditsa. I was expecting the final dragnet raid.

CHAPTER XLV

A CHAPTER FROM
THE FUTURE

One day in early December I went to Pushcha-Voditsa with
the boys to gather hand grenades and hunt for explosives.

The forest was mutilated and mangled. Shattered cannon, burned-out halftracks, turretless tanks, and stacks of
unused shells and mines were everywhere, under the pines
and among the bushes. But the chief thing was the mass
of corpses lying all around. Someone had been heaping
them together in piles three yards high—pyramids of
naked, bluish-gray Germans, rotting despite the slight frost.
I think there are many families in Germany that still do
not know how and where their men perished.

Should these lines be read by the children of the missing,
for example, the children of Franz from Hamburg, the
elderly artilleryman who took part in the seizure of Poland
and Norway, who captured Paris and fought under Rommel
in Africa, I would like them to know that their fathers
died in Russia with thousands of others and lay in a pile of
grayish-blue corpses all through the winter of 1944. Later

373

they were laid out in ditches and pits and covered with earth.

The forests have risen again, and it is impossible to find those places now. There are many forests in Russia.

The retreating Germans caught Bolik after all and took him along in a transport train. He escaped and returned to Kiev on the third day after its liberation. A neighbor had to put him up, since his home had been sacked and his relatives were gone. Then he was drafted into the army; and off to the front he went to do some real fighting at last. I was sure he had found his long-coveted machine gun there.

He did not return to Kiev until the autumn of 1944. He was still lanky, with the same bump of a forehead, but taller and more manly. He even had a rank now: junior sergeant. After fighting on the Finnish Front for seven months, he fell into the water somewhere, caught cold and lay sick in a village for a long time. Then something went wrong with his heart and lungs, and he was sent to Kiev for treatment. He was thin and pale, the kind who sways in the wind, as they say.

"Tell me all about it! Where've you been?" I threw myself on him. "Did you fight well?"

His hand rose sadly, "Oh, I was . . . with the medical corps, in a medical train."

"What about that machine gun?"

"It didn't turn out that way. I only got a chance to shoot at some planes with a rifle and waste some ammunition."

This fellow was moody and absent-minded—not the Bolik I once knew. Here he'd been in the war and he wouldn't even talk about it.

"They gave me a medal," he remarked indifferently.

"Show it to me!"

"It's at home."

We stood in my yard. The day was cold and gray. Grandfather (he, too, had survived) came in from the street and was surprised to see Bolik.

"So you're back?"

"Yes."

"Well, well, you've had bad luck, haven't you? The same thing could have happened to Tolik if he'd been a little older."

Grandfather regarded Bolik attentively.

In a few days Bolik was taken to one of the sanatoriums in Pushcha-Voditsa; I was glad, for the Pushcha-Voditsa sanatoriums were very good. It was difficult to be admitted there.

I was deep in my lessons at school at that time. Engrossed with mathematics, I pored over my theorems at night and did not think of Bolik very often. I was all the more surprised, therefore, when Mother hurried into the house one day and exclaimed mournfully, "They're burying Bolik! Go to his funeral!"

The procession moving down the street was headed by Bolik's uncle, who carried a solitary medal on a cushion. Then came two or three wreaths, and then an open truck bearing the open coffin, followed by a score or so of mourners.

There lay my Bolik, in a well-pressed suit, his skin yellow, his hands folded awkwardly on his chest. Sitting in the truck beside him was Auntie Nina, his mother. She was a bent little woman, as yellow as he, and she never took her eyes from her son.

The truck swayed as it rolled over a pothole opposite

375

our gate, and Bolik's mother clung desperately to the coffin. I guessed she was unable to walk and that's why she was in the truck.

I can't explain my state of mind. As the truck rolled by our gates, a stream of hazy thoughts flitted through my head. Why didn't Bolik get well in those good sanatoriums? Why hadn't anyone told me he had died? Why hadn't anyone called me when his body lay at his home? I knew where they would bury him: at Kurenevka cemetery, beside the tombstone of his grandfather Kaminsky. I knew the spot well, for that was where Grandmother lay. I would visit the place in a few days, but I didn't want to walk in that procession. I only wanted to see Bolik and remember him.

The casket, rocking in the truck with Bolik's mother, was so close that I had a good look. Mother kept nudging me, urging in a tearful voice, "Go! See Bolik to his last resting place."

But I hung back sullenly. The procession moved on and on toward the bazaar, and I stood watching as long as it was in sight.

Bolik had gone.

I saw a great deal of the world: I worked at various construction projects and later studied in Moscow. When I came home for a visit one day, Mother said:

"Vovka Babarik is back. He was injured by a mine near Warsaw, where he served as a sapper. He's just back from the hospital. May God save everyone from such a fate! He can't move, he's blind and he's lost an arm. He didn't want to come home, didn't want to show himself that way; but they talked him into it and brought him home after all. Why don't you drop in on him? He's always happy when someone comes."

This was the same Vovka Babarik with whom I had been friends and then enemies, whose birds I had freed from their cages and to whom I had even sold a moldy nut.

I crossed the street and knocked on the Babariks' door. The yard was the same. I saw the familiar garden and the trees on which he had once hung his bird cages. His mother opened the door and clapped her hands:

"Tolik! How happy Vovka will be! Come in, come in!"

I entered with some excitement and recognized the small outer room, the kitchen and the "big room," which now seemed very small. Dark-brown rabbits hopped about on the floor.

On a trunk beside the window sat a puffed and flabby Vovka, with an absurdly cropped head and only one arm. I did not even feel that he was sitting there, but rather that he had been propped up on the trunk like a sack of flour.

He was blind. Instead of eyes he had a pair of watery slits. His face was an unwholesome color, shiny and covered with dots and streaks, as if someone had scribbled all over it with an indelible pencil. Through his parted collar I saw gruesome wounds on his chest and neck. He was absolutely immobile, like a clay Buddha, and his one and only hand, a strong manly hand, lay on the edge of the trunk.

Then his mother did a strange thing. She came over to him, took his head as if it were an inanimate object, put her lips to his right ear and shrilled into it, in an unnatural piccolo-like voice, "Tolik Semerik is here! Tolik Se-me-rik! Remember him?"

I stood shattered, realizing that this was Vovka; that he was barely recognizable; and that he was deaf on top of it all. Vovka grew animated. His head moved.

"Tolik!" he shouted in a hoarse, husky voice. "It's good you've come!" His hand went up. "Where are you?"

"Sit here, on the right side, and talk into his ear," said his mother. She was deeply moved and smiled as she made room for me.

I sat down, leaned lightly against his ponderous body to let him know I was there, and surrendered my hand to his fingers, which were feverishly searching the air. His fingers took hold and pressed my hand again and again. He would not let it go, but kept squeezing and patting it.

"So you've come," he repeated. "It's good you've come. I heard you were studying at the Institute. Good for you! They say you'll be a writer."

He offered me his ear.

"Yes!" I shouted. "I've been writing!"

"They say you'll be a writer," he repeated, and I realized he hadn't heard me. "What institute, did you say?"

"The Literary!" I bawled desperately, as close to his ear as possible.

His mother came over, took his hand and again shrilled into his ear in her high, thin voice.

"He says he's at the Literary Institute, that he's going to be a writer."

"Uh-huh, uh-huh!" nodded Vovka happily. "That's wonderful. Smart boy! And how's Mother? Is she well?"

"Yes!" I cried, pulling his hand down to let him know that henceforth this meant "yes."

"And Grandfather Semerik?"

"He's gone. Dead!"

"Grandfather Semerik is dead!" shrilled his mother as before, and Vovka caught the message this time.

"You don't say? So Grandfather Semerik is dead!" he commented wonderingly. "I didn't know he died. I hope you'll excuse me for saying so, but he was a choleric old fellow!"

I pumped his hand up and down.

"Yes! Yes!"

"Well," he said, "you're really a bright fellow, and I'm glad for your sake. As for me, I'm as you see me. I couldn't move at all before, but now I seem to be loosening up a bit. I can sit up. My hearing is gone, except for one strand of a nerve. I'll be all right as long as Mama is alive. The fellows come to see me sometimes. We read the newspapers together. Amazing, what's happening! And agriculture! Who'd have thought it?"

"Yes, yes!" I shouted, plying his hand. I held on to his hand as the only link between us. I sat next to him, crowding his big flabby body a trifle too hard. His face was right next to mine, but I still saw nothing familiar, nothing at all! Only his voice, and perhaps his way of speaking, reminded me a little of the old Vovka.

His mother left us and went to the kitchen. Enunciating my words as clearly as I could, I bellowed into his ear, "Forgive me! For that nut at the bazaar! Remember?"

"Yes, yes," he answered. "That's how things are. You're a good fellow. But I remember how you let my birds out of their cages."

"That's right!" I bawled, pumping his hand up and down, and then from left to right.

"I keep rabbits now," he confided. "Mama, give me one of the rabbits!"

I steered his hand from left to right.

"Mama's gone out!"

I looked around, but couldn't see a single rabbit. They had hidden somewhere. Vovka waited.

"Have you been reading the newspapers?" he asked. "What's happening in the United Nations?"

I pumped his hand up and down.

"They ought to put me on the podium for a while," he declared. "I'd give them a speech, all right! Listen! D'you think there'll be a war?"

I moved his hand from left to right. He understood, but did not agree.

"Oh, yes there will! They've got us covered right now! We've got each other covered, with the safety catches off! That's how we live. Rockets pointing at all cities. As soon as anything happens and there's a fracas somewhere, the buttons will be pushed and the fun will begin. Mama, give me a rabbit!"

"Don't worry!" I yelled into his ear, not at all sure he would hear me. "There shouldn't be a war. Everything's all right for the time being."

"So that's how things are, Tolik," he said, affectionately stroking my hand. "Your Mother is well and you've turned into a man. But drop in again. Don't forget."

I shook his hand up and down.

"I can't hear anything with my left ear," he explained, "but I can with my right. Talk clearly and right into my ear."

"Vovka, Vovka!" I choked, pressing his hand.

"Don't forget me. Come again. Why don't you describe me, just as I am? So people will know what war is. Will you?"

I signaled, "Yes."

I have fulfilled my promise to describe my friend Vovka Babarik, who, as you read these lines, still lives in Kiev, at No. 5 Petropavlovskaya. He is one of the millions of the Second World War veterans who are still alive.

LA COMMEDIA
É FINITA

The whole cortege of German limousines pulled out in exactly three minutes that grim November day, leaving their telephone and all its wire behind them. (For years afterwards Mother used it to hang her laundry on.)

Trembling with excitement, I watched the troops retreating down the street. Never had I seen men so pale, worried and frantic. Words can hardly describe the scene; only a picture could truly convey it.

Trucks, carts and halftracks streamed toward Podol. There were batches of Germans, batches of Hungarians and *Polizei*. The trucks rumbled noisily, blowing their horns and running down their own soldiers. The horses were covered with froth as their drivers lashed them.

The Germans were retreating with our little Russian horses; their own big, fiery-brown draught horses had perished long ago.

I have never seen such a sight before or since. Bundles and phonographs fell from the carts. The road was strewn with articles of all sorts, including cartridges and discarded rifles. A submachine gun leaned deserted against a post.

The windows of the school were lit up, as they often were in the early evening when the panes reflected the setting sun. But this time there was no sun. The day was overcast and gloomy, and darkness had already fallen. The school looked strangely sinister. Suddenly I realized that it was on fire, ablaze on every floor. The departing Germans had flooded the classrooms with gasoline and ignited it. The troops pressed on, while the school burned slowly, almost lazily. It was a stone building and empty.

Black smoke erupted from the bazaar, as straight as a column. I did not know what the Germans had set on fire, but I could see they were carrying out a plan. I was utterly confused; in the general uproar and shooting it was impossible to make out anything. Then an explosion rocked the air with such force that our cottage began to sway, and a looking glass on the wall disintegrated. I crouched down, almost deafened. I thought the explosion had occurred right in our backyard. I had barely recovered my senses, when there was a second explosion as strong as the first, and I crouched down again.

"They've blown up the bridges!" cried Mother from the yard.

I looked and saw an empty space where our bridge had been; it was half-filled with sand and slabs of stone. Germans caught on the other side continued scrambling across the debris of the bridge. Others ran along the embankment. (When the debris was cleared later, an automobile with four officers was found in the wreckage. Some thought these men had blown up the bridge as an act of suicide; but others —more correctly, I think—decided that the car had been at the foot of the bridge when the explosion came, for many Germans had been stranded on the other side.)

Stupefied by all this, I wandered aimlessly about; I came to the shed, found Titus, took him in my arms and carried him about like a baby. I didn't want to watch the retreating troops anymore. I had several rifles hidden in the pantry, but the hand grenades seemed more reliable. My pockets were tearing under their weight, but I kept them there, not knowing what to expect. I never noticed when the last of the troops had passed.

Nightfall brought no darkness. Everything was flooded in red light. The reflections danced over the clouds as if they were screens. Flickers of light danced about, as though someone were playing pranks with a flashlight or looking glass. So many things were burning around us! It was like being in the heart of a bonfire.

It grew very quiet.

The stillness was disturbed from time to time by a thud from the school, where geysers of sparks were flying into the air; the ceilings were caving in.

Mikolai and Lyaksandra sat in the cottage crying under their mattress. If a stranger had come in, he would have been startled: the empty room, the strange-looking lean-to beside the stove and the queer, whining sounds. I never heard old people carry on so.

Mother took them by the hand, drew them out like little children and bundled them off to our shelter. I, too, sat in the shelter for a while, but was too keyed up to sit still. I felt as if needles were pricking me all over. So I climbed out and ran about again, thinking hard of my plans—I'd fight with grenades, keeping a rifle handy; then from the embankment, the meadow, the swamp and the reeds, I'd make them pay for my life, if only I weren't caught napping—my head swam with all this. I had been ready for the worst long ago, but still I wanted to live—very much so!

Naturally, no one could sleep. As for Titus, he deserted me disgracefully. The darkness restored his energy; he began to prowl after his rats—that fierce old tiger!

Friday, November fifth, was drawing to an end—the 778th day of the occupation of Kiev.

I stood on the porch, leaning against the wall with a rifle in my arm. A green rocket soared noiselessly from behind the embankment. A shot fell, and then another. Again a rocket took to the air. How queer they looked, those green rockets against the bloody sky!

Crackling and thudding noises kept coming from the school. "This is it," I thought. "The German incendiaries are coming!" I would like to write that at that moment I was serene; that I took out my hand grenades and calmly unscrewed the caps. But it wasn't so at all.

All my weapons instantly seemed inadequate. Hammers pounded inside my skull, but I could still catch shouting coming from beyond the embankment.

What to do? Where to hide?

An idea flashed into my mind: I would climb a tree and climb it high. To the very crown! They would be on the ground everywhere, burning everything, but not the trees. And if they noticed me, it would be easier to hurl my grenades from above like stones. By the time they got me, I'd have made them pay dearly. The cries from behind the embankment grew louder, as if many people were shouting.

"O-o-m-ades! O-o-m-ou!"

I leapt into a tree like a cat, breaking my fingernails;

but flying to the first fork in the boughs. Swallowing my breath, I listened.

There came a bawling from the embankment in the loveliest Muscovite Russian: "Co-o-mrades! Co-me out! Soviet power is back!"

And everything grew blurred, damn it!

I yelled incoherently and flung myself down from the tree. I ran into the street and pounded through that red street under the red sky toward the red embankment. Suddenly I stopped; I had a hand grenade in each trembling hand. I laid them down gently side by side and ran on.

The collapsed bridge was a terrible wasteland, gruesome at close quarters. Queer living creatures of some kind —humans or animals?—were crawling up the steep embankment on all fours. But I realized at once that they were people who had been hiding, just as we had been. I raced onward, outstripping them, but was not the first to reach the top. Up on the tracks, people were embracing wildly. Ragged old women, crying hysterically, hung on the necks of the Soviet soldiers.

The soldiers' questions were businesslike and to the point.

"Any Germans around?"

"No! No!" sobbed the women.

There were only a few soldiers, probably several men from a scouting unit. They exchanged a few words, and one of them fired a green rocket into the air. Another soldier came plodding up breathlessly on the opposite side of the embankment. He was a straw-haired, good-natured looking fellow with a bundle of some sort in his hand.

"Well? Did you have a hard time?" he asked cheerfully.

"A very hard time!" wailed the women in unison.

"Here! Take these things and hang them on your houses. It's a holiday."

The bundle he carried turned out to be a parcel of little Soviet flags, no bigger than the ones carried by children at parades. The women clutched for them, and I would have grabbed one too if the soldier hadn't cried, "You can't have them all! I have to have some for Podol, too!"

The soldier with the rocket gun sent another green flare aloft; then he and the others ran downhill on our side of the embankment.

As for me, I didn't run. I just soared home, dived into the shelter and roared, "Our soldiers have come!"

Without pausing to enjoy the effect I dashed out again, climbed up to the garret, rummaged about in the dark and found the red flag I had hidden there long ago. Next I went to the shed, broke off the handle of a rake and nailed my flag to it, sometimes hitting my fingers in the dim light. The world was red and the flag looked white in all that redness.

The liberation of Kiev went on all night. Here and there, street fighting broke out. Houses blew up and burned— the university, schools, warehouses and the huge apartment houses opposite St. Sophia Cathedral; but happily for Russian history, the cathedral itself was unharmed.

The main forces of the advancing army rolled into Kiev through Kurenevka. The dynamited bridges had blocked the streets, so the army advanced across the Park of Culture and over the railroad crossing on Beletskaya Street, which disgorged tanks, Studebaker trucks (new to us), artillery and long transport trains. The infantry wound their way single file directly over the debris.

Dirty, sooty and tired, these troops were painfully dear

to us, poignantly familiar—startlingly like the men who had gone away in 1941. They trudged along, a straggling line with prosaically clanking mess kits. Some, evidently terribly footsore, walked barefoot, their shoes tied across their shoulders. There they were—Russian soldiers!—treading firmly with reddened feet over an earth already chilled by autumn frosts.

A FINAL,
CONTEMPORARY
CHAPTER

I'm back in Kiev, in Kurenevka; my mother, much older now, is still living here in the self-same cottage. She's on pension now, after teaching for 40 years.

Nine-story houses, as white and modern-looking as ocean liners, have risen on the main street of Kurenevka.

St. Andrew's Church still soars over Podol. St. Sophia Cathedral continues to receive her processions of touring schoolchildren, and the Lavra continues to oppress the tourists with its ruins.

Kreshchatik, like the whole center of Kiev, is entirely new. The well-known Druzhba (Friendship) bookstore, where one can buy foreign books in many languages, now stands on the corner of Kreshchatik and Proreznaya.

Babi Yar is gone. It has been filled in, and there is a new highway through it now. Construction is under way on both sides of the road. But people working on the foundations still turn up human bones and clumps of barbed wire. The ashes have long since drifted away, though some lie deeply buried. Nothing remains of those who perished here but statistics and recollections.

Each of these dead was once a living being, a person with thoughts, joys, sorrows and talents. We shall never know exactly how many there were; the figures are only estimates.

Until recently, the house in the cemetery was still tenanted by the caretaker, M. S. Lutsenko, or Auntie Masha, as she was called. The Germans had forgotten all about her; they never knew that she had stolen into the brushwood and seen everything they were doing. As she showed me around, she told me again and again where it had all begun; where the slopes had been blasted; and how "they were killed there and there. How they screamed! Oh, Mother of God! And they were hit with shovels, hit and hit!"

I ponder over the thought that no social crime ever remains a secret. There will always be an Auntie Masha who has seen it all, or witnesses who have escaped; fourteen, two, perhaps only one. And if none survive, the dead will bear witness. History will not be cheated, and nothing can be hidden forever.

This story was begun in Kiev; but I couldn't continue it there and had to go away. At night I heard cries in my sleep. I lay down and was shot in the face, the chest or the back of my head. Or else I was a bystander with my notebook in hand, waiting. And the Germans wouldn't shoot. Instead they showed me snapshots of their mothers, their wives and children; or they just loafed around. This was their lunch hour, you see. They were boiling coffee on the fire, while I waited for it all to begin so that I could jot down everything conscientiously, for the sake of history.

These nightmares pursued me constantly, and I woke up with the cries of thousands ringing in my ears.

We dare not forget those cries, both because such things are unforgettable and because the problems of the Babi Yars hang over mankind like a black cloud. Nobody knows what technical forms they will assume in the future, or what names will be given to the new Buchenwalds, Hiroshimas and other horrors, still hidden from us but awaiting their hour.

Let me emphasize again that I have not told about anything exceptional, but only about ordinary things that were part of a *system;* things that happened just yesterday, historically speaking, when people were exactly as they are today.

Looking at our yesterday, we think of tomorrow. Life is the dearest thing we have. We ought to protect it.

Fascism, violence and war must end and be recalled only in books about the past.

Finishing one such book, I wish you peace.

Notes to the Text

Certain notes appear here in brackets; these were supplied by the translator for the American edition. All other notes were provided by the author.

THE EDITORS

1 The fascist newspaper *Ukrainskoye slovo (Ukrainian Word)*, September 21, 1941.

1 [Svyatoslav Igoryevich (died in 972) was a Kiev prince and prominent army leader.

The Ukrainian Princess Olga was the wife of Prince Igor, Grand Duke of Kiev and founder of the Rurik dynasty. She adopted Christianity in 957.

Vladimir Svyatoslavich (died in 1015), a prince of Kiev, adopted Christianity in 988–989 and spread the new religion to his people.

Zinovi Bogdan Khmelnitsky (1595–1657) was a Ukrainian statesman and army leader who united the Ukraine with Russia.

Mazepa (1644–1709) was Hetman of the Ukraine from 1687. He attempted to separate the Ukraine from Russia, siding first with the Poles and then with the Swedes. He fled to Turkey after the Battle of Poltava.

Taras Grigoryevich Shevchenko (1814–1861) was a Ukrainian poet, artist and revolutionary democrat.

Lesya Ukrainka—Larisa Petrovna Kosach-Kvitka—(1871–1913) was a Ukrainian poetess influenced by democratic and revolutionary ideas.

Simon Vasilyevich Petlura (1877–1926) was a Ukrainian

nationalist commander in 1917–1918 who opposed Soviet rule.]

1 [Vasily Leontovich Kochubei (1640–1708) was the Ukrainian Cossack leader who told Peter I that Hetman Mazepa intended to separate the Ukraine from Russia; he was executed by Mazepa.]
2 [Yury Dolgoruky (1090–1157) was Grand Duke of Kiev and founder of Moscow.]

1 The collection of documents entitled *Kiev Province in the Great Patriotic War, 1941–1945* (Kiev, 1963) quotes from "Memorandum of the State Security Committee of the Ukraine Republic Council of Ministers Regarding Sabotage and Reconnaissance Activities of a Group of Underground Fighters Who Operated in Kiev Under the Leadership of I. D. Kudrya."

This document tells of a series of exploits performed by the group of Chekists [secret police] headed by Ivan Danilovich Kudrya, otherwise known as Maxim. The group included D. Sobolev, A. Pechenev, R. Okipnaya, Ye. Bremer and others. The memorandum says: "The fires and explosions never ceased in the city. . . . They grew particularly intense from September 24 to 28, 1941. Blown up, along with other objects, were the storage premises filled with radios turned in by the population, the German military commandant's office, the cinema for Germans, etc. Though no one can definitely say who set off the explosions that brought hundreds of the 'conquerors' to their graves, there can be no doubt that members of 'Maxim's' group had a hand in it. The chief thing was that the explosions showed the insolent fascist 'conquerors' that they were not the masters of the occupied territory."

It is known that D. Sobolev perished in one of his numerous bold operations. A. Pechenev, who was wounded and helpless, shot himself when the Gestapo came to seize him. "Maxim," R. Okipnaya and Ye. Bremer were seized in Kiev in July 1942.

Notes to the Text

No one knows where they died. I. D. Kudrya—"Maxim"—was posthumously awarded the title of Hero of the Soviet Union in 1965.

CHAPTER VI

1 Central State Archives of the October Revolution, Collection 7021, Listing 65, Item 5.

2 [Podol is a district of Kiev where many poor Jews lived.]

3 ["*Karaim*—literally, readers (of the Bible). A people living in the Crimea, Lithuania and Turkey. They speak the Tatar language. They sprang from a Jewish sect that refuses to accept the Talmud and recognizes only the Bible."—*Ushakov's Dictionary of the Russian Language,* Moscow, 1935.]

CHAPTER VII

1 D. M. Pronicheva was nearly caught many times after this. She hid among ruins and, under the assumed name of Nadya Savchenko, in Darnitsa and in villages in the countryside. She found her children only at the end of the war. Then she returned to the Kiev Puppet Theater, where she now works. In 1946 she testified as a witness at the fascist war crimes trial in the Ukraine.

CHAPTER IX

1 *Ukrainskoye slovo,* September 29, 1941.

2 *Ibid.,* September 30, 1941.

3 *Ibid.,* October 2, 1941.

4 *Ibid.,* October 9, 1941.

5 *Ibid.,* October 10, 1941.

6 *The German-Fascist Occupation Regime in the Ukraine: Collection of Documents and Materials* [in Ukrainian], Kiev, 1963, p. 45.

7 *Ukrainskoye slovo,* October 25, 1941.

8 *Ibid.,* October 22, 1941.

9 *Ibid.,* October 25, 1941.

Notes to the Text

10 *The German-Fascist Occupation Regime in the Ukraine: Collection of Documents and Materials,* Kiev, 1963, p. 46.

11 *Heroic Kiev: Collection of Materials on the Heroism of the People of Kiev in the Great Patriotic War* [in Ukrainian], Kiev, 1961, p. 234.

12 *The German-Fascist Occupation Regime in the Ukraine: Collection of Documents and Materials,* Kiev, 1963, p. 55.

13 *Ibid.,* p. 60.

CHAPTER XVI

1 Subsequent investigations established that 68,000 died in the Darnitsa camp. There were similar camps in Slavuta, on Kerosinnaya Street in Kiev proper and elsewhere. I tried to find out what became of the administrative personnel at the Darnitsa camp, but so far I have not found anything. None of them, not even Bitzer, has appeared at any trial.

CHAPTER XVIII

1 There are few documents about the explosion in the Cathedral of the Assumption and the burning of the Kiev-Pechora Lavra; not everything about this affair is clear yet. I quote from Professor K. Dubina's investigation of fascist crimes in Kiev:

"As has been discovered, the fascist vandals mined the Cathedral of the Assumption and other buildings in advance, then waited for a convenient moment to blow them up. On November 3, 1941, Tisso, the betrayer of the Slovak people, visited the Lavra. This was deemed a good time for an act of provocation. Just as Tisso left the Lavra territory, explosions were heard. As already noted, the occupationists tried to ascribe this crime to Soviet patriots who allegedly tried to assassinate Tisso. But even such an inveterate bandit as the accused Scheier was obliged to admit that the crime was committed by the German fascist invaders. How the occupationists looted the Lavra, blew up the Cathedral of the Assumption and murdered the scholar N. N. Chernogubov has been described by the latter's widow, Ye. A.

Chernogubova-Yakovleva."—K. Dubina, *During the Years of Great Ordeals,* Kiev, 1962, pp. 96–97.
2 *Ukrainskoye slovo,* November 23, 1941.

CHAPTER XIX

1 [Taras Shevchenko (previously mentioned), Ukrainian poet and painter, was born a serf. As an adult he was freed by purchase from his master through the help of the poet Zhukovsky and others. He is known for his descriptions of the village life of his day.]

CHAPTER XX

1 *Novoye Ukrainskoye slovo,* December 14, 1941.

CHAPTER XXIV

1 *Novoye Ukrainskoye slovo,* April 19, 1942.

CHAPTER XXV

1 *Novoye Ukrainskoye slovo,* January 11, 1942.
2 *Ibid.,* March 3, 1942.
3 *Ibid.,* April 14, 1942.
4 *Ibid.,* October 11, 1942, signed "I."
5 From the collection *Pages from Fascist Captivity,* Ukrainian Political Publishing House, Kiev, 1947; the letters from Nina D., Katya P. and Nina K., pp. 7–8, 15–16.

CHAPTER XXVII

1 [As mentioned above, Petlura was an anti-Bolshevik Ukrainian nationalist of the period of the Revolution and the Civil War.]
2 From the directives of the *Reichskommissar* of the Ukraine to all generals and *Gebietskommissare* on the conditions governing the opening of elementary schools, issued January 12, 1942. *The German-Fascist Occupation Regime in the Ukraine: Collection of Documents and Materials,* Kiev, 1963, p. 71.
3 *Novoye Ukrainskoye slovo,* May 14, 1942.

Notes to the Text

CHAPTER XXIX

1 *Novoye Ukrainskoye slovo,* July 12, 1942.
2 *Ibid.,* July 18, 1942.
3 *Ibid.,* July 24, 1942.

CHAPTER XXXIII

1 *Novoye Ukrainskoye slovo,* May 23, 1942.
2 *Ibid.,* May 10, 1942. "Decree No. 88 of the Mayor of Kiev."
3 Announcement appearing in *Novoye Ukrainskoye slovo* in all issues during May 1942.
4 *Novoye Ukrainskoye slovo,* June 23, 1942.
5 *Kiev Area in the Years of the Great Patriotic War* (Collection of Documents), Kiev, 1963, pp. 282–283.
6 *Novoye Ukrainskoye slovo,* July 4, 7 and 20, 1942.
7 *Ibid.,* repeated in several issues.

CHAPTER XXXVIII

1 [Lieutenant-General Kopak coordinated the partisan movement with Soviet Army operations.]

CHAPTER XXXIX

1 Topaide's name was never mentioned among the condemned fascist criminals. He may have perished, although most of the Gestapo men who worked at the rear were able to escape and hide. It is possible, therefore, that he is still alive. Did he get rid of his nervous tic? Nobody was sentenced specifically for Babi Yar; and the fate of the German and Russian administrators of the Babi Yar camp, including Radomski and Rieder, is unknown.
2 Babi Yar was incorporated by the German authorities under the name of *Baukompanie* (construction company). This company had its own bank account, for all the materials, the oil, the wood and the machines had to be financed. In this, the systematic Germans were true to character.

Notes to the Text

3 The sisters were Natalya and Antonina Petrenko. Davydov later visited them on Tiraspol Street in Kurenevka, where I believe they live to this day.

Only fourteen of the 330 prisoners escaped. Fyodor Yershov perished. Nearly all of the survivors joined the Soviet Army, and many of them fell in battle.

V. Y. Davydov now lives in Kiev, where he works as chief of a construction crew.

CHAPTER XL

1 *Novoye Ukrainskoye slovo,* September 26, 1943.

2 *Ibid.,* Order of Major-General Wirow, the military commandant.

3 *Ibid.,* September 30, 1943; after which the newspaper ceased publication.

4 Figures were learned later. There had been 900,000 people in Kiev before the war. By the end of the German occupation, 180,000 were left—fewer than lay dead in Babi Yar alone. Every third person in Kiev was killed during the occupation. If we include those who died of hunger, never returned from Germany and so forth, we could say that every second person in Kiev perished.

5 The Germans loaded the people of Kiev into freight trains and shipped them westward. Many of them got away and scattered in the West Ukraine and Poland. Others perished en route. Some found themselves in Germany, and others even ended up in France.

CHAPTER XLII

1 [From the translation by Eugene M. Kayden, Antioch Press, Yellow Springs, Ohio.]